Travels with a Gypsy Lotus

STEFAN LAWSON

Nora & Bruna,
You are both wonderful
people & I appreciate
your support

Lawson

5/13/22
Jimmie made me
put this here

5/13/2022
Love you both very much
Jimmie Watson

TRAVELS WITH A GYPSY LOTUS

This work is based on a true story with many of the names of individuals and places altered for privacy. Some events, dialogue and timelines have been slightly modified to create a more consistent and enjoyable reading experience.

ISBN 978-1-7366966-0-6
Stefanlawson.com

1. India – Nonfiction / 2. Adventure – Nonfiction /
3. Travel – Nonfiction / 4. Culture – Nonfiction /
5. Biographical – Nonfiction / 6. History – Nonfiction /
7. Humor – Nonfiction / 9. Memoir - Nonfiction

Cover design by Lindsey Leflet
Editing by Paige E.L.
Author photo by Amber Locke

A percentage of the printed sale of this book will go to animal and humane causes around the world. Thank you for supporting this author and the causes associated with this text.

For my mom and dad, who have given me everything I could need to succeed.

******

A special thanks to all of those who helped me bring this book to the world, gave me feedback and left reviews on Amazon and Goodreads. Thank you to all the people I met during this journey who now have a place in this book. To everyone in my family. And finally, to those extra special people who gave me continuous feedback and support: Ally, Trish, Amber, Alyssa, Dr. K., Mike, and my dear Grandma. There are many more of you who deserve to be listed here, but you know who you are and my thanks go to you as well.

Travels with a Gypsy Lotus

Takedowns

I stood in the group room beside the monstrosity of a man holding a syringe in his freakishly large hand, my pulse faintly throbbing in my ears as I realized that I, a skinny, young man, inexperienced to any kind of physical combat, was moments away from a perilous altercation with this behemoth of a human. It was my first week on the job at the hospital and right now, the most reassuring thought I had was knowing that it was not me this needle-wielding co-worker was going to be fighting. Rather, he and I were currently trying to talk a patient into taking his nightly court-ordered medications. The black man was sitting across the room from where we stood, in a large chair filled by his girth. His big tree branch forearms were settled on the armrests as he gripped them with dinner-plate-sized hands. He was a bulky fellow and his oversized jacket and sweatpants gave him a homely look but also intensified his already apparent mass. He sat there with a blank stare on his face, oblivious or indifferent to our requests. When he refused to cooperate and come out of the group room, we had been left no choice but to evacuate all the other patients from the area and confront him.

My coworker, Fox, passed the syringe to the nurse standing with us and turned back to the still seated patient. Like me, Fox was a psychiatric technician and, on this particular day, was wearing the same shade of tan scrubs as me. Standing beside each other, we looked like a pair of severely disproportionate Twinkies. Fox was trying to talk to the stoic man across the room from us. The word *FAT* was etched into the thick window behind him, designed to be shatterproof but apparently not scratch resistant. An irreversible act of vandalism by another patient a few months prior. "This is it, brother," Fox said. "This medication is court-ordered. You can just take it yourself and make it easy for us all. We will have to give it to you whether you want it or not. Don't make us do that."

The man remained passively mute. He hadn't even bothered to look at Fox as he spoke. The silence held between the four of us and I could feel the unbearably thick tension in the room. My co-worker let the moments slip by, perhaps waiting for the patient to process the situation and wise up. To come to his senses and realize all this trouble wasn't worth it. When nothing happened, I knew things were about to take a turn for the worse.

The door to the group room opened. Our backup had just arrived. Another technician from the second floor had gotten our call and came down in case we needed some assistance. From the looks of things, we were about to need all the help we could get. John was a Boston native and a former member of a notorious biker gang. Like Fox, he was a built man with tattoos that seeped from the sleeves of his hospital uniform and stained a path to his meaty wrists. The patient's eyes tracked the newcomer as he entered and stood just far enough away from Fox and me to make our presence seem that much more spread out. Despite our numbers, the patient still made no show of complying.

"Okay then," Fox said, and, in unison, we all took a step toward the patient.

The man shot up from his chair at a surprising speed and stood rock still with his arms down by his side and the same blank expression stapled to his face. We all stopped in our tracks. "Stay the fuck away from me," he said. His demeanor was so flat that the statement was surprisingly void of any aggressive edge but still carried the full weight of a menacing threat. It made for quite an effect and, for a split second, I had wondered if the man had done it intentionally. However, I knew enough to recognize that this was not a thinking man, but a dangerous one.

As he stood there, I suddenly realized just how big he truly was. He was bigger than Fox for sure, much taller too, and the quickness in which he had stood up told me he was not a blob of totally useless flesh. He had deceptive speed. In the back of my mind, I hoped that my team would contain him before he had the chance to do much more of *any* kind of moving.

Both Fox and John took wide steps to flank him from both sides. He clenched his fists but I was amazed that he still only stared straight ahead, relatively undeterred by the two large men that had come just outside arms reach of him. I knew he was mentally unstable, so predicting his movements was next to impossible. I did my best to step forward into a position that would put pressure on the cornered patient while also trying not to get in the way of my two co-workers, who I was counting on to take the lead on what was about to happen next.

I noticed the man's view seemed to be fixated on the female nurse's syringe. She had wisely kept her distance and was now the center of his attention. Fox noticed this and took another step closer. The man's concentration broke and he snapped his gaze coldly toward Fox's hands, which were slowly coming up to take hold of him. It was then that John closed the distance and secured the man's left arm with one hand and braced his shoulder with the other. The patient quickly tried to spin toward his assailant, his free right arm working to break the tech's grip. Fox was on him in a split second and immediately worked to restrain the patient's right arm. It was a move they had both practiced for years in similar situations. Trapped from both sides, the big man began to panic and thrash, throwing his weight against Fox. In less than five seconds all three of them were on the ground. The patient struggled to break free and, in desperation, began using his only available weapons. His legs. I dove onto the hospital floor with the entangled men and quickly wrapped my arms around his two unsecured limbs, feeling a bulk of muscle beneath his sweatpants.

"Get off me!" The man yelled, flailing wildly in our grasp. "I'm being drugged against my will!"

The door to the room suddenly flew open and another mentally ill man with long disheveled hair barged in and joined in on the shouting. "He doesn't want that," he yelled over the noise. The nurse quickly turned to the unexpected newcomer and worked to remove him. She braced one of her arms across his chest, still holding the needle in her opposite hand. He looked past her to the scuffle unfolding on the floor.

"Get off me!" the restrained patient continued. "I don't want to be here."

"Yeah! Don't wanna be here," the other psychotic patient echoed.

"I know your faces," the black man hollered. "You're all dead!"

"Yeah, all dead!" The other patient repeated, the nurse still working to push him from the room. "You have to leave, sir," she insisted. "It's dangerous. You have to go."

"Dangerous! Have to go!"

"Get off me!"

"Get off me!"

Another co-worker appeared and took the long-haired man away from the door which quickly closed behind them. The nurse turned and hastily stepped forward with her gently sweating syringe. "Keep him steady. I'm going in for the stick," she said.

"You keep away from me with that needle!" The man shouted.

"Just relax man," Fox said. "It's gonna be real quick."

"Fuck you! I'm not crazy! I don't belong here! I don't!"

The man's right leg was suddenly ripped from my grasp and struck out, landing a harsh blow to Fox's side. I quickly reached out and wrapped the free leg up again and squeezed with all my strength to keep both legs in my arms. My face almost pressed against his body, I quickly deduced that the man had not taken a shower in several days. The nurse was now pressing one knee gently into the patient's lower back as she began working his pants down, exposing his bare, naked ass. "Keep him steady," she shouted over the scuffle.

"Keep away from me bitch! Don't stick me with that junk!"

As the patient began to thrash with renewed vigor and I worked to keep my hold against his massive legs, I began to wonder how it was that I came to be in this position. What circumstances had led me to a place where, at any given moment, I could be lying on the ground with three other men in an aggressive struggle for control? What were the odds that one of these patients might engage me like this when I had no help around? The fact that such an altercation had developed in the first few days of working at the hospital was more than enough evidence to suggest I would see much, much worse in the months ahead. Despite this, I would look back years later and marvel at how fortunate I had been to be at the Winded Willow at that exact time. I was fortunate because it was there that I met a woman who would eventually become a good friend and a travel companion to the far ends of the world. It was there at the Winded Willow that the course of my life would change and take direction in completely new, exciting ways.

Jimmie Wakefield & the Winded Willow

I met Jimmie Wakefield while working nights at the Winded Willow, an old, run-down psychiatric hospital along the murky waters of the Mississippi Gulf Coast. I had graduated from college a year ago and spent my time working various jobs while trying to figure out what I could do with my psychology degree. I had originally gone to school to work in the entertainment industry, but switched majors after deciding it might be wiser to have a degree that would afford me a bigger market to work in while pursuing my dreams of being a writer and musician. My uncle was the director of radiology at one of the more prominent hospitals in town and got word that a position was opening for a psychiatric technician at the Winded Willow, an in-patient mental health hospital. He knew the program director there, a man named Henry Stallworth, who told him about the job.

It was for this reason that I now sat in Mr. Stallworth's office at the Winded Willow.

"We get sick people here," Mr. Stallworth was saying. Outside the window behind him, a group of naked trees swayed in one of the last harsh winter winds which had found its way into early March. "Very sick people. A lot of them come off the street." He leaned back and sighed, his arms resting on the chair now. "*Most* of them come off the street," he corrected himself. "You name it, we've seen it. Severe drug addictions. Mania. Schizophrenia. Psychotic delusions. Hallucinations. These are the everyday staples in our workplace. Have you ever dealt with anything like that before?"

I reflected on my studies in school. All the words he was saying were just concepts in books I had read—the right choices to tests I had taken. Now, hearing these same words, a new gravity was placed on them as I realized they were no longer just words. They were human conditions that I would be in charge of managing and treating on a daily basis. I had almost no experience working with people afflicted by these ailments in real life.

"I'm sure you know the answer just from looking at that folder," I said with a smile, gesturing to the paperwork that lay before him.

"But I'll bet you've seen things on TV, right? Movies like *One Flew Over the Cuckoo's Nest?* Or Hannibal Lecter from *Silence of the Lambs?* I'm sure you've got some preconceived notions from stuff like that?"

I tried to laugh a little. "I know those movies are all just part of the Hollywood dreamscape. In reality, it's probably a much different story."

He tilted his head and gave me a look with wide eyes. "Well, you know what they say, art is created from that which we experience," he said. I tried to hold my smile, sizing up his words, his demeanor.

"I'm not trying to put you off from anything," he said. "Your uncle said you could use a job. You seem like a bright enough young guy. I'm sure you would be a good fit here. I just want you to be prepared. There isn't any other field quite like this. Mental health service is a demanding industry. I'm sure you're familiar with the level of burnout professionals experience in this field."

I had heard all about burnout.

"Yes sir, I have," I said.

"Ya, well, it's a real thing." He leaned back in his chair. "Is mental health a field you see yourself in the long term?"

I thought about the question, wondering if I should say something to make me look like a better candidate for the position. I took him for a straightforward enough guy. He seemed genuinely curious. "Perhaps," I said. "I feel like I just want to get a sense of what's out there. What goes on at in-patient mental health wards has always been a mystery to me. It all happens behind closed doors. Of course, I know it's all for patient confidentiality. If this line of work isn't for me, I'd rather figure that out now instead of later."

"What would you do if you weren't working in the mental health field?"

"I'm not sure. I guess that's what I'm trying to figure out."

"What do you like to do in your free time?"

I thought about it for a moment. I loved music. I had been playing guitar and recording songs consistently for nearly a decade. I loved to write and had taken an interest in journalism. I was finding a new passion in podcasts and was taking steps to start my own as a little side project. However, above all else, one thing seemed to be on my mind more than anything those days.

"I've been thinking a lot about traveling since I graduated."

"Traveling? That's great. Everyone loves to travel, right? Have you done much in your life?"

"I've gotten around to a few places." I reflected. "Right after I left school, I took my first trip out to Colorado. Something about Boulder had been grabbing my attention for years. I used a social networking site and met two students my age who lived there. Some people thought it sounded crazy and would never do such a thing, but I feel like that spirit of communal travel is becoming more prevalent these days. I had a fantastic time and the people I met were great. I'd love to see more of the west."

He nodded enthusiastically. "Any overseas travel?"

"A little," I replied. "I was in Jamaica recently for a week-long wedding. I've seen a little bit of Mexico with family, but the places we went to felt like tourist traps. I also spent a few weeks in Europe as a kid."

"What's the next destination on your mind?"

"*Hmmm.* I've always thought Iceland would be a great time. New Zealand or Australia, perhaps. Some people find this strange, but to be honest, I think about India a lot."

His eyes lit up.

"India?" he beamed.

"I know it probably sounds like a weird choice. Not a lot of people's first pick, that's for sure."

"Why India?"

"I just think it would be such an alien place to visit. Clear on the other side of the world from us. It's an ancient culture, steeped in so much history. I think of India and, to me, it's almost synonymous with the earliest roots of human civilization."

"That's something," he said, slowly nodding his head. "Very interesting."

"How so?" I ventured.

He leaned forward and flashed a coy grin. "I think you'll see what I mean at the right time." He reached forward and closed the folder on his desk. "That is, of course, if you take the job."

I analyzed his words, pushing past his curious remark to the more pressing matter in front of me. "Is this an offer, sir?"

He gave a small gesture of indifference with his hands. "If you learn the principles of the job and stay patient, you'll pick up on how things are done around here and you'll have the chance to do a lot of good for others. At the end of the day, that's what we're here for. We're here to help people get better. Is this something you feel you're willing to take a shot at?"

I would do just about anything to start establishing my young adult life. I wanted to buy my first home soon and upgrade from the hand-me-down Corolla I was currently driving around.

"Yes, sir," I said.

"Great," he said rising from his chair. He really was a big guy. "Since you're here now, what would you think about meeting some of the staff?" He glanced over at his clock on the wall. It read half-past six. The daylight had faded from outside his office window. "It's almost seven o'clock," he said. "The night shift will be coming on soon."

******

Henry Stallworth pressed his ID badge against the card scanner mounted next to the heavy metal door which separated the rest of the world from the patients inside the Winded Willow. A small *beep* was accompanied by a green light and Stallworth, with some effort, pulled back the handle to open the entrance that would lead us to the first-floor unit. An older, bald security guard was stationed in the lobby. He nodded to me as I followed Stallworth inside and watched the heavy door behind me glide smoothly to a close, a deep *thump* that echoed in the tile hallway before us. A curious odor played across my nose as I tried to match Stallworth's long strides to the far end where another heavy door, this one made of wood, stood waiting for us.

"I don't think there has been too much excitement on the unit today," Stallworth said as he searched his pockets for something. "All the same, we will just make our way directly to the nursing station." Stallworth produced a small chain of keys and quickly selected a long silver one which he then inserted and twisted into the lock. The door came open and we stepped onto the ward. "This is 1-South," Stallworth said. "Mostly for substance abuse but minor psychosis as well. One tends to follow the other in a lot of cases."

The curious smell I had detected was much sharper now. It was a strange blend. That awful smell you encounter walking through a hospital from all the sterilization, all the cleaning products, but also an odor of something old and rotting. I wondered if it was the building or the people inside of it. An old man in a worn gray jacket was slowly pacing up the hallway towards us, his hands tucked away in his pockets. He stared blankly ahead and barely seemed to notice Stallworth and me as we passed by. We came to a long community table that served as a place for patients to eat their meals, socialize and play games. Branching away from this community area was another long hallway where the patients' rooms were located, giving the unit an L shape. There was a series of windows looking into a large room in the middle of the unit where many of the patients were sitting in chairs, watching television. Several of them looked up to watch us go by. Some of them were asleep. One of them, a middle-aged man with disheveled black hair and glasses seemed to stare more through the TV than at it. His right leg bounced up and down at a million miles a minute. Behind them were large windows giving a view of the outside world. I squinted my eyes together. I could just barely make out the words etched into the glass.

FAT

"This is the nursing station," Stallworth said.

Next to the community table was a door leading into a glass-walled nursing station. The door itself was split in half at the center so that the bottom half could be kept closed and nurses could lean out and give patients their medications. Stallworth searched his key chain.

"Hey," came a voice from behind me.

I turned. A woman just shy of sixty years was standing behind me in a bathrobe and slippers. She had long stringy gray hair and sunken eyes. She leaned forward with her hunched posture, the concern quite evident on her face.

"I can't get near seamen," she said.

"Um, I'm sorry?" I replied.

Stallworth momentarily abandoned the search for the right key behind me.

"Oh, sorry, this is Barbara, one of our patients. Mrs. Barbara you'll have to excuse us. We were just-"

"I can't get near seamen," Barbara said to me again, "because if I do, I'll get pregnant. It's a condition. I keep trying to tell them. I swell up like a balloon. There are too many men here. I can't be around all these men."

"Okay, Mrs. Barbara, okay," Stallworth was practically pulling on my arm now. "We will remind your nurse. I have to take our new employee here into the nursing station. Why don't you go watch TV with the rest of the group, alright?"

Barbara slowly turned and began shuffling up the hall towards her room, her face like a medicated mask. "Don't let them fool you," she muttered. "There is something unusual about this place. Can't put my finger on it."

Stallworth had turned me back to the door. "Sorry about that," he said. "We've been trying to get Barbara's medications right. She stopped taking them a few weeks ago and ended up in the ER saying she was giving birth to the anti-Christ. Really nice lady." The key was in his hand now and the door opened freely.

The circular nursing station had computers lining the walls. In the middle was a large counter with storage underneath. Opposite of 1-South was another L-shaped hallway with a similar commons area and group room with a television and a line of chairs with idle patients. The configuration was the same on both sides and the nursing station was directly in the middle of it all. From inside, you had a clear view straight down to the patient rooms on both units. Several nursing staff were typing away on their computers or had their noses down in paperwork. Most wore scrubs. One or two of them were wearing more business casual attire. I assumed they were doctors or perhaps even social workers.

We were immediately greeted by a big, hulking man with a shaved head dressed in blue scrubs. He wasn't as tall as Stallworth or even me for that matter, but one look at him told me he had most likely either been a bouncer or bodybuilder at one point in his life.

"How's it going, Henry!" The man practically shouted.

"It's going great," Stallworth replied. "Just showing Stefan around. He's going to be our newest psych tech."

The man swallowed my hand with his own. "Nice to meet you brother," he said. "I'm Fox."

"Good to meet you, Fox. Try not to break my hand there, okay?"

He laughed. "Sorry bro, sorry, my engine runs a little hot, you know what I mean? I'm a psych tech too. Been here a couple of years. Really interesting work environment. You'll rarely have a dull moment, that's for sure." He was high energy and talking faster than a man who had just received a coffee enema. "Listen, I'll have to catch up with you later. I'm about to run one of our cognitive behavioral groups. We do a couple of different sessions throughout the day. You'll have to stop in sometime and be a part of one. It's really great stuff. We have to empower the people, ya know? Good to meet you, man!" He gave me a strong pat that I momentarily thought would dislocate my shoulder and went out into the commons area. The pacing old man in the gray jacket was shuffling past. "Come on, Bernie!" Fox shouted enthusiastically at the patient. "We're gonna have a great group today. You're not gonna want to miss it!" The man seemed to register none of his words, even though they exploded out of Fox like a cannon. He simply held his gaze forward and moved down the opposing hallway.

"Lot of energy in that one," Stallworth said.

"I feel like a tornado just came through."

He laughed. "Come on. I'll get you introduced to the rest of the team. Hey Natasha, say hello to your newest teammate."

Nurse Natasha was a tall woman who appeared to be in her early fifties. Her straight black hair was pulled back in a ponytail and rested between her shoulder blades.

"Oh, hi there," she said with an East Coast accent. "You're going to be joining us on the unit, yeah?"

"Looks like it," I said simply.

"That's wonderful. Have you ever worked in a psychiatric hospital before?"

"No ma'am. Do you have any advice for me?"

Her eyes widened. "Make sure you have health insurance. I'm telling you, it pays to have a good plan in a place like this." She quickly rolled up her left pant leg and exposed the side of her calf where a deep red and purple bruise was fixed into her flesh.

"See that? We were trying to restraint this guy to his bed and he sank his teeth right into me. Tore the muscle real good."

"Okay, Natasha," Stallworth said, pulling me along. "You're going to scare the kid off before he even gets done with his orientation. Let's wait a while before we start sharing our war wounds, shall we?"

She shrugged. "Sorry, Mr. Stallworth, was just giving an honest opinion." She turned back to me in a sudden surge of excitement. "Oh, have you met Jimmie yet?"

"No, he hasn't," Stallworth answered. "Jimmie is still on leave."

"Oh, that's right," Natasha said, her face falling. "So sad." A change in emotion again as she turned back to me. "Well, all the same, it was a pleasure to meet you, young man. Hopefully we'll be working together soon."

"Yes, ma'am."

Stallworth pointed across the station to another middle-aged woman with short brown hair and glasses. She was hunched over a stack of papers, a blue pen in hand, scribbling away. "That's Caitlin over there," Stallworth said. Caitlin waved from across the room and then returned her gaze to the papers. "She's another one of our nurses. She's been here several years. We get lots of compliments from the patients about her. As you can see, she is very focused on her work."

He pointed down the north-facing hallway to an African American man with a clean-shaven haircut and a neatly trimmed, close-cut beard.

"That's Brandon, another psych tech," Stallworth said. "Right now, it looks like he is just finishing up to help a patient shave. We of course have to supervise them for such activities."

Nurse Natasha chimed in without looking up, her fingers still tapping away on the keyboard. "Otherwise, they might try to pocket the razor and hurt themselves, or worse, one of us. We had an inattentive young tech here once and a patient gave him back a handle with no blade in it. Used it to cut one of the nurses clean under his eye. He looked like Scarface." She stopped typing and laughed. "Which is ironic because that nurse ended up having a bit of a drug problem. Started swiping patient medications from our inventory. He's *looong* gone now."

"Boy, you sure are chatty today, Natasha," Stallworth said. "Any more stories you want to share with the new guy?"

She held her hands up. "Sorry, Mr. Stallworth, sorry." She resumed her typing. "I'll make my coffee less strong in the future. Only good advice and encouragement from here on out."

"Great," he said. "Come over this way young man. It looks like John is just coming back on the unit."

Just as I turned to follow him, Natasha touched my arm and spoke in a low voice. "I've got all kinds of stories for you. You'll see." She turned back to her computer like she had just shared a secret. I looked up again in Stallworth's direction as he closed the distance between him and the other man. John was a big guy. With my skinny frame, I was beginning to wonder how I had been selected to work alongside these men. Were they looking for another technician or a part-time punching bag for the patients?

"Coming back from a discharge, John?" Stallworth asked. I was still standing on the opposite side of the nursing station.

"Yes sir," John replied with an exhausted sigh. "Old man, Martin," he continued. "Christ, I thought we were gonna keep that guy here forever. How long was it? Almost two months? It only took him throwing his shit all over the hall for us to get him a bed at the state hospital. I mean, I know the guy is mentally retarded but all the restraints and the bedwetting. It was exhausting. And I know his jackass of a son has just been using the poor guy's disability checks to buy booze. All those taxpayer dollars hard at work."

Stallworth quickly cut him off. "John, this young man over here is our new psych tech. I'm introducing him to the team." John turned to me as I stepped across the nursing station and shook my hand. Yet another massive palm that dwarfed my own, attached to some of the biggest forearms I'd ever seen, covered with an assortment of aggressive-looking tattoos. "Hey, howya doin', I'm John," he said in a distinctively Boston accent. He had a graying goatee and a bald head. He was wearing gray scrubs and a pair of faded white Adidas tennis shoes.

"Stefan Lawson," I responded with a smile. "Just getting a lay of the land. Sounds like this place is where all the excitement happens."

"Oh, you have no idea," John said. "You should have been here the other day. We had a young military guy who was cheeking his medications. Ya know, pretending to swallow them but not really. He built up a small stockpile and managed to keep it hidden from us in his room and took all of it at once one night. Three o'clock in the morning me, four other staff and the security guard were wrestling this big brute down onto the floor. He kept yelling, 'I am God! I am God!'" John's big smile revealed several missing teeth. "I'm sure we'll be seeing him on the news soon and not for his charity work." John turned back to Stallworth. "Say, is Jimmie back yet? Has he met Nurse Jimmie?"

"Jimmie sounds quite popular," I chimed in.

"No, Jimmie will be back later next week," Stallworth said. "I was actually going to talk to you about that for a second, John." Stallworth turned back to me. "Do you mind if I talk to John in private for a minute? We're just going to go into the hall here. You can hang out in the nursing station."

"By all means, take your time," I said.

Stallworth and John went into the hallway. I could still see them through the nursing station windows. I stepped back and scanned the opposite hall facing the north. A middle-aged Asian woman wearing a Minnie Mouse jacket approached the nursing station and waved to me. I waved back. She made a gesture with her hand. *Come here.* I looked around momentarily but no one else seemed to notice her. I came and stood at arm's length from her.

"Do you know when I'm getting out of here?" she whispered.

"I'm sorry, I'm new here. I don't know when you'll be leaving but I'm sure if you take it up with the nurses later on, they might be able to help you. What's your name?"

A huge grin spread across her face. "I am patient 317717. I've been here a long time."

"Is that a number the hospital gave you? What's your *name*?"

"That *is* my name," she laughed. "I am patient 317717."

I shook my head. "I'm not sure I understand."

She wagged her finger and took a step back, the smile never leaving her tired face. "You'll have to do better than that," she said. "Pay attention." She then turned and walked down the hall.

"I see you met our Jane Doe," Natasha said. "It's true. She has been here some time. We can't seem to figure out what her story is. No family that we can find. I don't even think she is from around here. They've been working on getting her a bed at the state hospital, but they are always booked and her condition is manageable enough. So here she stays. For now.

"What's with the numbers?" I asked.

"If there has been any one thing consistent about her," Natasha said, "it's that she has always referred to herself as patient 317717. If you can figure it out, I'll put you up for a promotion." From behind me, I heard the south door open to the station. Stallworth was coming back in as John walked down the south hall. "So," Stallworth said, "I was thinking of letting you hang here for just a few minutes while I pop into my office to sort something out. You can chat with the staff a little more and then one of them can let you off the unit when you're ready to leave."

"Sure," I said. "That sounds good."

"Listen, I have a question for you," Stallworth said. "How would you feel about working the night shift? You would be working on this rotation with some of the same people you've just met. They will train you well and nights are not as intense as the day shifts."

"*Hmmm*," I said. "I've never worked a night shift before. What are the hours like?"

"7 pm to 7 am," he said. "Twelve-hour shifts."

"Oh, wow." I did not like the sound of that at all.

"I know it's probably not the most ideal hours, but it is a pretty easy job compared to being on a day shift. I mean, on the night shift, you'll come in, provide patient care for an hour or two, give out some medications with the nurses and then the patients go off to bed. Then you'll just have to monitor them. Check in on them and make sure everyone is accounted for. If any excitement happens, you'll have the other techs and the lobby security guard to back you up. More often than not, you'll just be sitting here in the nursing station, socializing and catching up on work." He gave a wink. "You'll probably even get to do some of that writing you like to do in your downtime."

I reflected on what he was saying.

"And," he added, sensing my uncertainty, "it pays more than what you would make working the day shift."

I thought about the house I wanted to buy—my own little place. Somewhere I could establish my adult life. I thought about the traveling I might one day be able to do. The extra money sounded good and I was brand new to the job. I wanted to make a good impression and meet the team's needs. What did I have to lose?

"Okay," I finally said. "I'll do it."

Stallworth looked relieved. "Oh, that's great, you'll be doing us a huge favor. Nurse Jimmie is on this night rotation too and she needs a good tech she can work with."

My eyebrows see-sawed momentarily at his remark. "She?" I asked. "Nurse Jimmie is a woman?"

"That's right!" Stallworth laughed. He pointed down the hall where John had disappeared. "I was telling John we're thinking of putting you on the night rotation. John was Mrs. Jimmie's assistant for about two years, so he can bring you up to speed about what some of your duties will be. Do you have any questions before I go?"

"No sir," I said. "I don't think I do."

"Well, if you do, feel free to reach out. We'll be in touch with you about your schedule in the next couple of days."

"Thank you, Mr. Stallworth," I shook his hand.

He disappeared through the nursing station door we had initially come through and made for the exit hall. John was coming back down from the patient rooms. He and Stallworth exchanged a wave as the manager keyed out towards the lobby.

John reentered the nursing station and came to the big center table where I was standing.

"So," he said, putting his arms down on the waist-high surface in front of us. "You're coming to nights, yeah?"

"It would appear so," I replied. "I've never had hours like that before. I don't know what to expect."

He waved the remark away. "Ah, you get used to it. It's not so bad. All of us have been working nights for years."

"More years than I'd like to count," Natasha added from her computer. I was amazed at how well she could work and keep up with other people's conversations at the same time.

"You drink coffee?" John asked. I had always enjoyed the smell of coffee, but a few attempts in the past had never given me cause to pick up the habit.

"Not really," I confessed.

"Well, there's a first for everything," he said. "Don't worry though," he gave a wink and a nod, "we keep some pretty good stuff on deck around here. If you're lucky, Mrs. Jimmie might even let you try some of her special reserves." I shifted my weight at the table. In one of the hallways, a telephone rang. An outside call for a patient, no doubt, but they were all in the group still, so it merely echoed through the hallway without a response.

"I'm dying to know more about this Jimmie lady," I said. "Don't know that I've ever even met a lady named Jimmie."

"Yeah," John said with a somewhat puzzled look, "I can't remember if that's her real name…or maybe she started using it later in life in respect to her father. His name was Jimmy, you see?"

I nodded slowly. "Interesting."

"Oh yes," said the female nurse named Caitlin, speaking for the first time. She was just coming away from her desk with a stack of papers in her hand. "Mrs. Jimmie is *very* interesting," she confirmed. She quickly pierced several pieces of paper with a nearby hole puncher with such force that it sounded like a guillotine dropping.

"Yeah," John added, nodding enthusiastically. "She is a real character and with as many characters we see in *this* place, that's saying a lot."

"You'll want to bring a jacket to work," Caitlin was saying now as she turned to speak to me directly. "Jimmie keeps it cold in here."

"In the nursing station?" I asked.

"No," John said. "She freezes out the whole unit. The entire floor becomes a fucking igloo. She says it's good for her asthma."

One of the patients on the south unit, an elderly-looking white male in his fifties wearing a New Orleans Saints hoodie came up to the nursing door to ask for the television remote in a slur of untidy words.

"Don't take the batteries out of it." Natasha handed it to the patient and returned to her chair.

"Ain't gonna take the batteries out it," he grumbled.

"If you take the batteries out," Natasha said as she resumed typing, "then we're gonna go through all your rooms again and there won't be any more TV."

"Ah said I ain't gonna take 'em out!" the old man snapped. "Wasn't me that *foolt* wit it."

"I'm just trying to tell you-"

"Ayah ya, ya, you talk and talk," he said moving away from the door. "All you people do aroun' here. Talk, talk." He moved down to the group room whispering something inaudible.

"How old is Mrs. Jimmie?" I asked.

"Eighty-one," John replied. "She's one of the oldest working registered nurses in the country. We looked it up online once. She's been in the field for over fifty years, working and traveling everywhere in the world. In fact, she *still* likes to travel." He turned to Caitlin and Natasha. "Where all did she go in just the past year? It was Hawaii, New York and...?"

"London," Caitlin said. "She loves London."

"Yeah, London." John said. "She told me once she knew she wanted to be a nurse when she was a little girl, back when the U.S. was in the middle of World War II. I was her tech for two years. I'm sure Stallworth told you. Boy, I could tell you some stories." He gave pause momentarily. "But it's always better to hear it from the horse's mouth."

Caitlin laughed from across the room. "Watch out. You call Jimmie a horse in front of her and she might kick your ass, John."

"You're right. I should choose my words more carefully." He turned back to me. "Don't be fooled," he said. "She is livelier than some people half her age. I don't know where she gets the energy. I do know that her mother and her eight aunts all lived to be in their late nineties, so she must have good genes on her side. I'll just say this:

We've had a lot of techs come through that...didn't last long with Mrs. Jimmie. She is," he thought for a moment, "very direct."

"That's a nice way of putting it, John," Natasha said, crossing her hands in her lap.

"Jimmie is just old school," he said. "She was born and raised in New Orleans. Those people down there run on a different frequency. She commutes from there to work."

I thought of the distance from New Orleans to our location on the Gulf Coast. "That's over an hour away," I said in astonishment. "She makes that drive at her age?"

John nodded. "She usually goes to our sister hospital when she works back-to-back. They let her use one of the patient rooms." This, I knew, was the hospital where my uncle worked. "It's an uncommon practice," John continued. "I don't even know if they are supposed to allow people to use patient rooms like that, but they make an exception for Mrs. Jimmie."

I was watching the group room on the north hall again. The man in the Saints hoodie was flipping through channels while the other patients sat watching the screen transition from one shot to the next. All except for one. An older Hispanic woman with slightly graying hair. While the rest of the patients were occupied by the flashing television screen, she appeared fixated on a large black man who sat several seats away from her. He seemed oblivious to her gaze.

"Mrs. Jimmie used to be retired," John went on. "But I think she has so many cats and dogs that she had to go back to work to support them."

"Oh, John," Caitlin laughed.

"I'm serious! Do you know how much she spent on that enclosed outdoor patio for her animals?"

"She doesn't want to stop traveling. That's what it is," Natasha added. "Eighty-one and she's still not ready to stay at home. She's living her life to the fullest. You have to admire her for that."

"Is that where she is now?" I asked. "On vacation or something?"

The room seemed to become hushed for a moment. Nobody answered at first.

"No," John said in a low voice. "Not exactly."

Caitlin, sitting at a computer, cut the silence by turning towards us. "I hate to interrupt, but we've got another admit coming. It's our old friend, Anthony Edwards."

"*Oy vay*," John muttered and stepped around the center table towards her. "Anyone want to take bets on which staff member he tries to sexually assault first? Natasha, I think he had eyes for you last time. Might want to watch yourself."

"Oh no," Natasha said, "you're gonna be his personal bodyguard this time, John. No female staff will be going anywhere near him."

"Last time I was assigned to him he pulled out his dong and tried to use it like a nunchuck to attack me. No thanks, I'd rather clean up piss and vomit."

"Don't you feel like you do that enough already?" Natasha retorted.

"I don't understand how these patients keep getting accepted to us," Caitlin sighed.

"Because that's what the Winded Willow is for," John said with an air of sarcastic seriousness. "It's a dumping ground for all the patients that nobody else wants. As long as we're paying taxes for the insurance these people can't afford, this hospital will always take them, because patients mean money. That's how the system works. This Anthony Edward guy, you can look at a calendar and figure out when he's coming back. He got his welfare check the first of the month and now the money is gone. He can't get drugs off the street anymore, so he's at the ER telling them he wants to kill himself. Now he'll come here and he'll get free drugs that we give him. It's the circle of life."

"Ah, so sad," Natasha muttered, shaking her head.

"That's the American healthcare system at work," John said.

"Write your congress."

Caitlin pointed to her computer screen. "Says here in his chart he came in higher than Jesus on the space station and that he had an old needle in his pocket."

"How about that," John said, leaning in to study the information with her. "Maybe he should try a stronger dose next time."

"*John*," Caitlin said in a shocked voice, yet a smile registered across her face.

My eyes caught the Hispanic woman in the group room again as they talked. She had still not taken her eyes off the other patient a few seats over. He was still watching the television passively with a careless look on his face. Then I noticed the older woman had what looked like a scowl on her expression. She raised out of her chair, turned around and picked it up.

I stood up a little straighter. The woman was turning back around and started shuffling toward the man she had been fixated on. "Hey," I said out loud. The nursing staff had their backs to me and were still looking at their computers.

"Vital signs are elevated but he looks stable otherwise," Caitlin was saying.

"He'll probably be here within a couple of hours," John added.

The woman suddenly raised the chair above her head.

"Hey!" I yelled. All eyes in the nursing station turned to me. A crash from the group room. All eyes turned to the sound. The large black man shot up from his seat just as the woman brought her chair down on his head with a wobbly swing. At the last moment, he had thrown his arms up, softening the blow. He looked shocked but barely seemed to register what had happened. The woman who had assaulted him was yelling now. The other patients jumped out of their seats and ran out of the room, all except one man who appeared to have no sense of anything that was going on around him, likely the result of really good medication or a very bad mental condition.

The nursing staff raced out into the commons area and into the group room. I followed them, not knowing what else to do. John pulled the black man aside, no doubt fearing the much younger man would clobber this woman to death if he decided to. He seemed more stunned than anything.

"What is going on here!" Natasha asked the old woman. "Why did you do that?"

"He's got the puppy!" The woman yelled back, tears streaming down her face.

The staff looked around at each other momentarily. "What puppy?" Caitlin asked.

The woman began to shuffle away uncertainly. "His shoe! He put it in his shoe," she sobbed. The nurses stood by watching her, not sure what to say. John was outside the group room, looking the man over for injuries.

"Ma'am, there aren't any animals on the unit. We don't allow animals here." Natasha said.

"Look in his shoes. He's got it." The woman continued to plead.

Before long the puppy was in the garbage can, then it was in the air duct and the broom closet. The man who had been hit seemed no more concerned than if a bee had stung him. He had an almost sleepy indifference to the whole situation. We would see a different side of him a few days later when we would be forced to give him a court-ordered injection against his will.

It was a really bad week for the poor guy.

Things eventually began to settle down. The psychotic woman was given her medications early for the night and sent off to bed. The large man she had attacked had taken up his seat in the group room again and was now watching an episode of *Wheel of Fortune*. Around and around the wheel went, hypnotizing all that watched, the commercials in between feeding on the vegetated states of consumers across America, perhaps not so different from the big man who watched with a half slack jaw and fading eyes.

I felt a hand on my shoulder which immediately tensed up a little. "What do you say, kid, that enough chaos for one day?" It was John with his friendly smile that I had already come to like. "Don't feel like you have to hang around," he joked. "I promise there will be just as much action when you come back."

"Yeah, I guess I could call it a night," I said.

"I'll walk you off the unit."

I turned and waved to the two nurses. "Caitlin. Natasha. It was good meeting you both." I went with John out into the patient hallway. He unlocked the door to the connecting hall and we exited the unit. Back in the main lobby, the old security guard looked up from a book he was reading and smiled, the odor of cigarettes lingering about him. We passed to the front entrance and I stepped out into the chilly evening air. The sun had disappeared from the sky some time ago.

"Just think," John was saying. "In a week or two, you'll get the chance to work with a real legend. Should be quite an experience."

"I must admit, I don't know how to feel about this Jimmie lady," I said. "I can't make out what you guys really think of her."

"Oh no, Mrs. Jimmie is a good lady. She just might take some time to get used to. You might think she's a little blunt at first, but you'll have a lot to learn from her, so just try to be open-minded and listen to what she has to say." He thought for a moment. "One more thing kid. I feel like somebody ought to tell you this."

"What's that?" I asked.

"Mrs. Jimmie has been through a lot in the last few weeks. That's why she isn't here right now. She is very passionate about her work, but I know things will be rough for her first few shifts. It might be that it makes working with her a little trying at times, but please just bear with her. You'll probably be very curious to ask her about her personal life, on the count of she's full of stories, but take my advice and just try to focus on the work. In time, Jimmie will open up to you and share more about her life, but for now, it's probably best not to pry too much. I don't want you two to start on the wrong foot and we could sure use the help here. Based on what you've seen today, I'm sure you can understand why it's hard to keep good people around."

I took in what he said. Small clouds of steam had been seeping from my breath as I stood listening. Nearby, the rumble of Earth signaled the approach of a cargo train as it began to screech in the night, a distant warning.

"Sure," I said. "I understand."

John gave a knowing nod. "Welcome to the Winded Willow." He closed the door and I could hear it lock immediately behind him. In the distance, the locomotive wailed and traveled at an unnerving speed with a rhythmic, mechanical pulse that carried it briskly through the night.

******

I pulled up to the front of the Winded Willow in a state of exhausted delirium. Turning off my car, I sat in silence for a moment, closing my eyes and taking a few deep breaths. I had made it through my first week at the hospital on the night shift. My first two shifts had been to orientate on the day schedule. After that, I was more than happy to fill my role as a night worker. By the end of that second shift, I had come to dislike the level of activity involved with day work. All the patients were awake during these hours and were always locked out of their rooms first thing in the morning. Many suffered from severe drug withdrawals and only wanted to remain confined to their beds. When this wasn't afforded to them, they often became very angry and got other patients emotionally worked up as well. Duties during the day included escorting patients to the cafeteria, providing medications, facilitating groups, assisting the nursing staff and, most importantly, keeping an eye on every patient and charting their activities.

It was tedious and tiring work. I couldn't understand how some of the staff had been doing it for so many years. It seemed like every hour there was a potential for physical conflict. Many patients spat venomous words at one another and constantly complained about the facility's conditions, even though what we provided them with was often much better than what they had on the outside. The staff I worked with seemed stressed from clock-in to clock-out. Having no experience in such an environment, I felt as if I was walking on eggshells the entire shift, confused by the procedures, the paperwork and the level of attention that had to be given to ensure total safety on the unit. The tech who trained me those first few days was a woman named Lashandra and she made it crystal clear just how serious my job was. Everything we brought from home into our workspace had to be viewed as a weapon. The careless mistake of leaving any miscellaneous item around could result in a patient using said object to cause harm. A misplaced key falling into the wrong hands could mean an elopement. I was panicked when Lashandra asked to borrow my pen one afternoon and I couldn't find it.

"I had it just a second ago," I stammered. "It was right here in my pocket." She stood studying me. "Are you saying you lost your pen?" She had asked.

"I don't know," I said, hating the words as they left my mouth.

"If you don't know where it is, we will have to stop everything we are doing on the floor. We will have to get all the patients into the milieu while the staff search their beds and bathrooms."

"Oh my God," I moaned. "It has to be here somewhere. I just-"

Lashandra then casually pulled my pen from her shirt pocket.

"You left it on the table when we were out there a minute ago," she said coolly. "That was a mistake."

I had taken the pen from her and apologized. "I'm sorry, I'll be more careful from now on, I promise."

"Good," she had said. "Your life might depend on it," and with a note of serious finality, "so could mine."

After a couple of days, I went to the night rotation. The routine was different here. I began working with the same group of people I had met originally. Caitlin, Natasha, John, Brandon and Fox were some of my shift regulars. To me, nights seemed far less stressful. I would arrive just before 7 pm. We would hold group and socialize with the patients for two hours, giving them time to make phone calls, play games or watch television. Around nine, the nurses would administer the nightly medications and it was lights out by ten. For the next nine hours, I would be in the nursing station or out in the hallway, checking in on each room, cracking open the patients' doors, peering in to make sure everyone was accounted for, then chart these rounds on a clipboard every fifteen minutes. All through the twelve-hour shift, we might admit a few additional patients. These usually came from our sister hospital in town where my uncle worked. The patients would go to the ER there and then be sent to us via ambulance. Sometimes, if the person was violent or unstable, they would arrive in a police vehicle.

Upon arrival, patients were taken into a room connected to the main hallway between the lobby and the patient units. Newcomers would be stripped naked, a process that was always cringe-worthy and searched for hidden weapons, injuries and anything that might hint at a medical condition that should be addressed. We would bring their belongings into the nursing station and inventory everything in front of them. Any clothes given to them had to have strings removed. No belts. No shoelaces. Nothing made of metal. Every pocket was searched for weapons or contraband. I couldn't hide my shock (or disgust) when the pockets of a patient's jeans revealed a used needle and a cheap gas station condom.

The condom itself, fortunately, was not used.

Perhaps the most difficult aspect of the night shift was just being able to stay awake for the full twelve hours. Thankfully, the staff was very forgiving of this and provided me with a couple of breaks in the early morning to rest in a dark room and nap for a few minutes. As suggested, I began trying the coffee that Natasha would brew up for us after the patients began to bed down at night. I found the taste strong and not particularly to my liking, but it did give me a little more energy.

I opened my eyes and stared at the hospital from my parked car. March would soon be fading into April and new life was blooming all around the Gulf Coast. I felt a big yawn coming on but did my best to suppress it. A white truck pulled in a few spaces down from me. Fox, who seemed even too big for such a large vehicle, leaped out from the driver seat and went around to the passenger side to collect his lunchbox and book bag. I opened the door and stepped out of my blue Corolla which looked like something his vehicle might devour as a lunchtime snack. I waved to my fellow psychiatric technician and we met in the road before proceeding to the hospital entrance.

"What's up, bro?" Fox said with his usual enthusiasm. "How are you sleeping?"

"I've had better," I responded dryly.

"Don't sweat it. You'll adjust. Did you buy the blackout curtains like I told you?"

I rubbed my eyes as we approached the front door. "I did. I still feel like my body isn't fooled though. Guess it just takes time."

Fox knocked on the door and the security guard let us in, a smell of cigarettes as we passed him. Once on the unit, we made our way to the break room located at the back of the north hall. As we passed the commons table, I saw the older Asian female patient from my first day on the unit. The patient who called herself 317717.

She waved at me as we passed. "So nice to see you again, Doctor," she beamed.

"You too," I said. I had given up trying to explain to her that I was not, in fact, a doctor. I placed my lunchbox in the fridge back in the break room and secured my belongings.

"What unit are you on tonight," I asked Fox, making small talk.

"I'll be on 2-North," he responded. "But if you need anything during the shift you give me a call, alright?

"Thanks, Fox. I appreciate that."

From behind me, the door opened and in stepped John.

"Hey, how's it going," John asked in his thick Boston accent.

"Hey, John, what's new?"

"Oh, not much. I just wanted to introduce you to somebody before the shift starts."

"Okay, who is it?"

He opened the door to the break room. "Come on," he said. I followed him down the hallway and we entered the nursing station. I waved to Caitlin and Natasha who were at their usual computers facing the north hall. They appeared to be a regular duo and provided care together on all the night shifts I had been a part of so far. In front of me, John was walking over to the computers that faced the south hallway.

"Hey, Jimmie," John said. "I got someone for you to meet."

I came around the center table in the nursing station as the gray-haired woman spun around in her chair, which was sitting up a little too high for her. She was short in her old age and the misaligned height of the seat kept her feet from touching the ground. She wore silver-rimmed glasses, purple scrubs and a pair of gray New Balance shoes. A large rolling suitcase was positioned near her desk and my imagination ran with what could possibly be inside. As she faced us, I could see her fondling with a gray necklace around her neck, which she quickly tucked away into her uniform.

"Oh, now who is this?" she asked.

"Mrs. Jimmie, meet Stefan. This young man is going to be your new assistant, Mrs. Jimmie," John said.

"Oh! Well, that's wonderful," she beamed with a great big smile which I couldn't help but match with my own. "You can put the medical charts together then," she added. I tried to keep my smile from fading completely at her remark. Assembling medical charts was one of the most tedious tasks on the unit. I had discovered my distaste for putting them together almost at once. In fact, everyone regularly voiced their despair for putting new charts together. Most of the other nurses I had trained with were fair when it came to making charts. They would usually assign me one and then do the next one themselves or suggest a team effort for all of them. Mrs. Jimmie, it appeared, had just given me the job of assembling every single one.

"So, what other hospitals you worked in?" Her raspy accent seemed a bit east coast but, knowing she was from New Orleans, I recognized the melting pot of tongues representing the city.

"None," I confessed. "This is my first real job out of college."

"Oh, well you just a baby then."

I laughed halfheartedly, though I didn't much care for the comment. I knew I wasn't as experienced as everyone else there but didn't feel like I needed to be reminded in such a way.

"So, Jimmie Wakefield, is it?" I asked. "Is Jimmie your real name or some kind of nickname?"

"What's wrong with the name Jimmie?" she asked. "Lots of girls were named Jimmie in the 1930s."

"I see," I said, searching for something to carry the conversation forward. I wasn't sure I was doing such a good job making a first impression.

"Listen here," she said pointing to a spread of charts on the desk in front of her. "We'll have plenty of time for formalities later, but we got a load of work ahead of us tonight. Patients are coming in from the emergency room right now. I read their charts, we know them. Both dope heads. Mark my words, they are gonna try to stir up a whole pot of shit when they get here, cause that's how they like to do. Trust me, I been a nurse for over fifty years and know what to expect. My instincts are very good. That's all you gotta know.

"Now, I been away for a while and need to get back into the swing of things. You, on the other hand, you young and need *lots* of practice, so you're going to help me with everything, okay? And so you know, if you're gonna be my assistant, I'm gonna teach you how to do everything the *right* way. The proper way, you understand? Your work reflects my work and I'm too old for a bad reputation. On my unit, we don't do anything half-assed. We do it whole-assed, you follow what I'm sayin'?"

My tired brain did its best to keep up with her fiery words. I felt my blood pressure rising a little.

Who does this lady think she is, I thought.

"Um, yeah," I muttered. "Sorry, I'm just kind of tired. Still getting used to this night shift thing."

She waved her hand. "Oh, you shouldn't be tired. You young. I been a night nurse for my entire career. I never worked days. Don't like all the extra administration. All the social workers and doctors running around like chickens with their heads cut off. It's too much. Do you drink coffee?"

"A little," I said. "I've been drinking some of Natasha's coffee."

"Agh," she grimaced. "The coffee Natasha buys is shit. You gotta have the good stuff. Life is too short to drink garbage."

From across the room, Natasha shot back. "There is nothing wrong with the coffee I buy, Jimmie. You can keep those remarks to yourself if you don't have anything nice to say."

"Natasha, you'd buy a bag of dirt if it was put on the store shelves. Don't talk to me about good coffee. You haven't the slightest." I stood somewhat dumbfounded by the exchange taking place before me.

"Okay!" John exclaimed, cutting into the conversation. "So it

33

sounds like you two have a busy night ahead of you. I'll leave you to it." He opened the door to 1-South. "If you need me, I'll be upstairs on the adolescent unit." There were two units upstairs, laid out in the same fashion as the downstairs units. One side was for patients who weren't as sick as the people downstairs and the other side was for adolescents. It was a much cleaner unit and far less chaotic. Needless to say, I envied John's departure.

"Okay, John," Nurse Jimmie said. "Take care, Darlin'." She turned to me as he walked away. "John was my assistant for almost two years. Good guy, but he used to ride with a rough group of men."

"What do you mean," I asked.

"Motorcycles," she said. "I'm sure you can imagine the type of organizations I'm talkin' about, but luckily he left that life behind. Not everyone gets to." She seemed to become distant all of a sudden. "Oh, but I shouldn't be talking about this. I'll get worked up."

"How come?"

"Nothin', don't you worry about it," she said, but I couldn't help but be puzzled over her statement. She rose from her chair and grabbed a clipboard from her desk. Standing up and against my tall frame, she barely made it to my chest. "Now I've got to go run this group," she said. "You start working on these charts, okay?" She was halfway out of the nursing station when she turned around. "You do know how to put the charts together don't you?"

I nodded. "Yes, ma'am."

"Okay, good." She took off down the hall towards the group room, almost shouting as she went. "Alright! Everyone into the big room here. We're gonna have group now. You, over there on the phone, tell 'em you'll call back. Come on now. We ain't got time to play around. Y'all move any slower and I may be dead before we even have the chance to get started." I watched her go as the patients slowly made their way into the group room. I turned to find nurse Caitlin looking at me from her chair.

"So that's, Jimmie," she laughed.

"Okay," was all I could think to say.

"Don't worry young man," Natasha was saying. "We're here to help you make it through the night."

I sat down to the charts in front of me, took a deep breath and began the arduous work of arranging the papers into the folders one at a time.

****

I was trying to catch up on my rounds, charting the patients' whereabouts at the ten o'clock mark. Lucky for us, most of them had gone to bed without complaint, except for one female patient who refused to be treated like a child. "You have to go to your room now," Mrs. Jimmie was saying. "It's lights out. Nothing else to do out here so you might as well go on. Get some sleep, why don't ya?"

"You can't boss people around like you do," the young woman spat. She was a tweaker in her early twenties. Black, matted hair that looked like it could start falling out any day. According to the staff who saw her regularly, she specialized in turning tricks for drug money out on the streets. "I didn't ask to be here. I don't *want* y'alls help."

"Well, I'm sorry," Jimmie said. "But that's neither here nor there at this hour. You can't leave tonight, so you might as well try to get some rest."

"Just leave me alone you old bitch!" the woman barked in her trashy redneck tone. She was wrapped in a blanket and sat unmoving at the commons table just outside the nursing station.

"Okay, suit yourself," Jimmie said coolly. She closed the nursing door completely so the patient couldn't hear us inside. "These young junky girls," Jimmie said aloud to no one in particular. "What a fuckin' mess. Young girls back in my day would *never*. Hey Natasha, did you give her scheduled birth control this evening? God forbid that girl ever reproduces. She don't wanna go to bed? Well, we'll see how long she stays out there when I bump the air down." She shuffled over to a thermostat on the wall.

"Oh, Jimmie, don't do that," Natasha pleaded. "It's already freezing in here."

"We have to," Jimmie snapped back. "This girl will not go to her room so we gotta get it good and cold. Those meds are gonna hit her soon and then she won't be able to stay at that table, even with the blanket."

"You put the air down *regardless* of whether patients are out there or not," Caitlin chimed in. "You're gonna freeze the AC system again and then it will be broke for another week."

"That wasn't my fault! Everything is cheap in this building. What kind of place in the deep south doesn't have a proper working AC unit? You know I can't work in a hot room."

"I don't see how seventy degrees could be considered *hot*," Natasha retorted. "Just leave it be, Jimmie."

"I'm puttin' it down Natasha and don't you touch it! You hear me? If you touch it, I'll know."

"Fine, have it your way," Natasha said passively.

"Right," Jimmie said, walking back to her chair. She gave a series of coughs as she sat. "Besides," she wheezed, "the cold is good for my lungs. I got the asthma." I couldn't help but feel like I should make small talk with my new nurse. "Have you always had asthma?" I asked.

"No, I got it from smoking cigarettes. Smoked for thirty years, since the age of fourteen. Everyone did it. When I started, they were twenty-five cents a pack. We'd go on our lunch break from school across to the sandwich shop and the owner would let us light up there. I smoked in the libraries, the hospitals, the airplanes. Anywhere the two-legged animal smoked, I smoked. And I was a *real* smoker. I could go through two packs a day, no problem. That's why my voice is so deep. I never smoked the left-handed cigarettes though." This, of course, being in reference to joints of marijuana. "And you wanna hear something else?" She turned to me, our knees were practically touching as we sat at the desk. "When I decided to stop. I did just that. I just *stopped*." She used her arms to animate the remark and paused for greater effect. "And I'm gonna tell you, if you want to beat an addiction, you have to know this one thing. You have to know that you're *always* an addict. If I smoke one cigarette - just one! - I won't be able to go to sleep until I smoke the entire pack. Ninety percent of the battle is knowing you're a slave to the drug. All this...*other stuff*," she waved her hand at the 1-South hallway, the group therapy room, the patient rooms. "It's all bullshit."

She pointed a finger at me. "And don't you go tellin' people I said that, cause I'll just look at them like they're crazy. I can't help I've seen a lot of things in my time and occasionally want to speak my mind. Most of the patients that come through here, their lives are stuck on repeat. They are in a cycle. They say, 'Oh ya, I'm gonna quit this time, I'm gonna change,'" She shook her head. "But their heart isn't in it. They haven't accepted it. You must be able to do that. Don't get me wrong, I think about those cigarettes all the time. I think, yeah, a cigarette would be real nice sometimes, but I know, if I smoke just one, I'll be a chemical prisoner all over again and, at my age, it's a slim to none chance of survival. Then again, over enough time, everyone's survival rate eventually drops to zero I suppose."

I tilted my head curiously. "Is that a line from *Fight Club*?"

She looked puzzled. "What the hell is a fight club?"

I gave my own questioning look. "You don't know the first rule of Fight Club?"

"No. I don't know what you're saying to me right now."

I was tickled a little by this for some reason and decided to amuse myself further. "Humor me," I pressed her, "If you had to guess, what do you think the first rule of Fight Club is?"

The confused look never left her face, but her eyes fell to the floor as if searching for the answer there. After a few seconds, she looked up again, an uncertain tone in her voice.

"Wash your hands?" she said meekly.

I opposed her previously searching gaze and found myself staring just above her at the ceiling tiles before slowly nodding my head and meeting her eyes again. "You know...that's probably not a bad suggestion."

"Yeah, you tell your little club I said that." She leaned against the desk. Her eyes studied me behind her silver glasses. "Back to what we were talkin' about. You ever fool with any of that stuff?" she asked.

"What, cigarettes? No, I've never smoked."

"Yeah? What about alcohol? You drink?"

I was beginning to feel like a patient being interviewed for my own admission.

"Sometimes," I said. "I tend to avoid it though. Never liked how it made me feel afterward." Which was true. I was fairly athletic and tried to keep healthy most of my life. "Yeah, I don't drink much myself," she said. "People get different once they take that monkey on their back. It's usually not until years down the road that the effects start to take hold." She stared down the long hall towards the patient rooms. "But our country *loves* its drink. Even after it has caused so much suffering. I have seen that suffering. I certainly have. If you don't do drugs as you say, then you should make a point to never pick it up."

I felt like I was getting lectured by my grandmother who, like Jimmie, was eighty-one and had made a life-long career out of being a nurse. My grandma was also a devout Catholic, a passionate patriot and a firm believer in living a straight-edged life. "Yeah, yeah," I said. "I hear you."

"That's good. Take it from me."

There was silence for a time in the nursing station. Outside, the female patient sat brooding at the commons table. I noticed her eyes dropping occasionally before she would open them suddenly, trying to hold to her defiance. The telephone at our desk rang.

"Oh, shit," Jimmie said. She stood up and walked away, the fastest I'd seen her move that night. "Let me get away from this damn telephone. Somebody's always got questions about something." I was left sitting there to answer another phone call. Another task I was not fond of. I didn't know whether I found her actions humorous or frustrating. I took the call. It was a doctor inquiring about one of his patients. I had to pull the individual's chart and stumble through a sea of papers to answer his questions. At least twice I made stammering remarks about being new. I could hear the physician on the other end of the line sighing as he waited for me to get it together. After several painstaking minutes, I finished the call and hung up the receiver. Jimmie was on the opposite side of the room with Caitlin and Natasha.

"I just don't understand how they can keep this place in the condition it is," Jimmie was saying. "I mean we got sick patients here. There's dust behind the computers. There's black mold on the ceiling tiles for Christ's sake."

"I hope that isn't really mold up there," Caitlin said.

"Hope doesn't pay the bills," Jimmie said. "And we breathin' it in. Y'all will be fine probably. I'm old though. This isn't good for my condition."

I sighed and stood up from my chair. Something about this woman's voice was wearing me down. There was a small bathroom in the nursing station. I went inside, turned on the light and lifted the toilet seat. After relieving myself, I washed my hands with cold water and soap. I looked at myself in the mirror and found a tired gaze in return. A small stubble of hair was forming across my face. I hadn't bothered shaving in the last few days. The work environment was pretty liberal in terms of work appearances. I could grow my hair out, get tattoos, wear scrubs, jeans or professional business attire. I would come to find such leniency was common practice in most mental health facilities. We were encouraged to be comfortable because we worked behind closed doors, away from the rest of the world. As long as our attire and appearance didn't affect our ability to forcefully take down a violent patient, it was usually a moot point. However, I quickly learned that I would have to have a certain level of mindfulness towards how I presented at the hospital. This was highlighted graphically in a story told to me earlier that week. "Doctor had her long hair in a ponytail," Fox had said. "One of her patients found out the doc was holding her a few extra days for treatment. Later that day, the patient saw the doctor talking to somebody in the hallway. Went right up behind her and grabbed that ponytail like it was a rope. One strong pull straight down was all it took."

I groaned into the bathroom mirror. I ran the water once more and splashed my face with the cold water. It gave me a momentary sense of refreshed energy that I desperately needed to survive these long, tiring nights. I turned the light off, went back to the nursing station and sat down. Nurse Jimmie, seeing me return, came back to our desk. "When's the last time you checked on them patients?" she asked. "Did you go on the hour?" I glanced at my watch; it was almost a quarter after eleven now.

"Damn," I said under my breath. "No. I forgot." I stood up and reached for my rounds clipboard.

"You can't forget about that stuff," Mrs. Jimmie was lecturing. "That is a *very* important part of your job."

"I know, I was just doing all these charts," I said, trying to keep my growing frustration in check.

"Don't make excuses. It's better to offer no excuse than a bad one. These patients are unpredictable. You know last year we had a black man go into a female patient's room and put his penis on her forehead? Is that something you'd want to happen to you?"

"I...what?"

"These people depend on you to keep them safe. As much from themselves as from each other. We housin' the animal kingdom in here. Don't you forget that, because if you mess up the administration will come after you, believe me, and if it's your ass, it's my ass too.

"Okay, okay, I got it," I was already hurrying to the nursing station door in an attempt to put distance between myself in her bombardment of criticism. My legs carried me quickly down the hall. I shook my head and made another heavy sigh. Carefully, I went to the first wooden door of the patient room at the end of the hallway. Out in the hall, the lights emitted an unbearable white radiance much too powerful for this hour. I cracked the first door and peered in. There were two beds in each room and a bathroom. I heard the snores of the sleeping men inside. I went to the next door and slowly opened it. Another male room. The light from the hallway fell on the face of the person in bed closest to the door, his dirty, unshaven features twisting in the sudden illumination. "Close the cock sucking door!" he shouted.

"Uh- sorry," I said out of instinct, quickly shutting the door. It wasn't until I walked away that I remembered it was my job to look in on the patients and I had done nothing wrong in doing so. I went down the line, opening each patient room slightly and peering inside cautiously, hoping to avoid another outburst. I returned to the nursing station and closed the door behind me. Jimmie, who was at her computer, turned to face me.

"So. Are they all alive still?"

"Yeah," I responded. "But I think the Asian guy in B1 is jerking off. Is there like...hospital protocol for that or something?"

Jimmie barely moved from her chair, her hands resting casually in her lap. "Is there another patient sharing the room with him?" she asked.

"No, he's by himself."

"Oh, well, just leave him be then. He can't hurt anybody." And with that, she spun back around to face her computer screen. I sat at my desk again. I was finally down to putting the last chart together. I thought to myself, maybe after I finish this one, I'll go have some lunch.

"Oh, listen," Jimmie said, turning back around. "I meant to tell you we got some more patients being admitted later tonight." She dropped two stacks of papers in front of me, followed by two empty medical charts. "Go ahead and put those together for me, would ya?" I looked disdainfully at the new mountain of work in front of me. I took a breath that seemed to reverberate deep in my bowels. "Sure," I muttered. A few minutes went by. Caitlin and Natasha were chatting with each other between their work on the other side of the station. The only other sound I could hear as I worked was Jimmie's slow typing on her keyboard. After a time, she began talking to herself.

"These crummy computers," she said. "They are just barely better than an Etch-a-Sketch and are so frustrating to use I wanna shake them just as much." I kept my head down on my work, punching holes, organizing papers, filling out dates, checking information, putting them all neatly in the right places.

"Unbelievable," Jimmie was saying now. "Just unbelievable."

I glanced up at the screen over her shoulder. I felt myself turning a shade of red when I realized she was just reading world news events. We were a year and a half away from the 2016 presidential election, so it was most likely something unrelated, but I couldn't tell exactly. All I knew was I had to put together a bunch of dumb charts while she browsed headlines. I held my tongue and turned back to my work. After a few moments, I saw Jimmie get up and go to the nursing station bathroom, the door closing behind her.

"How are you making out over there?" Natasha asked from her desk.

"Fine, just fine," I said from my side. Just then I heard something. It sounded like a small shriek. My eyes shot up in front of me, out the windows and into the patient hallway. I listened closely but heard nothing after that. Nurse Caitlin got up and came over to my side. "Got a lot of charts there, don't you?"

"Yeah," I said, forgetting the noise. "Big fun these things are."

She reached down and picked one of them up. "I'm not too busy right now," she said. "I can do this one for you." I looked up at her. She had a kind smile. "That's nice of you, Mrs. Caitlin. I appreciate that."

"Don't mention it." She went back to her side and sat down. I turned back to my chart. A couple of seconds later, I heard the door to the side bathroom open. A shuffle of footsteps coming closer to me. "Hey," Jimmie said. I looked up and found her face twisted in an awful scowl. She was breathing heavily. "What's the matter with you," she said. "Were you raised in a barn?"

I sat dumbfounded, not having the slightest clue where her angry words were coming from.

"What?"

"You left the toilet seat up," she snapped. "*I fell in!*" From across the room, Caitlin attempted to contain her laughter which was so strong that it came out as a snort at first. My mouth was now hanging open slightly.

"Don't you know when you're among women *you put the seat back down!*"

I was at a loss for words. Natasha spoke up from across the room. "Jimmie, don't you turn the light on when you go in there?"

"Well, my eyes aren't that good! It don't matter about that damn light." She turned back to me. "You need to go put that toilet seat back down. Go on."

I stared at her in disbelief. "You couldn't just put it down yourself," I said, feeling my face swell with blood. The interaction had suddenly shot my body temperature up and the freezing nursing station was like a sauna all of a sudden. "No," she shot back, "*you're* going to do it because that's what should have been done in the first

43

place." She was fuming. As much as I wanted to snap back at her, I couldn't. She was technically my superior and I didn't want to stir the pot being so new in my position. I put down my pen among my sea of medical charts, stood up and walked past her.

"And next time, have a little situational awareness of what you're doing," she said from behind me. "My mamma used to say, if you're not using your head, you might as well have two assholes."

I practically broke the bathroom light switch with an aggressive gesture of my hand and stared at the lifted toilet seat. I had never felt so much anger for such a trivial inanimate object in my life. I walked over and grabbed the seat with full intention to slam it down but, as I gripped it, I decided to take a deep breath in. Instead of relief, all I got was an overwhelming smell of urine. This bathroom desperately needed a deep clean. The attempt to calm my nerves had backfired, but it was enough to make me consider my actions. I set the seat down gently and walked out. Mrs. Jimmie was sitting in her chair, her hands on her knees, waiting for me to come out. This bothered me a great deal. "Now that's better," she said before turning back to her computer. "We might be able to turn you into a good technician after all."

I sat down to my work and wondered how long I would last at the Winded Willow under these circumstances.

******

"I don't know how long I will last under these circumstances," I said. I was on the phone in the break room talking to my mother before my shift. She was doing her best to convince me to stick it out and hang in, but so much of the job was already playing on my nerves. "It's so hard to sleep during the day," I said, "and the clientele they are housing in this facility...they can be really difficult to work with. The staff isn't too bad, but this Jimmie lady...I just don't know if we're going to get along very well."

"I'm confused," my mother said. "Jimmie is a woman?"

"Yes, her name is Jimmie. Something to do with her father I think. I don't know."

"Well, just hang in there, Honey. This is your first real job since you graduated. You're finally putting your degree to use. You don't want to quit out too soon. It might make it difficult to find work elsewhere. You don't want that to be the case so early in your career."

"*Ahhh,*" I moaned. "My career." The thought of working under conditions like this for that long of a time was unnerving.

"Give it a chance," my mom encouraged. "Who knows, the job might surprise you."

"Oh, it surprises me plenty," I said. "When you walk in on a patient doing martial arts naked who says he is training to be a movie star, that is surprising. The other day I was out in the commons area drawing with the patients and I tried to throw a crumpled piece of paper into the wastebasket across the room. It missed and landed next to an old Vietnam veteran who screamed, 'Grenade!' and dove under the table. That was surprising. We have a patient here who has numbers for a name and nobody knows anything about her. I have to watch my back everywhere I go and consider everything around me as a potentially dangerous weapon. Do you know why this hospital doesn't serve those little packets of butter with dinner anymore? It's because some guy started hoarding them in his room. Then, one night when he had saved up over a dozen packets, he stripped naked, rubbed all the butter over his body and ran out of his room to fight the staff. They could barely hold onto the bastard he was so slippery."

"I'm sure it's incredibly challenging," my mom said, "but you're a hard worker. The management will see that and after some time, you'll find another hospital to work at that is more to your liking. You'll see."

I sighed into the phone from the chair I was sitting in. I glanced at the cheap Casio sports watch on my wrist. I had paid all of ten dollars for it. It read a quarter till seven. "I hope you're right, Mom."

"Mothers usually are my son."

I smiled. "Oh, good. I guess I don't have to worry too much then. I hate to cut us short, but I have to go now. My shift is about to start."

"Okay, Honey. Have a wonderful day. Be the light for someone in need."

"Okay, Mom. I love you."

I hung up the phone, leaned back into the chair and closed my eyes. For a moment, I thought sleep would take me right then and there, so I opened them again and stood up quickly. After a few minutes, I exited the break room and made my way to the nursing station. I was not so much greeted by Nurse Jimmie, rather, she anxiously acknowledged my presence to inform me of the work ahead.

"There you are," she said in her gruff voice. "I know it's early but we need to be on high alert. We have a patient coming to us right now via ambulance. He's a young kid. Nineteen years old and he is in *bad* shape. They think he did the Spice."

I knew the name well. Spice had become a popular street drug in the last few years. Some weird, synthetic cannabinoids that reacted with receptors in the body in a similar fashion to which the cannabis plant attaches to, only these substances were causing users to have severe mental breakdowns and episodes of psychosis. This didn't stop thousands of people from using it though, especially since it was not detectable in standard drug tests.

"We've got Brandon here for backup just in case. You've met Brandon, right?" She gestured over to the other side of the station. Brandon, who had been studying a computer with Caitlin, turned and nodded toward us. His pearly white teeth looked radiant against his dark complexion.

I waved. "Sure, I remember Brandon."

Jimmie was moving about her desk now. "This kid will get here just after the other patients are going to bed, which is perfect because we don't want to deal with too many people at one time. He is very spaced out. He was having some minor hallucinations in the ER but has calmed down now." She dropped a red patient chart on my desk. "Go ahead and put this together while we wait."

******

It was almost one o'clock in the morning when the screaming started.

"What the hell was that?" Mrs. Jimmie said from her chair.

"Sounded like our boy down in A1," Brandon said, already darting for the door. The boy named Ricky had been pale and slack-jawed when he arrived a few hours ago from the ER. The brow below his fire-red hair was damp and his words were nonsensical stammerings as he fought off what looked like a dimension-shattering Spice trip from Hell. The young man had been incredibly lethargic in movement coming off the stretcher and appeared as though he needed a *bunch* of naps. We had put Ricky to bed without issue, but now it was clear that something had gone very wrong as he lay alone in the dark abyss of his room.

I quickly followed in line behind Brandon with Jimmie bringing in the rear as fast as her old feet would take her. Halfway down the hall, we broke into a run as the screaming suddenly erupted again with piercing clarity. Brandon burst through the door and the shouting spilled out into the hallway and filled the unit. The light from the hall poured into the darkness and fell onto the bed where the boy was thrashing about in his sheets.

"Fire!" he screamed. "My skin is on fire!"

Brandon was at his side in a second and was working to stabilize him. "Ricky!" he shouted. "You're okay, Ricky! Try to relax!" But the boy screamed and thrashed as if he was being dipped in a vat of scalding hot wax. His eyes were shut as if he feared opening them would sear his retinas to a pulp. I ran to the opposite side of the bed to help hold him down.

"Make it stop! Make it stop!" he desperately cried out.

The arm nearest me came loose from my grip. His whole body was soaking. The arm went flying at an alarming speed so fast I didn't even have time to register that I had been struck. I stumbled backward and tripped over my own feet in the close quarters of the tiny space, falling to the ground.

"Are you okay!" Jimmie yelled over the struggle.

Suddenly the boy had thrown his entire weight against Brandon and the two of them went to the ground as well. They were now both thrashing together, a mix of sweat and flailing bed sheets. I stood up in shock, my vision spotted with bulbs of dark circles in the already dim room, the light from the hall still the only source for visibility. I caught my breath.

"Should I call the security guard out front?" I shouted to Jimmie.

"Hell no, that security guard doesn't know his ass from a hole in the ground! Run back to the station and call upstairs for John! Tell him it's a code green! Brandon will hold him." I took one last look at the two men on the ground. I wasn't convinced Brandon would be able to hold him, but I dashed to the nursing station and dialed the number for the upstairs unit.

"2-North this is John speaking, how can I-"

"John! Code green downstairs on 1-North!"

"I'm on my way."

I slammed the phone down and sprinted back to A1. Several of the patients were now peering from their rooms down the hall. "Stay inside!" I yelled. I ran back into the room. Brandon was locked up with the patient still on the ground. He was a big, muscular man, but still appeared to struggle against the psychotic break the boy was suffering.

"Fucking pigs! I don't have anything here! I flushed it all!" The boy was raving.

"What can I do Brandon? Tell me what to do!" I shouted.

"I've got him! Get Mrs. Jimmie back!"

A door flew open with a forceful jerk from down the hall, and John flew around the corner and into the small war zone unfolding inside A1. He dove into the fold without missing a beat and immediately began to wrap the young man up in a vice grip. Between the two of them, Ricky was no match.

"They're killing me! They're killing me!" he screamed. "They threw me in the oven. Jesus fuck! Burn alive!"

"Get him into the isolation room!" Jimmie shouted.

The two technicians found their footing and brought the boy to his feet. He jumped about and continued to thrash, but the men positioned themselves in such a way that his flailing head would not hit their own. It was a well-executed hold they had performed dozens of times.

"Grab his feet, wouldya?" John grunted.

Doing my best to avoid another blow to the head, I wrapped my arms around both Ricky's legs, hoisting them up into the air so that we could carry him perpendicular to the floor. He couldn't have weighed more than a hundred-forty pounds, as rail-thin as he was, yet his body jerked and convulsed unnaturally against our grip.

"They'll eat me alive!" Ricky yelled. Through all of this, his eyes had not opened once. It was like he was fighting his own nightmares more than us. "Eat me alive! Dogs are out of the closet! Fire in the hallway!"

"Christ, he has lost it," John gasped. We were just a few steps away from the isolation room.

"The skins falling off! Where did it go!" he shouted incoherently.

"Lay him flat," Brandon instructed. "Where are the restraints?"

"I have them here." From behind us, Caitlin produced several straps from a black bag.

"Keep his legs steady kid," John instructed me. "Caitlin, get those straps across his chest."

Caitlin worked frantically to secure the patient to the bed. There were hooks down at the bottom that she worked the straps through, then over the patient's chest and to the other side. "Chest strap secured," she said. "Moving to the legs."

"They'll paint the house red with my blood!" Ricky cried. "Hide the knives!"

"Okay, I've got them," Caitlin said breathlessly.

"Ricky! You've got to relax!" Jimmie shouted over his wailing. "You're okay, Ricky, you are okay."

"It's crawling all over!" he protested. "Get it off me! Get it off!"

A high-dose sedative was ordered up and drawn by Caitlin, who administered the concoction with Jimmie's assistance. After several minutes the patient relaxed, but he continued to experience violent hallucinations, the likes of which I had never witnessed. For the rest of the morning, I was assigned to stand by Ricky's side. For the next several hours he lay there silently for several minutes at a time and then, without warning, would sit bolt upright in his bed, eyes shut and shout hysterically. "Hey! Why would you leave a fish tank in the bedroom! You can buy a twelve-pack of Coke for fucking twelve ninety-nine!" Then he would fall onto his back and lay motionless in a cold sweat. After several minutes, another outburst. "God damn piece of shit radiator, this junker won't go!" Always screaming. Always yelling. Imprisoned in a nightmare landscape. He sat upright again, his arms shooting out as far as they could within the confines of his restraints. He fumbled in front of himself desperately. "Floor it, God damn it! Go!" I realized his hand was reaching for a gearshift, the other a steering wheel.

Every time he fell back down, I thought it would be his last outburst. That his body couldn't possibly contain the energy needed to so much as lift himself up from off the mattress again. But it never stopped. For hours he wailed and hollered. A doctor returned in a futile attempt to assess him once more, but it was hopeless. He couldn't even be heard over the yelling. Eventually, I brought in a chair and sat down, my nerves fried from the tension, the excitement. I had never seen anything like it. I had no idea someone could break down so easily. I didn't know this boy's history, but I was terrified for his future. Could someone even come back from something as traumatic as this? Would he just be broken for the rest of his life? What was his life like just twenty-four hours ago? Is sanity so fragile that it can leave the body with just a single administration of a substance?

My mind raced with questions, with fear. I sat there and stared at the hopeless boy. I wondered where his mother was and if she knew where her son lay. With every outburst I found myself trying to piece together the reality this young man came from. Everything that came out of his mouth seemed to sting with a level of vulgarity that would make any modest, good-natured human blush. His thoughts were projections of hatred, violence, substance abuse, conflict, desperation and deep-rooted fear. The kind of fear that inexperienced young men turn away from and block out with anything they can, any mental projection that will shield them from the troubles, the insecurities that would normally eat them alive if they truly came face to face with them. The kind of fear that turns a lost, scared boy into the man that beats his wife, kills animals for pleasure and has no real connection to another person, the void in his life filled instead with a hunger for money, abuse or sex.

In short, this kid was totally Fucksville.

It was just another day at the office.

"Hey."

I jumped in my seat. I had not heard Jimmie come in through the isolation room door. "Sorry about that," she said. "Didn't mean to scare you."

"I'm not scared," I blurted out, but it didn't feel at all like the thing I meant to say. Jimmie regarded me with careful eyes. "No, of course you aren't," she said softly. "You're just tired. Go grab your belongings and head home. Sleep it off."

"You can't send me home. We have to watch this guy. What about the other patients?"

"Honey, you been in here so long dealing with this shit you don't even know what time it is. Go look outside. The sun is coming up. Our shift is over."

I stared at her blankly for a time. "It's seven o'clock?"

"Just about."

I stood up slowly and made my way past her. At the door, I turned around to face her.

"What about him?"

"Him? There is nothing more we can do for him. He has to ride this out. The other rotation will look after him. Give him medications as needed. But he has to go through that lonesome valley. Can't nobody go through it for him."

Back home, I stood in my shower for close to a half-hour. The water eventually faded from warm to cold. I walked to my room and climbed into bed, the blackout curtains making everything pitch black. I tried to fall asleep but I couldn't. My mind raced with the events of the night. I wondered how I could ever go on working in a place where I would be exposed to such traumatic occurrences on such a frequent basis. It seemed unnatural. I closed my eyes and began to meditate, a practice I had taken up in college around the same time I began going to yoga classes and studying deeper into eastern religions. I felt like I needed a sense of center more than ever now. I let my breath rise and fall, feeling the steady rhythm of my chest beneath the blanket. I searched for the loving smiles of my family, a kind word from a friend, the great fortunes of my existence. Whatever I could tune my consciousness to that would take me to a higher state. A state of peace. A state of rest.

Eventually, I came to that place and sleep found me shortly on the other side.

Life Stories in the Late of Night

Several nights passed after the incident with the red-haired boy. By the time I came back to the hospital, he was already walking around and performing normal activities. He was put on the opposite unit, so I never spoke to him directly. He always appeared quiet and moved about with sunken eyes, carrying his head low as if banished into shadows by some great unseen Reaper. The nursing staff said he had recovered from the episode, but he may never recover from the damage done. After several days, he was released. To where, I cannot recall.

I shifted my thoughts to the present. It was nearing one in the morning and I was painfully combating the effects of sleep deprivation. I closed my eyes. It seemed like only for a minute, but I felt my body becoming light and my mind began to flirt with the world of dreams.

"Hey," Jimmie said, "if you can't sit down and stay awake why don't you go stretch your legs."

I stretched my legs to the backroom for some coffee and hoped it would give me the boost I needed. In my first month at the Winded Willow, I had become accustomed to drinking the coffee. I didn't find it particularly enjoyable unless it had sugar and cream and I was worried I would develop a habit, but I felt like the ritual and the energy it provided more than justified my fears. I reached over in a haze of half-sleep and pushed down on what I thought was the bottle of coffee creamer we usually kept out. When I saw the white liquid coming out was much too thick, I thought the cream had gone bad. I then realized that the coffee creamer was sitting at the other end of the table. Someone had placed an industrial bottle of lotion in the room to use in between all the hand washing we did on the unit, which stripped our hands of moisture and made them dry.

"God damn it," I said, at first frustrated, but soon began laughing out loud. "Good grief," I said to no one. "I need sleep." I poured my soiled drink down the drain. A perfectly good cup of coffee gone to waste. I made another cup, pouring the hot liquid slowly, savoring the smell and the look of it. Again, I tore open a pack of sugar and dumped it in. I found my spoon and stirred lazily, allowing myself to momentarily become hypnotized in its circular motion. Out of delirious habit, I once again put the cup under the pushdown squeeze bottle of lotion but caught myself just in time before committing the mistake again. I was that exhausted. I chuckled to myself a second time. "Okay," I said and reached for the creamer at the far end of the table.

I walked back down the north hall to the nursing station, passing a shuffling Filipino woman along the way, recalling John's words about this particular patient. "That's Maria," he had said. "You think she's the silent type now? You should have met her a year ago. She was a raving mad lunatic druggy back then."

"What happened?" I had asked.

"She got into an argument with some petty street dealer. He shot her in the head with a pistol and she went into a coma for several weeks. They never could get the bullet out. The operation would have killed her, so that lead is just buried in there among all her brain tissue and cerebral fluid like a trapped spelunker in a labyrinth of darkness." He had nodded his head approvingly at this statement. "Yep. Mrs. Maria really mellowed out after she took that bullet to the head. She's so much more...well mannered."

I entered the nursing station. I lifted my cup to Natasha and Caitlin as I passed their desk back to my own. Jimmie sat at her computer and turned to me as I approached. I took my first sip of the murky, brown liquid and sat down next to her.

"Boy, that was a hell of a group earlier. One of the patients told us he had a dream last night that he was swimming in a dump truck full of Lortabs. You can't make this stuff up."

"That is something," I said.

She regarded my cup. "What you have there?" she asked.

"Coffee," I said.

"Where'd you get it?"

"The break room."

"Who made it?"

"Think Natasha did."

"Oh no," she said with a grimace and stuck her hand out. "Give it here. Let me taste it."

I wondered momentarily if I could tell her no, that I had gone through great lengths and that this cup of coffee was the first good thing that had happened to me tonight. Instead, I handed her the cup. She put her nose close to the rim. She smelled it. Her wrinkled hand brought it gently up to her mouth then came away. She sat there reflecting a moment and then waved her hand.

"Oh no," she said again, standing up now. "This will not do."

"What do you mean?" She was now walking away from me with my precious cup of coffee, right to the garbage where she promptly disposed of it in a great show of disgust.

"Hey!" I said. "I was going to drink that." Yet another cup of coffee wasted.

"Honey, that coffee tasted like asphalt. You gotta widen your palate. There is so much more to the world that you are missing out on. Come here, I'll show ya somethin'." She turned and went out the south-facing door. She went around the commons table to the patient snack room. With her key, she opened the door and went inside. She pulled open a waist-high drawer. It contained a bunch of utensils I had never seen before. Behind it all, she produced a gallon zip lock bag.

"You ever had Hawaiian coffee?" she asked.

I had never been to Hawaii, nor had I had their coffee, but the sound of it made my mouth water with anticipation.

"This is *100%* Kona," she went on. "Straight from Hawaii. I was just there recently and thought I'd bring some to work tonight. Did you know Hawaii is the only state in the U.S. that grows coffee? They have about eight hundred farmers that grow the beans there and it's all done at higher elevations. Really adds to the flavor. Sometimes they try to sell you *Kona blends,* but they don't tell you they only have to fill ten percent of the bag with actual Kona beans. The other ninety percent they can put whatever the hell they want. But I know better so I only get the real stuff." She was beaming as she spoke, her passion for a good brew becoming more apparent to me. I studied the bag she held. She opened it and the small pantry was at once filled with a sweet, rich aroma. "Ya see, they have all them volcanoes on the islands and it adds loads of nutrients to the soil. They get lots of rain there too and all the trees give the beans a certain amount of shade from the sun. It's like the perfect balance of soil, sun, fresh rain and calm winds. The smell of the Kona island is out of this world." I was transfixed by her words, the imagery she created of a place that sounded almost mythical in its description. A perfect paradise at sea. "This is my favorite coffee in the whole wide world," she said, "and I'm gonna let you try some."

She held the bag out to me. "Wow," I said. "Thank you." She turned around and produced a small coffee pot from below the drawer. I had no idea she kept all that stuff stashed back there. "Just wait till you try it," she was saying. "You can use my pot here," and with a sly grin, she added. "This one only brews the *good* stuff."

I smiled back. "Okay then."

"Make sure you wash it out and put everything back where I had it," she said as she went back to the nursing station. "Don't want any of these crumb snatchers around here getting into my stash."

After placing the grinds in the filter and letting the hot water drip over the beans, I pulled the pot from its housing and slowly poured the liquid into a new cup. This one I was determined to keep in my possession. I went back to the nursing station where Jimmie sat. She gave me a look as I entered.

"Give it a taste," she encouraged.

I put the cup to my lips and took in the full effect of the drink. A surge of delight across my taste buds. Hints of brown sugar, milk chocolate, honey and bright, fruity flavors filled my senses. It was crisp and clean. Smooth with a somewhat syrupy body. It was rich but not overpowering for a novice coffee consumer such as I was. A medium roasted color with floral aromas.

"It's amazing," I said.

Mrs. Jimmie grinned. "And that," she said, "is what *good* coffee tastes like."

I had gone my whole life avoiding coffee and had never had any interest in its taste. Within the course of one night, Mrs. Jimmie had introduced me to what I imagined was one of the best forms of coffee on the planet. I would become spoiled with coffee this good regularly.

"I'm gonna leave it all in that snack room," she said. "You know where it's at now. Anytime you need a cup, just help yourself."

******

Later that night, around three o'clock, I roamed the halls of 1-South. I held the ward keys that dangled from a retractable chain at my hip in one hand to keep them still as I moved down past the patient rooms, silent as the night, carefully applying just the precise amount of pressure to the doors in just the right places to open them without a sound. I scanned the dark rooms, now completely familiar with each layout. The patients slept on, oblivious to my watchful eye. Some nights I would walk up and down the halls dozens of times, just to avoid becoming sedentary at my desk for hours.

In the middle of the night, I would go out to the courtyard walled in by twelve feet of concrete and walk in circles under the moonlight, the trees blowing casually as I rounded the enclosure over and over, the grass and rocks crunching softly beneath my feet. Other times, I would take a yoga mat that I kept stashed in a nearby office and go outside to stretch. Sometimes, I would just lay on my mat when I was exhausted and allow myself to nap for a half-hour under the stars, coming alive again to the sounds of crickets. I was just beginning to feel comfortable in my new workspace. Even my relationship with Jimmie seemed a little less strained, her offering of this most sacred Kona coffee appearing to me as a gesture of goodwill. Maybe I misjudged her at first.

I checked the last patient rooms and stood at the end of the hallway. Everything was *quiet*. A word the nursing staff was somewhat superstitious of. They would scald anyone who uttered it aloud while at work, as such verbalization, they believed, would curse them to a series of admissions or a suddenly unruly patient. I was less concerned with such practices but found it all in good fun. As I stood observing the silent hall, I thought it might be best to take the time to grab my lunch from the back. Moments of inactivity like this were rare at the Winded Willow and I wanted to take full advantage of it while I could.

I made my way to the nursing station. Jimmie was reading a newspaper at her desk. U.S. politics from the looks of it. She turned as I entered.

"How's it going out there?"

"Everything's fine, Mrs. Jimmie," I said. "Silent as the dawn of time."

"Ya, well, you keep talkin' like that and it won't be for long," she joked.

I found myself smiling at her words. A real smile.

"What are you reading?" I asked.

"Oh, bunch of nonsense," she said dismissively with a great sigh. "I swear, this country is in deep trouble if we don't change things soon. Something has to give. We can't continue on this course like we've been doing. The generations before you fought too many wars for us to let it all go to pot now."

From across the room, Natasha and Caitlin were sitting at their desks.

"I agree with you, Jimmie," Natasha was saying, "but I don't know what you expect to happen. The young people won't vote and the older generations that get put into office aren't getting the job done."

Jimmie spun in her chair to address her. "That's because y'all keep voting in these white-ass republicans over and over again!" she exclaimed. "Now don't get me wrong, I'm a white woman, I've voted republican plenty times, but *these* people," she pointed to the paper in front of her, "My God, they barely people at all. They're *characters* at best. Puppets! Catering to the corporations, to Big Pharma and the one percent. They are ruining this country, going to war in places we got no business bein' in. Look at what we dealin' with now in the middle east. You can thank that dry drunk, Bush for that. And the hits keep on comin'. They're driving up healthcare costs, putting young people in debt for their education and cutting the social programs." She became animated and changed her voice in a mocking tone. "*Oh, look at me, I'm a prim and proper politician. My hair is so straight and my suit fits just right. I'm your friend. I'm fighting for you and your family. I'm for middle America.*" In her normal voice again. "That's all bullshit. Our system is in shambles. We don't have the leaders we need to run this country and the bill is going to come due soon, mark my words."

I began making my way towards the door to leave. I could sense things were about to get heated and, while I was a little surprised by

Jimmie's progressive words, I wasn't currently interested in being a part of a political debate, especially given how hungry I was at that moment. Behind me, Jimmie spun back around in her chair towards her paper.

"I'm telling you," she said, "sometimes I think I should just go back to India and stay there for good."

I stopped in my tracks and turned back around to face her.

"You've been to India?"

Jimmie spun her chair around once more, an almost surprised look on her face, as if her declaration that I had now brought into question was irrefutable common knowledge.

"Oh yeah," she said matter of fact. "I lived in the Himalayan Mountains of Kashmir for almost ten years."

"You did *what?*"

"Yeah! I absolutely love India. It's like a second home to me. It *was* my home."

I sat down next to her on the edge of my seat.

"I can't believe I'm just now hearing about this," I said. "You're a born U.S. citizen, right? How on Earth did you come to live in India for so long?"

"Well, that's a story," she said. She was leaning on the desk now, studying me. "What interest do you have in India?"

"It's hard to put into words," I said, "but a couple years back, when I was still in college, I had big dreams of traveling. I was taking a lot of world religion courses and had just started getting into yoga and meditation. I made friends with a guy who was big into a lot of the same stuff, especially anything having to do with eastern cultures. He had a small library of books and would let me borrow different ones and then talk to me about them. I started taking an interest in Buddhism as well, which I know has strong ties in India."

"Oh yes, I love the Buddha," she said.

"I had this professor at the University of Southern Mississippi, Dr.

Cappers," I continued. "Every year he hosted a trip to India for the university's religion program. He was one of my favorite teachers and he always spoke so highly of India. He studied deeply in the Buddhist tradition too. I'll never forget the words he said to our class one day. He said, 'Stepping off the plane in India is like stepping into another world.'

"Since then, going to India has become a life goal of mine. I want to know what that world is like. I want to understand why people love it so much. I want to taste the food and sit with the people. I want to understand what folks talk about when they describe it as a spiritual journey of the soul."

A smile came across her face. "Oh yes," she said. "India has a hold on you. I can see it now. You've really got the bug for it." She laughed to herself. "Ain't that somethin'." I could hardly contain my excitement. I was sitting with an American who had spent almost a decade in a place that I was quietly passionate about. "Will you tell me how you came to be there?" I asked.

She quietly searched her memory.

"I went with Tulane University in New Orleans back when I was working in the area. An Indian doctor at a medical seminar was running a trip to his home country and his group was looking for volunteers. I thought, well I'd like to go to India, so I raised my hand. A few weeks later, we were on our way.

"Now, I may have grown up in the Bible Belt like you have, but I am not a religious person. I don't worship any god. Nature is my God. The birds and the big cats. A river runnin' through the valley in the mountains. I don't put a lot of weight into the spiritual talk outside of those things. I think when you die, you do just that. I've never really believed in any kind of reincarnation either but," she is looking at me but I can sense her eyes are seeing another time and place entirely, "the first time I got off the plane in the Himalayan Mountains...I felt like I had been there before." She held up a hand. "Now, I've traveled all over the world, Darlin', and I've seen all kinds of places, but nowhere have I ever had a feeling like that come over me. It was like having deja vu. It lasted several minutes and then it was gone. I knew I was somewhere special."

She leaned forward and smiled. "And I tell you, I had the *best* time there. I fell in love with the place almost immediately. The people, the food, the temples, the mountains! It was all so breathtaking. It felt like being home. Like I was reconnecting with a friend I hadn't seen in many years. I still remember that feeling. I sure do." Any sense of exhaustion seemed to flee from my body. She had me totally hooked with her words, her enthusiasm.

"What year was this?"

"I had stopped smoking by that time," she said. "Must have been 1984."

"I half expected you to say the seventies."

"What do you mean?" she asked puzzled.

"Well, everyone was going to India in the seventies," I said. "Once the Beatles went it seemed like everyone had to go. Then we had all the alternative thinking, the peace, love and drugs thing going on. The counter-culture they called it. You had *The Harvard Psychedelic Club*. Timothy Leary, Ram Dass, Huston Smith and Andrew Weil, along with countless others all advocating for westerners to look closer into the deep spiritual and cultural maturity of the east."

She gave a great laugh and pounded her tennis shoes against the ground. "Boy," she exclaimed, "you've done your homework, haven't you? The Beatles, huh? I never cared much for 'em. Their voices were too high. I like a man with a low voice, but for a bunch of men singin' songs and carryin' on, I guess they weren't all that bad." I suppressed my instincts to argue with her about the merits of one of my favorite bands that she so easily dismissed, not wanting to detract from the core of our conversation, as it was proving to be the most unifying discussion we had yet shared.

"So, what happened?" I asked. "You just left everything behind? Your family, your country, your career?"

"Not all at once," she said. "I came back to the States and eventually made a few more trips out to India again, but every time I visited, I had to make myself get on the plane to come back home. It felt wrong to leave. So I retired for the first time from nursing in the late eighties and left the country. I bought a house in the mountains around Srinagar. Big house. Six bedrooms, six bathrooms. And I had two live-in servants, Javani and Rashid. I lived upstairs and they lived downstairs." She leaned forward and said in a whispered tone. "One of my favorite things about India is the American dollar goes a *loooong* way."

"Holy shit," I said. "Sounds like it."

She went on. "My servants would come up every night with homemade yogurt. Oh! It was the best yogurt you ever had. Just out of this world. Rashid liked to cook and clean the house. Javani enjoyed being outside. He would tend to the garden and plant things. I brought him seeds from America, corn and such. He loved planting those. I had two dogs when I went over there and I had to pay my servants *triple* to take care of them. Muslims don't like dogs, ya see. It's ingrained in their religion. They think they are filthy animals and neither one of them had ever touched a dog.

"One of my dogs I brought with me from Miami was a big, purebred Basset Hound named Rex. As soon as I got there, I went to New Delhi and I picked up a newspaper and started looking for another dog so that Rex wouldn't be alone. I wanted him to have a friend. So I found this black Dachshund, and the owners wanted six thousand rubies. I called them up and they lived in Kalkaji, which is kind of like the Metairie of New Orleans, but a little more upscale. It's the bedroom of New Delhi. They told me they would bring the dog to me and that he was six weeks old." She rolls her eyes. "Well, his eyes weren't even open so I know he was probably only about two weeks old but they knew I had that money and they wanted it. So I bought the dog and we named him Puppy because he was just so tiny. It's funny though because this breed of Dachshund was from Moscow, and those types are bigger than the ones Americans see most often.

"After several years living with those dogs, both my servants came to love them dearly. When I eventually had to leave the country, Javani begged me not to take Puppy. He had grown so attached to him. Of course, I couldn't do that because he was my dog and I loved him too. That was one of the best dogs I ever had." Her tone becomes solemn now. "He just passed away recently," she said.

She looks off down the hall, her mind replaying a thousand memories of lost love and happiness in what feels like another lifetime. "I sure do miss him sometimes," she says softly. I sense a sadness in her that moves me. It's a compassionate side of her I have not seen before. Not wanting to lose her train of thought, I try to push the conversation forward to India again.

"Why did you come back?" I asked.

She seems to shift in her chair and finds my eyes again. Her voice was more hard and raspy again.

"War," she said. "The great undoing of man."

In my mind, I quickly analyzed the time frame she had described. "You left because of September 11th?" I inferred.

She nodded. "It was late at night when it happened. Javani came up to my room in an almost frantic state. 'Madame! Madame! Something has happened to your country. I must turn on your television.' I didn't know what he was talking about. He said there was an attack. We turned on the television and the first tower had already been downed. I thought it was a mistake. 'Javani,' I said, 'This can't be right. This is a movie or something.' He said, 'No madam, it's on all the news stations. This is happening right now.' We flipped through the other channels, but we only had about four or five channels. Every one of them was broadcasting the attack. Then we saw the second plane hit. We stayed up all night, my servants and I, watching the news until the sun came up. I knew our country would never be the same after that. Worse yet, my life in India would most certainly change."

The hospital was silent as she spoke. From across the room, Natasha and Caitlin stopped their work to listen to her story, which they were undoubtedly familiar with but transfixed by all the same. "Sure enough," she said, "I'd be proven right not long after that. Attacks started occurring all through Northern India. The border of India and Pakistan were always under tension, but things started to escalate and I knew it wouldn't be long before that conflict was going to come to my front steps and when it did, I didn't want to be the American who answered the door, you know what I'm saying?

"I had a close call," she continued. "at this beautiful park in Northern India. There is a point where all four major rivers in the region meet up. For the life of me, I cannot remember its name, but it is perfectly round and they say the water goes down almost a hundred feet." She leans forward with her hands together and says in a low voice, "But you can drop a coin in it...and you can watch it sink all the way to the bottom." She lets the last statement hang in the air before covering both arms. "Oh, it's spooky. I'm getting chicken skin just thinkin' about it." She becomes livelier again. "Almost nobody is ever there at this place, because it's a disturbed area. The Muslims fight over it. We went on motorcycles from Srinagar. It was maybe a two-hour run."

"*You* road a motorcycle through the mountains," I asked in surprise.

"Well sure," she responded. "We went up into the mountain range, me and a girl I knew from Germany. She was later killed in a car wreck on the Autobahn when she was about fifty years old. Very tragic. But this party I was with at the time, there were maybe four or five of us. They went down from the mountain into the town below to get chickens. We were gonna have a good ole fashion barbecue that night.

I stayed up in the mountains by myself to cut the onions and potatoes.

"As I said, everything was closed because of the fighting in the area. There were curfews, but we were granted access anyway and we were staying in this little cabin. I'm cutting my potatoes, I look up and I see something that catches my eye. Four men. I could see the beards on them." She grabs at her chest. "My heart skipped a beat. They came out of nowhere and I was all by myself. I kept on peeling the potatoes, just sitting there on them steps.

"That's when I saw the machine guns. Ah oh, I said, but then there was nothing else I could do. I knew there were patrolling militias in the region fighting the Indians, but I didn't expect to come across one alone like that. Everyone at my party, besides my friend from Germany, were all Muslims too, but that didn't do me any good with them all down in the town. Finally, they came upon me, and the group leader asked me how I was doin'. He spoke English. I told him I was doin' fine. He asked if I was an American and I said I was. He said, 'Let me see your passport if you're an American.' I said, 'Why you wanna see my passport?'"

"He said, 'Because I want to see if you're a Jew or not.'

"I told him, 'If you gotta ask if I'm Jewish then you don't know anything about the Jewish people.' He didn't understand what I meant. I said, 'First of all, if you look at my passport, it's not gonna tell you if I'm a Jew or not. Second, if you look at this nose, it's not a Jew's nose. The Jewish people typically have noses you could land an airplane on.' Now I would never make such a comment but, at the time, I feared my life was in danger. I needed to break his concentration. Shake him up instead of the other way around. Well, it worked. That got him laughing."

She leans forward in her chair. "Do you know why I was able to get myself out of that situation? It's because I didn't show fear," she said sternly. "Men of power with ill intention in their heart thrive on fear. If they sense it in you, they will know you're weak. Maybe it's the generation I came from, the hardships of war, but I always told myself I would never live a life of fear. I would never show weakness. I would only show my strength." She reached over and grabbed my bicep. "I don't mean this stuff here," she said. She pointed to her head. "I'm talking about what's in here. No amount of muscle will serve a person like a strong mind. But you gotta believe it. It's gotta be something that becomes a gut instinct."

She sat back again. "The man asked me how long I was gonna be there and who I was with. I told him about my friends down in the town. He said, 'I watch over these mountains and I will spread word to my men that you and your friends shall not be disturbed.'" She nodded her head in approval. "He was good on his word. For the rest of our stay, we were never bothered and when my Muslim friends came back from the town, they told me who he was. He was *the* highest-ranking commander in the region. I've got his picture somewhere because I saw him come on the BBC one time. That tickled me. I believe he's living in Pakistan now."

She folds her fingers together and cackles to herself, letting the tension of the close encounter slip from her thoughts to the memories that she cherishes the most. "That was such a beautiful place," she said with a hint of childish innocence. "The water ran down from the mountain and you could hear it rushing past all night long as you drifted off into sleep. Yeah. The park where the four major rivers met. You could see all the way to the bottom. A hundred feet they say."

Her demeanor changed as she reflected on the tensions that forced her from her home overseas. "I remember when I finally made the decision," she said solemnly. "I was driving from Kashmir to Srinagar with Javani and Rashid. You might find it funny that *I* was the one who drove my servants around. They didn't know how. We passed a military jeep going the opposite direction carrying a group of a half dozen men or so. Moments later there was a blast and my car shook violently. It was so severe that the back bumper was smashed in. We turned around and went back. We were the first people on the scene to find the jeep almost completely destroyed by an IED. All that remained was the frame and four smoldering tires that had flown fifty yards from the explosion in every direction. Other military personnel showed up with bags to put the soldiers in, but they left with those bags empty. A few weeks later, two bombs went off at a shopping center I frequented in Srinagar."

She shook her head slowly recalling the events. "That's when I knew it was time for me to leave. My children feared for my safety. I had to return to my country, back to my family and away from the life I loved in India." Her thoughts drifted away for a time. For a moment, I thought I could see her eyes mist over behind the glare of her glasses. She brought her hand to her mouth and then to her cheek. "Oh, how I miss it," she finally said. "I've longed to go back ever since I left. To feel that connection again. To see my friends. To walk in the places where I took so many pictures."

"You have pictures of India?" I asked.

She shook her head. "I use to have thousands of pictures from India and everywhere else I went in the world. I use to pull them out late at night and go through the pages of my albums. I'd look at those images and think back on all the good times I had. But then Katrina came in 2005 and the city of New Orleans went underwater, my house along with it. I lost all my pictures, even the digital copies. They're all gone now. All that's left are my memories."

"Oh. I'm so sorry to hear that, Mrs. Jimmie."

She gave a great sigh. The hospital was eerily quiet in the early hours of dawn. "There was a time when I thought I might return with my son. He traveled with me to India often. Even lived with me for a while. We traveled all around the world, he and I. My daughters, they didn't care to travel as much. Everyone likes to travel to some degree, but it's to get away from something a lot of times. To leave their lives or their responsibilities just long enough so they can continue to tolerate them when they return. I've always embodied that wandering gypsy soul. Traveling was a way of life. I was born for it."

Her hand slid down to the front of the purple scrubs she was wearing and came to rest on her heart as if there was a growing sorrow buried beneath her palm. "But I have to face the reality," she said in a trembling voice, "That part of my life is over with. Things have changed and I just don't see myself making it clear to the other side of the world like that anymore. Besides, gets hard for me to walk far now. Then there is the asthma too. Some parts of India, they got really bad air. No. I can't do that. It hurts to say it out loud, but it's the truth and I am learning to accept that one day at a time."

My heart sank with her words. I realized just how important India was to her. I wasn't exactly sure if it was her age or her general health that kept her from traveling again. Like most Americans, I was completely ignorant of the political turmoil in the country or what it meant for Americans to travel to certain parts. I watched as tears filled her eyes, the torment of cherished memories being the only remaining comfort to an American woman who felt as if she belonged on the other side of the planet. I was filled with sympathy and my mind scrambled for words to console her. Anything that may give her some peace.

"Do you believe you could still travel such a distance?" I asked.

She breathed deeply from her chest and fought through her sadness. "Perhaps," she said, "it would be much more difficult now, but I think I could manage. I don't know."

I now felt strangely connected to her cause. I continued to voice my thoughts at the risk of seeming foolish in my thinking. "Is it the political unrest that worries you? Would it be too dangerous for you to go back?"

"No," she said, rubbing her hands. "It's more than that."

She took off her glasses and rubbed her eyes. Her face had become flush. At first, I was thrilled to be speaking with someone, an

American at that, who had spent so much time in the one place I wanted to visit more than anywhere else, but now, seeing her in such distress, I was emotionally conflicted by our seemingly innocent conversation. Mrs. Jimmie took a deep breath, adjusted in her chair and once again appeared to regain the composure of her former self, the woman I had come to recognize over the last few days.

"I'm sorry," she said. "I didn't mean to get all emotional like that. I've had a lot on my mind these last few weeks and sometimes it just bubbles up." She turned to me and laughed, her eyes clearer now, more familiar. "You know, us old people, we can get like that when we start digging up those old memories, especially for the people and places closest to our heart."

I smiled. "I understand," I said. "Thank you for sharing your story with me."

"Oh, Honey," she laughed, grabbing a stack of papers and starting to spin away in her chair. "You haven't heard that half of it."

Her words sparked a new interest in me. I wondered what other treasures of life she had experienced. Where she had traveled. What fifty years as a nurse had taught her. What life in New Orleans was like as a small girl during World War II. I suddenly had a million questions.

"I'm all ears," I said.

She laughed again, a sound I was thankful to hear after she had poured so much out to me. "Those are stories for another time," she said. "Look out the window. The sun comes again to meet the day. Maybe on the next shift, we can talk again like this."

"I'd like that," I said. She rose from her chair and began to walk past me. "Okay then," she wheezed, standing up from her chair, "why don't you finish up the last rounds on the patients and we can call it a night. I'm gonna go to the bathroom and then sign off on all my charting." She stops and turns to me, raising a cautious finger in my direction. "You put down the toilet seat since the last time you've used it?"

"I may never leave it up for the rest of my life," I said.

"Excellent." She turned and began to shuffle away. Her voice hard like whiskey barrels and burnt cigarettes, fading as she went. "At first, I had high hopes we could make a good technician out of you. At this rate, you might get yourself married to a nice young lady and make a good husband someday too."

******

I watched the scene unfold before me. The patient was tall with a lean athletic build. Black facial hair and glasses that sat crooked on his pointed nose. He was holding the patient phone in his hand. I knew he had just spoken to his soon-to-be ex-wife about the custody battle over his kids and most of the money he had worked his whole adult life for. A gambling problem mixed with an unquenchable thirst for hard liquor had brought him to where he was now after years of slipping down to rock bottom. At first, the phone call out in the commons area had been tense and his voice had risen. The staff had been watching, sensing the coming escalation. Then he had started yelling into the phone. Protests about taking his kids, taking everything he had earned.

He stood up from the chair, gripping the heavy-duty receiver corded to an old telephone box, made of metal and thick plastic. He began to slam the receiver against the mounted machine in several lighting fast blows, over and over again until the cord was ripped from the housing, years of similar abuse from other patients causing it to finally give way. Patients all around him watched silently as Fox and John ran from the nursing station and approached the man from behind. They shouted to him. He stopped. His left hand was now braced up against the wall. His right was still gripping the receiver with the long metal cord hanging like a whip, blood dripping down it and gently falling onto the floor. The man stood there, taking hurried breathes through clenched teeth. The two techs approached slowly from behind, saying things I couldn't hear. Come with us, I think they might have said. Let's go somewhere to talk.

The man held his ground, still facing away from them. They crept closer. The patients began to move toward their rooms at the pleading of the nurses. Just as the techs were within a few feet of the man, he suddenly spun around and began lashing out with the phone, the cord-cutting through the air and sending thin streams of blood that painted the walls. Obviously, official protocol went out the window immediately as John and Fox dove headfirst towards the man after quickly evading several furious swings. John connected with the patient first, tackling the man at his waist. He exerted such force in the movement that they both went back several feet and collided with the meal table, flipping over it in unison and collapsing on the floor at the other side. Fox was there instantly, along with several other staff members who rushed in after the skirmish had begun. Within seconds, there were six people on top of the patient and the phone was removed from his death grip. The man's face twisted and his mouth opened wide in a wild and silent scream.

Silent, because the recording I was watching, produced no sound at all.

"Holy shit," I said, leaning away from the computer. "That was crazy."

John clicked the mouse and froze the image before us. "Oh, just another day in the life," he said with a smile while stroking his gray goatee. "I'm not proud to say I've lived a life of bar brawls and street scuffles all along the east coast, but that was the gnarliest fight I've had at the Winded Willow. The only other person that bruised me up worse was that sixteen-year-old girl upstairs that kicked me in the nuts last year." He gave a great sigh and his face was troubled, as if from a wartime flashback better left forgotten. "Good thing I'm not planning on having kids."

I discovered that going through old video footage of patient takedowns was a common pastime at the Winded Willow, especially when a new guy like me was brought in. The old recordings, kept for legal and training purposes, provided hours of enjoyment for the hard-working staff. It seemed appropriate, given the dark gallows humor that flowed through this unit. As time passed by into the early hours of the morning and all the patients were asleep in bed, our conversations morphed and descended into the bizarre and hysterical. I imagined it was a similar vibe in the circles of cops and firefighters, sitting at their stations for hours on end. Having been a lifeguard for eight years at a local pool growing up, I felt right at home with this type of banter.

"Luckily this guy wasn't too big," John was saying of the man still on the screen, his face frozen in a tormented howl of anger. "He might have presented a real problem then, but if there's one thing I've learned working here, you can never be too sure how strong someone is when they go into a blind rage like that." He started clicking through other video folders. "Here, let me show you the video of this autistic guy from a couple years back. He couldn't tie his shoes to save his life but he had a right hook that *put me on my ass.* And the grip on this guy, my God. It took half an hour to get him sedated enough to pry his hands off from around my neck. I swear, it's a mystery to me how this dude ever managed to jerk it without ripping his own dick off."

"Alright you two, come away from there," Jimmie said from behind us. "It's too early in the night to be talking about shit like that. At least let me get a cup of coffee first."

"Sorry about that, Mrs. Wakefield," John said. "I have to get back up to the second floor anyway."

"Take care then. Hopefully, we all have a good night."

******

"If you don't move me to another room, I'm gonna kill that boy."

The large, black man standing at the nursing station window had uttered these words as casually as if he had been discussing the weather with a friend. He was about fifty years of age with a shaven head and a big scar down his left cheek. Mrs. Jimmie, who was scribbling away at papers, stopped to regard the man, her poor ears grasping for his muttered words.

"What's that now?" she asked with a squinted face.

"That boy y'all got me with, he a sugar foot."

"A sugar what?"

"He a sugar foot," the man repeated. "That boy sweeter than sour sauce. He fruity for the booty. I don't sleep with no gay man. Y'all better move me or something bad gonna happen." I sat at my desk watching this new exchange. Jimmie shot up from her seat. "No, no, no! There isn't gonna be any of that!" she fumed as she approached the man head-on. He was leaning on the door. "Come on now, move your body so I can get through," she barked. The man seemed a full two feet taller than her. He lazily moved aside and Jimmie shot passed him down the hall to the patient's room. "Listen to you," she said. "Talking about killin' other people this close to bedtime, that's no way to behave."

The man followed her as she went. "The boy wants to get fresh with me," he mumbled. I watched them go, keeping a close eye on them both, but I knew Jimmie had control of the situation. "Nonsense," I heard her say. "That man is only worried about his treatment. He is just doing what everyone else is doing to get out of here and that's to be on his best behavior. You go making threats like that and you think the doctors will let you back out into the real world? Like hell they will." They both disappeared into the room.

It seemed like it was always nighttime when the patients became the most bizarre, their words and actions becoming more unpredictable. Something about the day ending, all of the groups suspended, all the phones unplugged, no one to socialize with, only their thoughts to reflect on as they confronted their demons. Nothing to distract them from the fact that they were temporary medical prisoners, forced to consider the circumstances that had brought them to this point. So they acted out. Resisted. Talked back. Fought the staff. Anything to not have to deal with the lonely nights of restless sleep from withdrawals and tormented memories. *Sundown Syndrome*, Jimmie called it.

The rest of the unit was fairly quiet. I put my paperback copy of Rick Strassman's *DMT: The Spirit Molecule* down onto the desk and went to the patient snack pantry to get some coffee. I went into the hall. I could hear Jimmie talking to the man still, her voice level. I unlocked the door to the snack room and rummaged about for the coffee pot and the zip lock bag containing the black gold I now knew as Kona. I placed the filter and dumped several tablespoons of the fine, dark grinds inside, just like Jimmie had shown me. I used a fresh water bottle to fill the pot and hit the ON switch. I cracked the door to the pantry. Still quiet out in the hall. I let the door go and it closed with its heavy weight, same as all the other doors on the unit. I listened to the sizzle of the water droplets fall through the filter and begin to drip slowly into the clear pot. That delightful aroma I remembered filled the small space. I smiled to myself as the murky liquid effortlessly descended with each passing moment, my heart filling up in unison with the glass container. I poured out the portions and dressed them the way Jimmie took hers, a little cream, a little sugar. I cleaned the pot and flicked off the power switch before taking both cups and exiting to the hall.

"Hello, Doctor," the Asian woman who called herself 317717. "How are the proceedings going?" I stopped to make momentary small talk. 317717 was a weird bird, but she was always pleasant and did stroke my ego with her delusions of wrongful identity. "Everything is going just fine, ma'am," I replied cheerfully. "Just getting the nightly fix."

"Oh, I'm so happy to hear that, Doctor," she said with a big smile. "I once drove a red Lexus into the heart of the sun. It was lovely." And with that, she shuffled past me towards her room. I tilted my head and thought about her words for a brief moment and watched her go up the hall. Coming back into the nursing station, I found Jimmie already back at her seat. I extended one of the cups to her.

"Oh! What's this?" she said.

"I thought I'd make us some coffee," I said. "I think you've got me hooked."

She laughed. "Yeah, no one in their right mind can turn down a fresh cup of Kona. Boy is this stuff good."

"Cheers."

"Cheers."

We clanked our mugs together gently and took cautious sips.

"Yep," she said in approval. "That's the ticket."

"Was everything okay back there," I asked, nodding down the hallway.

"Oh yeah. That man thought that young guy was gonna try to poke him in the night or somethin'." She leaned forward and brought her voice down, giving a dismissive wave of her hand. "That boy is as skinny as you are. He wouldn't dream of messing with that big black man, but that fellow is so psychotic he isn't thinking clearly. He's paranoid. He don't wanna sleep in the same room with a gay man? Fine. I moved him. Why deal with the drama? Preventive action, you understand? I put him in the quiet room by himself. Cold as shit in there, but he isn't going to mind. I gave him an extra blanket."

I lifted my cup in admiration. "Strong work, Mrs. Jimmie." I saw Jimmie's tablet computer on the desk. I noticed she used it often and seemed fairly competent with it. The same went for her smartphone, a large Apple device. I was somewhat surprised that she embraced such forms of technology to the extent that she did. "What are you reading," I asked.

"Oh," she said turning to her device. "It's the obituaries. I like lookin' at them sometimes. Can you believe it? All these people are dead and I'm older than all of them! I get a kick out of that. It's the simple things in life, ya know?"

"I guess so," I said. "You like those tablets don't you? I see you using it a lot."

"Yes, I've always loved technology. It helps me stay connected with the rest of the world. I started using social media recently to keep up with all my friends around the globe. I still like to write letters and send postcards, but it's nice to see more into the lives of the people I love."

"I get that. You seem pretty savvy with it."

"You shoulda been here earlier. I tried to install a music app on my phone. It started playing shit kickin' music loud as hell. Couldn't figure out how to turn it off."

"I see you always putting in a pin code to log in," I commented. "Would you like me to set it up for you so you can just scan your finger to unlock it?"

She shook her head. "No. It wouldn't work. I don't have any fingerprints."

"What do you mean?"

"I mean just that," she said. "I don't have any fingerprints. There's nothing there. They just faded away over the years." She held up her digits for me to inspect in the light. The tips of her fingers were smoothed over like the surface of a stone.

"How is that possible?" I asked.

"I can't say. All I know is that for all the good that little tablet will do me, it won't ever be able to do that. If the FBI couldn't get a read on my fingerprints then I doubt Apple could either, and trust me, the FBI *did* try." I began processing whether or not Jimmie couldn't tell me why she had no fingerprints or if she *wouldn't* tell me the reason.

Before I could press her, she took a quick sip off her mug and carried on. "All this technology is something else. So much has changed since I was a little girl livin' in Louisiana. In some ways, it has been so drastic that it feels like I've lived more than one lifetime." I clasped the coffee mug in both hands, feeling the warmth of the liquid seep deep into my palms. "What was your childhood like?" I asked.

"Oh, we goin' way back now," she smiled. She placed her coffee mug down and her eyes lit up, reaching back far to the early roots of her family. "I come from the Haines family," she said. "A well-known and respected family. We came into the country starting with my great grandfather. He and his brother that came over from England. Both brothers came down from New York and they were heading to California and, for some reason, one of them stopped in Alabama. Maybe he met a girl or something. The other brother went on. They never heard from him after that. But my daddy's grandfather was the one that stopped in Alabama. We got a little genealogy up there. I think *my* brother did some research about thirty years ago and he found the other family in California. Apparently, they became very prominent in Redwood City.

"Here in the south, our family started to make a name for themselves, doin' business and getting established. Eventually, my dad's father came to take up residence in central Louisiana in an area called Grant Parish, where eventually he became the richest man in the area. It was 1869 when they established that parish. He owned the store, the funeral home and the sawmill. I still have 40 acres out there. Anyway, he died in 1966."

"What do you do with all that land?" I asked.

She shrugged her shoulders. "Nothin'. It's just sittin' there. Don't know what I'll ever do with it. About eight acres is on the Mississippi River." The phone suddenly rings in the nursing station. "Hey Natasha, get that would ya?" Jimmie practically shouts across the nursing station.

"Why do I have to answer it?" Natasha said defensively from her desk.

"Just answer it. It's an easy call, I'm sure of it."

"Sure, Jimmie."

She turns back to me. "Anyway, that's where my childhood starts, right there down in Louisiana. I grew up back and forth between Baton Rouge and New Orleans depending on the time of year. That's where you go if you want to develop an accent like this and taste some of the best food in the world. Nobody knows how to use spices and create flavor like we do in New Orleans, besides India of course. I been to just about everywhere worth goin', but New Orleans is still my first home. My daughter and I still live there, next to each other, side by side in a little duplex with all our cats and dogs.

"But I'm getting ahead of myself. During World War I, my daddy worked on the Higgins boats as an electrician. He lived in a hotel on Canal Street and I would go stay with him in the summer. I still remember the name of the man who worked the front desk there, Mr. Bagget. He would watch over me while my daddy worked. Across the street was Dickie's Potato Chips, and they were on a conveyor belt that would come out on the sidewalk and you could pick them up and eat them right there on the street. I would eat a few of them and then just go walk around. A six-year-old girl strollin' *Canal St.,* can you imagine?"

I reflected on the city of New Orleans as I saw it now. A checkerboarded city of beautiful neighborhoods lined with French-inspired architecture, juxtaposed by areas of extreme poverty and crime. The sprawling city park filled with massive oak trees and Spanish moss, with the gray city of high rises and bustling streets in the downtown region. The French Quarter with all the charm and excitement that draws millions to it every year and the feverish partying that takes place on Bourbon Street. I thought of the massive Mardi Gras parades that the city was known for and the chaos of being deep inside a crowd hungry for cheap plastic beads, moon pies, stuffed animals and the occasional display of public nudity. Considering all of this, it was difficult to imagine a girl walking down a place like Canal at such a young age.

"He was a rounder, my dad," she continued. "He had a woman on every corner. He was also an alcoholic. A drinker. No good. A whole lot different from my mom who never drank, smoked or did any drugs. She was a Red Cross nurse, but not a real nurse. She didn't go to school for it or anything. Before she met my father, she was a governess for a rich New Orleans family. My dad had just come back from World War I. A good-looking bachelor and an old maid.

"So, I guess you and the rest of your family weren't too close to your father," I ventured.

"Oh no, I loved my daddy. He was a drunk but he'd put me on his knee and sing to me:

"Mexicali Rose stop crying, I'll come back to you some sunny day.

Every night you'll know that I'll be pining, every hour a year while I'm away.

Dry those big brown eyes and smile dear, banish all those tears and please don't sigh.

Kiss me once again and hold me, Mexicali Rose, goodbye."

She laughed. "I use to love when he sang to me. He may have been no good, but he was still my daddy."

"So your parents were divorced?"

"Oh, no! They were never divorced. He just started a new life and dated all the ladies. That was how he did. Sometimes he'd come home for a while, but then he'd always leave again."

"So your momma must have had boyfriends too then?"

Jimmie slaps the desk. "Oh, *nooooooo*. Not in those days! Absolutely not."

"Because of the church?"

"Oh yeah, probably why they never divorced either. She was a pillar of the church. She would wake us up at five o'clock every day.

When my dad still lived with us, he would say, 'Wake up, your momma wants you to go to church,' and we would go and he'd sleep in. Even after he left home, we still had to go to church. It was dreadful."

"So Dad had all the fun and Mom ran the circus, huh?"

"I guess so," she replied. "He stopped practicing when he started the womanizing, but, when he got to be too old to chase the ladies, he came back home and my mother accepted him. That's when he started to practice again. Real convenient timing, if you ask me."

"That's crazy," I said.

"Crazy lives next door to the truth," she said. "He was a World War I veteran though, so my momma stuck with him. They are buried next to each other at the National Cemetery at Baton Rouge. He's been dead since 1966 and she passed twenty years ago in 1994.

"Now my mother," Jimmie continued, "she had *eight* sisters. That's right, eight. And they all lived to be in their nineties. I might not make it that far because of my smoking. Nature never forgets. Way I see it, I'm all on borrowed time at this stage. A long history of cigarettes will get me but, my mother, she went out naturally."

"How do you mean? She died in her sleep?"

"No. She was climbin' a fruit tree and fell out."

I flinched so hard an observer would have thought a fly had hit me in the face. A splash of coffee, now cool at this point, fell onto my pants. "What?" I said in shock. "Why on Earth would she be climbing a fruit tree at ninety-something years old?"

Jimmie looked puzzled. "To get the fruit of course!"

I could not contain my laughter.

She went on. "My mother lived a straight-edged life. She never did anything the so-called civilized animal ever did. She never smoked. She never drank. She never drove an automobile. She walked everywhere she ever went. She went to mass and communion every morning of her life for about seventy years. One morning, a Hispanic man knocked her down in the churchyard and grabbed her purse, but it was wrapped about her arm. With her other free hand, she pointed her finger and said, 'God's gonna *get* you.'

"He ran! He let go and took off. From that day forward she never carried a purse at all. Don't think she ever ate a sandwich in her life, but she ate a slab of bacon every morning. Two eggs and fried them in the bacon grease with a tall glass of cold milk. I asked her one day, 'Momma, what is your cholesterol?' She sat and thought about that. She finally turned to me and said, 'What's cholesterol?'

"I said, 'Forget about it.'

"She ate whatever the hell she wanted. She *loved* junk food, loved sweets. In her old age," she counted on her fingers as she went, "her diet consisted of cupcakes, regular cakes, chips, cookies..." she thinks for a moment, "-and fruit. Ironically enough, I guess it was the fruit that eventually killed her." She laughs. "But anyway, she passed sometime after that. Was it directly related to her fall? Hard to say. What I can say is, she led a long, full life."

"Did she work in her old age like you?" I asked.

"Yeah, she worked. She cut her grass." She said this without a hint of humor but I found her remark funny all the same. "My family," she continued, "they lived on this beautiful, big plantation out in the country along the River Road just outside of Baton Rouge. It was called the Longwood Plantation, built sometime at the end of the 1700s. It's now on the *National Register of Historic Places* as of 1983. You go across the street and there's the levee holdin' back the Mississippi River. They would load the crops up on flatbed boats and then glide down the river—a real sight to see. There are only three or four plantations in Baton Rouge that are still in good, original condition and Longwood is one of them. The land was originally given as a grant by the King of Spain.

"During the school year, all my cousins and I would be living in New Orleans and, in the summer, and for all the holidays, we would be out in the country. That's how families did in those days. We made corn syrup with sugar cane out on that plantation. They had cows and cattle and I used to love riding those horses bareback. And of course, they had the quarters where the servants would live and all. They weren't slaves mind you. We were past those times. They were paid, hired hands. They had free housing, free water, free meat and vegetables...You know that song by Johnny Cash? 'Owed my soul to the company store'?"

I did know the song and, played it regularly on my guitar at home in the style of Tennessee Ernie Ford.

"Well, that's how they did. Over the railroad track, they had a country store, so they would buy everything from the store and it had these wooden floors and you could smell the feed as soon as you got near the place. The workers would go to this store and spend their money there. Wasn't too many other places to spend it! They'd get cigarettes and liquor, those kind of things."

She reflected for a moment before her face lit up with another memory. "We had these fireplaces. Oh, they were so wonderful. That's how we stayed warm in the cold months. And we had these wonderful feather beds. You would get on the mattresses and just sink right down into them. It was heavenly." She closes her eyes tight and wraps her arms around her herself, reconnecting with the distant sensation. The conversation then turned to the harder realities of life during the time.

"We had outdoor poo-poo houses," she says with a straight face. "So you had a slop bucket. If you had to pee at night or whatever, you had to use the bucket. You couldn't go out at night because there were snakes in the tall grass! If you did want to go out, you'd have to have a lantern and that's more work than you want to deal with in the middle of the night, so you just squat on the bucket." She turns away and I can see she is lost in the deep well of her former life. In a whisper, she says, "I'll never forget that. Not as long as I live."

Not wanting to lose her in her thoughts, I searched for another question. "You said you had a lot of families out there at this plantation?" I asked.

She turns back to me. "Yes, my Uncle Pot, he was an overseer there. He managed different groups to make sure production carried on as it should. He and his wife Neti were there all the time. They owned thousands, *thousands,* of acres." With a smile she adds, "I named one of my dogs at home Neti, after my aunt."

"That's nice," I said returning her smile.

"Yeah. But my Uncle Pot, he was a real character. He used to *love* gambling. Loved playing cards with the men. Only thing was, he couldn't drive a car and my Aunt Neti didn't like him gambling so she wouldn't take him. So, when I was nine years old, he put me in the driver seat of his Forty-One Plymouth and had me take him down to St. Gabriel so he could get on with his pals."

"What? You're joking!"

She seemed undeterred. "So then it became a ritual that I would drive him down to St. Gabriel's on Saturday nights," she said matter-of-factly. "Any other kids that would be there would bring a mattress or a blanket and just lay there on the floor while the men played cards. I remember that was during the war and all of his sons were in the war. My first cousin, Fontain, was in the Battle of the Gulch, just southwest of Normandy. Medi, was in the Battle of Leyte in the Philippines, quite possibly the largest naval battle in history with some two hundred thousand naval personnel. My brother Harry was in the Battle of Iwo Jima. Uncle Pot's daughter, Ellen, my first cousin, was an army nurse in New Guinea and Australia. Everybody was at war. We had no men in the country. None.

"It was Pot and Neti's daughter, Ellen, that made me want to be a nurse," she confessed. "I remember her coming back from the war and us sitting on the front porch together. I was the baby of the family. Just a little girl watching my family go off to faraway places for reasons I didn't totally understand at the time. My cousin Ellen told me about being a nurse in New Guinea and Australia. Gave me a taste of what war was like but, more importantly, why nurses like her were critical for our country's success.

"We were losing so many men in those days. In our little neighborhood, nine boys were killed. We only had a hundred and fifty million people in America. And remember, women weren't serving in the military back then. They did nursing and sometimes went to the factories to work. The older women kept the children. We had to have tickets or coupons to buy shoes or sugar. Me and my brother would have to agree on who would get what because you couldn't just go out and buy whatever you wanted. Gasoline, tires, rubber...all that went to the war. That was just how it was and everyone accepted it."

She has a new memory then. "I'll tell you another story about Alma," she said. "Alma was a young girl who was a little bit older than me, a rich girl who lived in the big house on the plantation. Just like *Gone with The Wind*. It was a big, two-story place. Gorgeous house! Her daddy, an American, had made all his money in the sugar cane trade in Cuba and then came to the south to buy land. Well, what's a bunch of land without a good horse for a little girl? So her daddy had this big black stallion brought over from England. They shipped it down the Mississippi River just like they did all the other goods. Alma loved that horse dearly. I use to watch her ride around the plantation on that majestic animal of hers. They were a beautiful pair.

"Well, Alma fell in love with one of the sharecropper's sons. His name was Frank and he was one of the hired hands, but she couldn't marry him in those days because he wasn't of the same class as her. Her parents would never allow it because they planned on arranging for her to marry a man of their choosing, like how they do in India. So they discouraged it and she only kept him as a boyfriend. I'd watch them around the plantation, her on top of that black horse shipped from overseas, him pulling her along through the grass in his bare feet. They seemed so happy. I thought that must be what true love looked like." Her tone changes. "But, they both eventually realized that it was never meant to be. Frank left to work in Baton Rouge as a mechanic, maybe to escape a broken heart.

"One night, shortly after that, the stables caught fire. I remember waking up and wondering how the sun could already be on the rise, but when I heard the shouting, I knew something had happened. We ran out into the yard and watched the chaos unfold, the men working frantically to save the animals and supplies. At first, all I could smell was the overpowering smoke that surrounded us, but then it was something else. Something I have never been able to get out of my mind, even to this day. It was the smell of burning flesh. The men threw the barn doors wide and that black stallion came bolting out. It was completely engulfed in flames. It darted across the plantation in a frenzied panic at such a speed you would have thought it was a comet skipping across the surface of the Earth. I remember being both shocked and totally transfixed by the tragic beauty of it all. The plantation was lined with dense trees and fences around the property, except for the entrance at the end of the driveway left open in the pandemonium. I don't know if that horse was running blind or if it just knew it needed to be at the water, but it ran all the way to the levee and stumbled into the Mississippi and never came back out." She shook her head slowly at the dreadful memory, one that no doubt haunted her dreams for many years afterward.

"By the river the black stallion had come," she said ominously, "and in the end, it was the river that took it back."

Her words hung eerily in the air and chill bumps danced across my skin. In the distance, the familiar sound of an oncoming train worked its way between our silence and brought us back to the present moment. "Not too many years later," she continued, "Alma married the man her parents had selected for her. On the surface, it seemed like a good match, but things slowly started slipping away from them. Alma became an alcoholic and had episodes of depression. Some say it was because she was too privileged or had made the wrong choices in life. Others thought that maybe she didn't have *enough* choice in her life, that too much of it was structured for her." She pauses and makes a contemplative face. "But I've always wondered how her life would have turned out if she had been allowed to love Frank. Perhaps things would have been different then. Frank, on the other hand, was still working as a mechanic in Baton Rouge. He and Alma kept in contact over the years, even though she was married, and when she finally did divorce from her husband, there were rumors that the two of them may have gotten together." She shakes her head slowly. "But I think their love was too late. By that time, in a tragic twist of irony, Frank had become an alcoholic as well."

She becomes silent for a time, considering all the possibilities of a romance gone wrong. The tragedy of a lost connection that could have given two souls all the happiness in the world instead of a life of sorrow. "They're all dead now," she finally said. "Not even the horse survived."

I quietly absorbed her sobering story, reflecting on what it meant to have independent choice in one's life and the complicated dynamics of love. I thought about the messy intersection of love and social acceptability. The politics of family finances versus what we feel at heart. Do we achieve peace of mind through union with another because of their status, wealth, or from an instinctual, emotional weight that is otherwise intangible? Do our religions and cultural practices set the foundation for what we seek or blind us from it? Would I be put through similar trials? How would I know to make the right choices when the time came? Mrs. Jimmie sat stationary, appearing deep in her thoughts. As I studied her distant gaze, I wondered what difficult decisions she had been confronted with in her long life.

"Whatever became of that plantation?" I asked.

The question seemed to rouse her from her internal dialogue.

"Alma and her brothers split up the land and divided it. Eventually, it was sold. Couldn't tell you what the state of the area is now. I'd like to think that property is still as pristine as it is when I imagine it in my mind, but who knows. Perhaps it's better I just remember the place I came from with my memories. It's all about what you choose to focus your thoughts on. Some of my fondest memories were when my older brother, Connie, took me to military dances in the city when I was a teenager. He had fought in the Battle of the Bulge, along with many other great men, but he would never talk about his time there. You hear that a lot, men not wanting to speak about those years at war. To this day, all my brother *ever* says about the war is, 'God damn it, that was the coldest I've ever been in all my life!'

"When he came home, he was twenty years old and I was fifteen and we made plans to attend one of these events in New Orleans. Well, we knew our mother wouldn't have taken lightly to her young daughter goin' off to dance with a bunch of military boys, so we just decided it'd be better not to mention it. We would sneak out of the house and push the car down the road almost a quarter of a mile before we would start the engine. Then we would drive into the city and dance all night." Her face lights up as she describes the events. "Boy, those were some great times. I loved to dance and I was a *good* dancer. Those young men back then, they were real gentlemen. They respected me and of course, my older brother always looked out for me. We never had any issues, just good fun.

"Well," she rolls her eyes, "I guess I can't say I didn't have *any* issues. I was attending a Catholic school then and it was all run by nuns. Old-school nuns, mind you, like the flying ones on television."

"Flying nuns?" I said confused.

"Never mind, you too young," she said. "But one of the sisters got word that I was going to these balls with an older man so they expelled me from the school. They didn't realize that older man was my brother! My mother went down to the school and raised hell, but they wouldn't change their minds. I guess I was just too much of a rebel to do any learning under their roof. Had to finish out my high school years at another institution altogether."

"Oh, that's hilarious," I chuckled.

"Yeah, and I was a perfectly fine student otherwise. Do you know, I've never called out a day in my life from work as a nurse in all my fifty-plus years? Not once! I can tell you don't believe that. My brother Connie, the same one that took me to those dances, called me up the other day. He told me he was lookin' through some old boxes and he found my old school reports. Would you believe I had perfect attendance there too? My brother found the award they gave me and everything. I had no recollection of that. I forgot about it completely.

"But anyhow, I think those balls were worth it, even though they expelled me but, as I said, things change quickly and soon it seemed like the whole world was spinning with change."

"World War II," I said.

"That's right," she nodded. "I recently watched one of the documentaries online. WWII footage in high-definition color. What an amazing program. I'm fascinated by that war because of how it changed this country and my home life. I told you about all my siblings who went to war, but just briefly.

"My brother, Harry, when he realized we were going to war, couldn't tolerate to stand by and do nothing. The gravity of it all was so serious that I'm sure it inspired just as much pride out of him as it did fear. He believed in this country and wanted to protect it." She hesitates on her next words but doesn't pull her eyes away. "He wanted to protect his family."

She finds her composure again and clears her throat before continuing. "To be honest, he was too young to join the Marines. He was only sixteen, but the military were desperate. At first, he told my mother about his desires, but she forbid him to go anywhere near the recruiter's office in our town. He pleaded, but she wouldn't have it.

She couldn't bear the thought of losing her youngest son to war, especially when her oldest was already out on the front lines. After several failed attempts at changing her mind, Harry went down to the recruiting office out of his own stubbornness. When he got there, they told him the age to join the military was eighteen. The recruiter said, 'Take a walk around the block and then come back to us.' So, he went around the corner, returned five minutes later, and told a different recruiter he was eighteen. He signed the paperwork and became legally committed to the United States military.

"When Harry came back to the house, he confessed his actions to our mother. I'd never seen my mother so upset. She marched straight down to the recruiter's office and threatened to have them all fired. She caused quite a stink but, ultimately, it was a lost cause. My brother was property of the United States Marine Corps now.

"Not long before he left to serve, my mother caught him smoking a cigarette which, as I'm sure you're aware, was a very common habit for men in the military those days. She put our heads between her knees and gave us a good and proper whippin' when we needed to be punished as kids. Well, when she saw Harry smoking, her instinct was to do just that. My brother, who was six foot two at the time, decided that he wouldn't take those whippings anymore and he picked my mom clean up off the floor. She started hollerin', 'put me down, put me down!' and he said, 'Momma...don't you think I'm a little too old for this?' They both had a good laugh and shared a long hug after that, my mother coming to tears as they held in that solemn embrace.

"I hate to think what went through her poor mind in those days. The ache in her body from the emotional pain. Her son had chosen a path that would take him far away from her and turn him into a different person. I'm sure she knew he did it for us. Put forth his own life so that the people he loved wouldn't have to give their own, but it was still hard all the same. He told my mother in a letter a year later, 'I will *never* let the Japanese get my little sister.'"

She gave a great sigh, her thoughts coming to her in waves. "My brother was as tall and skinny as you when he went into the service, but they fed all those boys meat and potatoes because they were Great Depression babies. They needed to be fattened up. He went off to undergo boot camp and all the other training the military put them through. Harry came back home to visit the family for a short while, about a year after joining. To my young mind, it was like he had changed overnight. He had put on fifty pounds, all muscle. He was an athlete now and a diving champion. He had always been a good-lookin' guy, but now, he was the most handsome fella you *ever* saw.

"In the span of just a few months, he had become a man. You could hear it in the way he talked, how he carried himself. He treated me with the same love he always did. I was still his little sister and they could never harden him so much that he lost that. I remember being so proud of him. I knew what he was doing was a very noble and honorable deed. I still remember seeing him off at the train station with his military duffle bag. I remember him waving to us as he faded from sight."

As she has been speaking, Jimmie's gaze slowly drifts away to somewhere else and she becomes silent for what seems like a long time. For a moment, I wonder if she has forgotten something, but then I recognize the change in her character, a sudden deflating in her voice. She speaks in a near whisper as she continues again. "That was the last time I saw him," she said. "A few months later he was sent to the bloody battlegrounds of Iwo Jima and never returned. He was in Platoon Company A of the 5th Marine Division, trained at Camp Pendleton an hour north of San Diego.

"It was one of the bloodiest confrontations in all of the war. It was the first battle on the Japanese home front, strategically chosen so that U.S. Forces would have an island base to coordinate and execute attacks further into enemy territory. Seven thousand marines were killed out of our seventy thousand men. The Japanese only had twenty thousand, but they fought from tunnels on the island, like gophers. They would pop up in one place and open fire on our boys, then a few minutes later the same squad would be shootin' from another spot. Only about two hundred were captured or surrendered of all those twenty thousand Japanese. They fought viciously to the very end. That was the only fight in World War II where there were no women, no children or civilians. It was man against man, soldier against soldier.

"When the U.S. troops stormed the island, they took over an airport near the center. My brother's squad went after a hill on the island's west side. There was a machine gunner's nest on this hill. My brother and the other men were hunkered down in a foxhole, trying to make progress. Those men had been fighting for nine days and nights and I guess my brother just lost his mind. Without saying a word to anyone, he jumped out of that foxhole and ran up the famous Hill 362. He cleared the enemies out with grenades and then, as he was running back, he saw another enemy outpost and decided to go after that one too. Just as he was about to drop in another grenade on the enemy, a sniper shot him in the head.

"His platoon sergeant witnessed the whole thing. He was the one that wrote him up for his medals. Handwritten, I still have the papers. That sergeant lived in Ontario, California and died just a few years ago. He wrote my brother up for a Bronze Star at first, but it went all the way up the chain to an Alabama-born man named Holland M. Smith, who was a big general during the war, often referred to as the father of modern U.S. amphibious warfare. They called him 'Howlin Mad' Smith and his accolades go back to World War I.

He read the account of what my brother did and said, 'This marine deserves the Silver Star.' And so, my brother Harry has a Silver Star and Purple Heart to his name." I could sense the pride in her voice. "Out of all our seventy thousand troops," she continued, "only 384 received the silver star for their efforts on Iwo Jima."

She is silent for a moment. I do not speak, but wait.

"I was the one who was home when the telegram came," she said. "I was twelve years old, just sittin' on the front porch. It was a young boy on a bicycle, maybe sixteen. He had eight other letters to deliver in just my neighborhood. The boy asked where my momma was. I told him she was working. She had a job at the local laundry mat at the time. He wasn't supposed to leave the letter with me because I was so young, but I told him that I would call my aunt to have my mother come home, so he gave me the telegram anyway. I called my Aunt Betty and said, 'Aunt Betty, they just delivered a telegram.' *Everybody* knew what a telegram meant. My aunt said she would get my mother right away. They couldn't tell my momma why she needed to come home and she was such a hard worker she didn't want to leave because she still had several hours left on her shift, but they insisted she go home immediately. I'm sure it didn't take long for her to piece it together.

"When she got home, she put her purse down and I handed her the telegram." Jimmie shook her head and a tear rolled down her face. "She wouldn't open it. She just took it and went and sat down somewhere. She started screaming. To this day I can still hear those screams. I'll never forget her grief. To lose a son–"

She stopped, wiping her eye momentarily and then pushing forward. "Harry did everything he did with his family at heart. He used to work at Kaiser Aluminum as a teenager. They would pay you with cash inside a little brown envelope back then. He would bring it to my momma and split the money with her so our family could get by. My dad wasn't around to help then. Before he went into the service, Harry had a girlfriend he loved dearly that he wanted to marry. Her name was Anne. I have pictures of them together somewhere. He said, 'Ann, as soon as I get back, I'll marry you. The day I hit California, I'm going to make you my wife, but I can't marry you before that because I've taken out double insurance in case something happens to me so that my mother and my sister will be alright.'"

She reaches for a tissue and wipes tears away from her eyes, still pained by the loss of her brother almost a lifetime ago. "He was buried on Iwo Jima for three years with the rest of the men before the government brought all our boys back home. They brought them to the Punch Bowl in Honolulu, but Momma wanted his body brought to Louisiana. He's just a few rows down from my mother and father at the National Cemetery in Baton Rouge. My brother Connie and I visit all three of them when we can. We bring them flowers."

Time passes, seconds like minutes with the heaviness of her stories sinking into us like soaked overcoats. The hospital exhales silently around us. "He died on February 28, 1945," she finally said. "Next year will mark the seventieth anniversary of the battle that claimed his life. That will be a hard day. Yes it will."

Suddenly, I feel as if something clicks in my brain. I realize all at once the significance of the date of her brother's death with her absence when I first arrived at the hospital. I understood now why my co-workers had encouraged me not to pry into Jimmie's personal life. I had started in March of this year and she had not come to work until almost a week after I was hired. "You weren't on vacation," I finally said. "You were gone because of your brother. Because he passed in late February all that time ago." The tears seemed to build behind her glasses with renewed vigor as I watched her.

"No," she whispered, shaking her head. "I wish that was all it was." She seems to get caught in her words momentarily. I watched her fight the emotions attached to memories I didn't fully understand.

"What is it, Mrs. Jimmie?"

She sits quietly for a long time. We are wrapped in a bubble of tension and sorrow. Just as I am about to speak up again, she turns to me. "I don't think I can say right now," she said. "What I will say is this: I have enjoyed talking to you. You're a nice young man and I appreciate you taking an interest in my life as you have. I've been through a lot lately, and talking to somebody like this has been very nice. Reliving the memories of my life brings me a certain kind of joy. Everything else you have in life is temporary, but your memories stay with you. Even talking about the hard ones can be good for you I suppose."

I reflected on her words and again found myself wondering what to say next. In the end, I simply reached out and took her hand. She returned my grip instinctively, without hesitation. Her hands cold and weathered but kind. "I understand," I said. "and if you do decide you'd like to talk to somebody," I pointed to the chair I was sitting in that was always positioned right next to hers, "you know I'm never far." As I had hoped, this was just enough to rouse a small laugh out of the old woman and she took one final dab with her tissue and smiled at me. "Tell you what," she said. "The next shift we work, I'll tell you a little bit more about my life. Some stories you might find interesting. A few things about my fifty years as a nurse. What do you think about that?"

"If you sold tickets and advertised it as a show, I'd be first in line," I smiled.

She pat my hand affectionately and smiled back, the radiance in her eyes finally begin to return again. "Well hang on to your seat, Honey, because the shows just getting started.

The Offer

The next shift didn't come until later that week. The midnight hour once again brought Jimmie and I together over hot cups of coffee. As usual, we had knocked out our work assignments within the first couple hours of the shift and merely had to observe for patient safety and hope there would be no new admissions from the ER across town. Jimmie, wearing a particularly colorful floral set of sky-blue scrubs, set her steamy mug down to address me.

"Last time we spoke, I told you I'd share a little about my career as a nurse. You still interested in hearing about that?"

Interested was an understatement. "I'm all ears," I said, feeling the subtle effects of my own brew beginning to warm and ignite my insides. The hospital stage was set perfectly in silence to accommodate the stories she was prepared to share. "Tell me about your nursing history. Where did you work? Did you ever practice in India?"

She gave a thoughtful look. "I never worked in India, only lived there. It was Miami Beach where I worked the longest amount of time. I moved there 1982. I went to India for the first time in 1984. I would spend months there in India. I made so much money in Miami Beach, that I would work maybe four months, travel three, come back to work five, then travel another couple months again. I did that for years.

I would work at huge hospitals that had seven and eight hundred beds. Hospitals so big nobody wanted to go on smoke breaks because they made you go a block away from the facility and it would take your whole break just to get out of the damn building. I went to school and worked at Charity in the beginning. That's in New Orleans. But eventually, it was Miami that became home for my family and me."

"You were married then?"

She nods her head. "For decades. There was a drive-through restaurant back where I lived. It used to be called Alley's, but today it's a Burger King. This is way back in 1949." She says the name again. "Yeah, Alley's. Anyway, I was driving through with this guy friend. He was my date. It was a convertible. A Towning Country Chrysler, I remember it well. We pulled up and there was this other car next to us. I stared at the man driving this other car and then I said to my date, 'Do you see that man?' He looked over and said he did."

She pauses a moment and one might have thought she was looking back through that convertible window all over again.

"I said, 'I'm gonna marry that man.' My date looked at me and said, 'What you talkin' about?' So I told him again, I was gonna marry the man in the other car there. He looked at me like a deer in the headlights and said, 'Well, who is he?'

"I said, 'I don't know, but I'm gonna go find out.' I got out of the car and I walked over to him..." She stops. I am waiting to know what their initial exchange was but it alludes her. "I don't remember what I said to him...but I gave him my number and he called me not long after that. Sure enough, we were married six months later in Baton Rouge, February of 1950."

"Come on," I said. "You're pulling my leg."

She laughs. "That's a true story!" She thinks for a moment. "Can't remember what I said to him. I *do* remember the name of my date though. His name was Humphrey."

"You remember the name of the date you abandoned but can't remember the words said to the man that you wed six months after meeting him." I shook my head. "Humphrey, I imagine, was probably not as tickled."

"No, probably not."

Jimmie sips her coffee and thinks back on their time together. "We were together some fifty years," she said. "We traveled a lot together. We lived on a Native American reservation in Wyoming for about six weeks working at a Pizza Hut chain. He did tiling on the floors, owned his own business, and took contracts to places all over the country.

"We went to Riverton, Salt Lake, Church Falls, Virginia and Salem, New Hampshire. I can't even remember all the places we went to. I would fly to meet him, me and my dog, and he would do the jobs and I would just stay in the hotel. After his work was done, we would explore whatever city we were in. Those were good times." She sighed deeply then. "But eventually we got old. No surprise there. Only difference was I wanted to keep travelin' and my husband didn't. He said, 'I can't keep up with this life of movin' around anymore.' He wanted to stay at home and watch the grass grow. So I said to him, 'that's fine, we can still be friends' and then we split ways."

"What! Just like that?"

"We stayed best of friends and neither one of us ever remarried. I just wanted to keep seein' the world. That feeling has never left me I suppose." She gave me a sideways look then. "Am I right to assume you are not married?"

"Me? No, I'm not married."

"You got a girlfriend?"

"Not currently. It's been a while, to be honest."

"Oh," she said and her look of curiosity seemed to intensify.

"Well, are you gay?"

"No."

"Oh, okay. Well, you a handsome enough young man. You got a good job. Said you bought a house here in town? Yeah. You doin' pretty good for a twenty-four-year-old. How come you don't have a girlfriend?"

"I don't know what to tell you," I said, trying to hunt for the words. "Guess I just haven't found that special something I'm looking for. I don't like to waste my time with anything I'm just halfway interested in and I sure don't want to waste anyone else's time. My passions fuel me, so if it's not there for me I don't bother with it. Besides, I've always kinda felt a little out of place living here, like maybe I'm supposed to be looking for love somewhere else altogether."

"Well, don't worry your mind too much about it," she said. "You'll find you a lady, I'm sure of it. Maybe sooner than you think."

"Thanks, Mrs. Jimmie, I appreciate that." My mind backtracked to our previous conversation before the examination of my sexual orientation. "Your husband," I asked, "Is he still alive?"

"No. His electricity went out during Hurricane Katrina while he was asleep. He lost power to his oxygen machine."

"Oh, I'm sorry."

"That's alright. We all have our time."

Her mind floats to another related memory, the dots of her scattered life weaving together in the most interesting of ways. "Years later, one of the richest men in all of Nepal proposed to me at a party. He liked me because I was an American woman. I told him that was nice of him but that I'd have to decline." She looks away and taps her fingers on the desk. "Although, sometimes I wonder if I shoulda said, yes. I'd probably be sittin' really pretty right now. Wouldn't have had to come out of retirement, that's for damn sure." She turns back to me again. "But to be honest, I just couldn't ever warm to the idea of getting married again. I don't wanna walk through the door every day after work and hear, 'What's for dinner? Where my socks?' My cats and dogs don't ask for any of that stuff. 'Can you clean my litter box when you get a moment? Maybe get me some food?' Things like that, but never what you have to deal with living with another person."

"Your cats and dogs ask you about those things?" I asked with a cheeky grin.

"Well you know what I mean," she retorted. "In their own way."

"You have a lot of cats?"

"Six. All of them spoiled and all of them have a bad habit."

"What? Like smoking?"

"No, no, I mean just funny characteristics. One of them, he's a bully. He is mean to one of my oldest cats. Another one keeps poopin' outside the litter box. Can't catch whichever smart ass is doing that. Another wants to be loved all the time, can't be away from me. The last one has Downs Syndrome, he plays with his water bowl and makes a mess, but he's just as happy as could be so I guess that's alright." She waves her hand. "But we're getting sidetracked here. Let me go back to the nursing stuff. You'll have to forgive me. Us old people, when we get to ramblin', sometimes we lose our way."

I was used to our conversations going off the beaten path from time to time. In my mind, it was part of the charm of the whole experience. "Quite alright," I assured her. "You were talking about Miami earlier."

"That's right, Miami. Boy, that was one hell of a place. Never liked it there but the money was *gooood*."

"How did you end up working there?" I asked.

"Got a job with a travel agency for a while. They would send me to different places in the city. I used to work in all kinds of crazy settings, like the city post office."

"What's so crazy about a post office?"

"Oh, Honey, it was huge! It had ten thousand workers and I would see about forty patients a night. I had a regular pharmacy. I could give anything you could buy in a drug store and I had six examination rooms. This was over twenty years ago.

"Another place they used to send me was a small little ER outside of town. This man came in while I was working once. Said his name was Charlie Brown." She rolled her eyes at this. "He came in and he had this baby...oh, it was so sad. The child was dead. This man, Charlie, said the little boy fell or something like that and you could see he had a bump on his head. Who knows what really happened, but one thing we did know was that that man did something to that child. We had a long hall in that ER. Back in those days, when the cops *knew* they had a bad man on their hands, they would say, 'Come here for a second, we wanna talk to you.' They'd bring him down to the end of the hallway, I would turn the radio up real loud and they'd beat the shit out of him. Nobody would hear him hollerin'. They knew how to beat him so you couldn't see the bruises. I don't know how they did it. Then, they would haul him to the freeway and say, 'If we see you in this town again, we'll bring you down to the swamp. Feed you to the alligators. Nobody'll ever find ya.' That was the last we saw of Charlie Brown. That's definitely not standard protocol anymore."

"My God," I said, shaking my head. "Did you ever get hurt on the job? Like being here on a psychiatric ward?"

She exams the ceiling for a time, searching her brain. She brings her eyes level again. "I tell ya, they taught us this in school. We don't like to think about it, but the dirtiest part of the human body is our mouth. If you gonna get bitten, get bit by a dog, not a human. I got bit by a fifteen-year-old girl that was on LSD." She scanned her arms. "I don't know where the scar is now but seven policemen were holding her in the emergency room and I went to try and take her blood pressure. She bit me clean through my sweater. I was on medication for a solid month running a fever. I have to be careful in my old age because now I bump into things, my skin turns black and blue.

"Anyway, there was a great doctor who I admired dearly that worked at that hospital. If you couldn't put a sixteen-inch Jelco in a patient, you didn't work in his ER. He was that strict. If you overdosed and went into his ER, he would stick a tube this big around down your throat." She makes a sizable circle with her index and thumb. I cringe at the gesture. "When they regained consciousness he'd say, 'You ever overdose again, don't come to my ER.'" Again, she begins to laugh. "We had a wall, not where patients could see mind you, but it had pictures of all the things we had pulled out of peoples' asses."

I to laughed, unable to help myself against her confession.

"Toothpaste tubes, weird sex toys…a glass Coke bottle. Patient had to go into surgery for that one. Never did find any gerbils though."

"Gerbils?" I questioned.

"Never mind, you don't wanna know." I gave a sour lemon expression as she continued. "You'd be surprised what we pulled out of those peoples' asses. It was almost *always* men. Only men are foolish enough to stuff shit *back* up their holes. Christ almighty." She shrugs her shoulders. "Anyway, that wall with all those pictures at that hospital is probably long gone."

She appears to be struck by sudden inspiration. Her eyes grow wide and I wonder what memory has found her next. She leans forward and puts a hand down on the desk. "Speaking of which," she says, "it was when I was living in Miami that we first encountered AIDS. They had a whole floor of HIV patients at Cedars Hospital. All male homosexuals. The mothers would come and take care of their sons, but the fathers never came. Not once." She shook her head in disgust. "Sometimes there would be male nurses or doctors working that wouldn't allow the infected men to call their partners as they laid in those beds dyin'. They were homophobic. They were cruel. When those male doctors or nurses weren't around, I would get the numbers of their lovers and I would call them. I told them they didn't have long and what room the patient was in. I did that because it was the humane thing to do. Sometimes you gotta stand up for others and follow your heart. Society will tell you one thing when you know it isn't right.

"Now, do I think grown men should be pluggin' each other from behind? Not necessarily. But then again, that's not really any of my goddamn business now, is it? You keep that in mind. You'll be faced with tough choices like that in your own life, especially in the medical field, but don't let anyone decide where your moral compass should point."

She settles back into her chair and continues. "Sometimes, I'd be tasked with going to HIV patients' houses to give injections to help manage their symptoms. I would go and the medicine would already be there. None of the other nurses wanted to do it, but I wasn't afraid."

"How many places do you think you worked in your entire career," I asked.

"That's hard to figure out. I worked in California, Vermont, Maryland, New York, Colorado...all over the place. I have stories from every different state. That was when my traveling first started and it was really fun back then. All your plane tickets, housing, food and all of it was taken care of. I would be home in Miami and then I would travel for a few months to all those other places."

"How much has nursing changed since you first started?" I asked.

"A lot!" she exclaimed. "First of all, corporations own everything now. They get together and conspire. All of medicine is for-profit now. They've got the doctor by the tail. They're squeezin' the nurses and, at several hospitals, they are already stopping the pay differentials. My base pay is almost ten dollars less an hour than when I retired in Miami Beach in 1998.

"So much back when I was in the prime of my career was negative charting," she continued. "You could tell which shift was handling what and it made sense. You didn't have to say '*Weeeeell*, they went up there and they watched the idiot box, then they had a bowel movement and then they scratched their ass...' none of that. You were to the point and it was simple and it did just as much good as all the stupidity we do now. It was the parishes or the counties that owned the hospitals then. All that's changed. Now, it's not about *patient care*. It's about *paper care*.

"Medicine should not be for profit," she fumed. "It doesn't work. Greed and corporate control only seek to gain for themselves and pay no mind to the needs of the patients. All this paperwork we're doing isn't for the patients. It's for the lawyers. It's for the suits that came from the schoolyard but have never actually worked in a nursing or physician position. All this paperwork is so that if the patient does do something like hang himself, the family can't sue the corporation. Instead, they'll just fire your ass because it was your responsibility. It was your job. You're replaceable. With all the money they got, it won't take but two seconds to find somebody to train and fill your shoes."

She leans back in her chair and stares off through the nursing window into the hall. "This here...this is nothing but a big ass disaster. The corporations took over thirty years ago and it's become more and more a disgrace as time has gone on. Corporations want to own everything. They own America. They own the White House. If they had things their way, they would own our very minds. It affects all areas of consumerism and institution: the medicine, the banks, the government and the schools. There is no limit to how far the disease of greed will corrupt man. What's it gonna take? When the hospital starts charging five dollars for the ten-cent aspirin, are people gonna take notice then? It's unbelievable the direction this country is headed. I feel sorry for all of you young ones. You're the ones that are gonna have to deal with it, not me."

"I think we may have made your coffee too strong, Jimmie." In actuality, her words made me wonder what the future would hold, as the election year was two years away and the country was always divided on the issues at hand, especially health care.

"Nah, my coffee just fine," she retorted. "It's the rest of the world that's drinkin' the Kool-Aid. They need to get with the program."

Her breath seemed to suddenly escape her and she began to cough. I waited for it to pass but she seemed to struggle to regain herself. "Are you okay?" I asked, but she merely bent over and started up another series of coughs. From across the station, Caitlin spun in her chair and leaned back to see over the large center table in the room. "Jimmie? Are you alright?" She held up a hand to show us she was okay and, eventually, began to recover from the spell. "Yeah, I'm fine," she managed to say. "Just my damn asthma."

"Are you sure it's not your passion? Here, calm yourself down a moment. Why don't you trade that coffee for some of this water?" I reached across the desk and took the pink canteen Jimmie always brought with her, along with a rolling suitcase that she was now pointing at across the room. "Alright, go grab my luggage over there would ya?"

"Can I get you something, Jimmie?" Caitlin asked.

"No, no, I'm fine, really. Just need my medicine."

"What the heck do you lug around in this thing?" I pulled the suitcase around and put it on the nursing table. Jimmie stood up and came over, beginning to unzip it. "Just a couple things every go-gettin' nurse should have on hand. Spare clothes, hygiene things and such. But most importantly-" she removed a large device that took up most of the space inside her luggage, complete with a clear plastic hose that snaked all about in a strangled mess. "My asthma treatment. I gotta bring this with me to work because of moments like this." She brought the device over to her desk and plugged it in. I sat down again and watched. After a few seconds of adding some distilled water and a medication of some sort, Jimmie flipped the ON switch. A gentle hum emitted. A stream of white vapor seeped from the mouthpiece at the end of the hose. Jimmie sat down and began to take large inhales. After taking a couple of breaths, I asked how she was feeling.

"Much better," she said. "but I gotta do it all or it's not as effective."

I went off to do rounds on the sleeping patients. No one on the unit stirred. I came back a few minutes later to find Jimmie again sipping at her coffee with renewed vigor. The asthma machine lay spent and silent. "Oh good, you back," she said. "Sorry about the interruption. Sometimes it just comes on so strong."

"That's okay. Better safe than sorry."

"Was that a bong you were smoking, Mrs. Jimmie?" Natasha asked with a grin. "Some of the friends from my teenage years would use those to feel better too."

"Sure, Natasha, sure. I get it flavored and everything." She squinted her eyes and tilted her glasses so they sat crooked on her nose. "Where are the cookies and chips," she said, putting her arms out in an exaggerated stupor. "I got the munchies. Ha!" She adjusted her glasses back and turned to me. "You know I've got an appointment with my pulmonologist coming up and it's a good thing because it has been terrible lately. I've been under too much stress. But he's a good doctor. I'm sure he'll be able to help. He's gonna have a heart attack when I tell him I'm still livin' with six cats and four dogs."

"What if he tells you you have to get rid of them?" I asked, half-jokingly.

"Well I'm not, that's all there is to it. They're like my children."

"Did you ever work with children when you were a nurse?"

"You mean in pediatrics? Only briefly. I got to know this one child very well when I started out. This was in the fifties at Charity. Back then, if parents had a kid they couldn't do anything with, they would drop it off at Charity and never come back for it. So it got to be where the nurses would take some of the kids home every so often because they were there together in the hospital all the time anyway. Well, I had this little guy, he was about five years old and he had cystic fibrosis. I had him for four months. He taught me how to drum on his back the right way to loosen up the phlegm. So one day I came in from a weekend off. I walked into the pediatric ward of Charity and his bed was empty."

She shook her head slowly.

"He had died. That ended me completely from pediatrics forever. I never wanted any part of it ever again. The only other time was when I had a child that fell out of his bed and hit his head. We thought it was just a little spill and that he would be alright. They sent him home but then he got sick. This was before they knew about stress ulcers and things like that.

"He died from internal bleeding. He was two years old. A beautiful young child. I had to go to the autopsy." She frowns and looks away in disgust, "I couldn't believe I had to do such a thing. I went into this autopsy and the doctor started making incisions with his knife. Well, I up and started hollerin' at the doctor. 'What are you doing! That boy is still alive!' They had to drag my ass out of there. Never put me back into another one after that, either. My whole fifty years I never went back to do anything in pediatrics. I couldn't do it."

"I can understand that," I said sympathetically. "I can't imagine how I would handle such a thing. And not knowing when or how it could happen. For it to be a part of your everyday life. Losing a child like that must have been horrendous."

I feel a slow tension take shape between us. Having spent enough time talking to Mrs. Jimmie, the feeling is something I've become accustomed to. It was the pain of her past stalking her like a ghost. The demons that haunted her memories resulting from decades in such a strenuous field. But this pain was different. It was deeper. As her eyes began to fill, she uttered a single heartbreaking phrase.

"Yes," she softly wept, "it is even more difficult when it's your own."

"I'm sure you felt very connected to that young boy," I said.

She shook her head. Her tears flowed freely now. She had produced a tissue from her pocket and did her best to dab away and hold back the stream of sorrow. She sat still for a time before she spoke. "I don't mean that boy." It was like her words were uttered between skipped heartbeats and my palms became warm.

"I've seen some terrible things in my fifty years," she said. "I saw men come back from the Vietnam War hopelessly addicted to pure heroin. Countless car collisions and bar fights. I've seen gunshot wounds, stabbings and overdoses. None of that compares to the day I worked at the Miami hospital. They rolled in a young man on a stretcher from one of the ambulances. All that my team knew was that he had been in a motorcycle accident and was unresponsive."

She covers her mouth to keep her voice from quivering. Regaining herself, she goes on. "When I looked down at him, my heart fell out from under me. The teenager lying in the stretcher was my own son. He was only seventeen. He hadn't been on the floor but for a few minutes when he stopped breathing. I pulled his tongue out and put a breathing tube down his throat. We worked around the clock to keep from losing him and by God we did. He was in the hospital for three months and then confined to his bed for another year. His back was broken in five places and they had to put those dreadful metal rods inside him. His diaphragm was completely ripped to shreds. He was written down in the medical books for that. He shouldn't have been alive, because you can't breathe without your diaphragm, but his heart was strong.

"He was eventually able to walk again and lead a life for himself, but it was never the same. He was always in pain but he was the happiest, kindest person you ever met. We traveled the world together. We went on safaris in Bahrain. We went up into the Himalayan Mountains in India. We went to Amsterdam, England and Paris, our dogs always coming along for the journey.

"He was an artist. He would do these beautiful tile murals for people in their houses. He never stopped living life just because of what happened to him." She sits quietly for a moment, sorting through her emotions. She seems to summon all her strength to continue. "But it was that accident that eventually took his life. He fought it for decades, but he just couldn't keep fighting it. His heart was strong but his body couldn't handle the stress anymore." She looked off into the distance, reflecting in silence. "That's why I wasn't here when you started," she confessed. "We had just lost him then. And of all the days," she cried. "The 28th of February."

My mind raced with her words. I thought that perhaps I had heard her in error, that maybe she was mistaken in her dates. The confusion must have been apparent on my face, because she slowly nodded her head, much to my sinking astonishment. "You hearin' right," she said. "February 28th...the same day I lost my brother, Harry, to Iwo Jima."

I processed her words. I didn't want to believe such misfortune could befall a person.

"He was my best friend," she said, voice cracking. "My whole life, I hoped I would never have to contend with the kind of loss my mother experienced all those years ago when her son was taken from her. Yes, mine went on to live much longer than Harry did, but in the end, I too have suffered as my mother did before me." Her breath was a tremble of anguished pain. "I sure do miss him."

"I'm so sorry, Jimmie," I said. "I truly am."

She nodded and continued to wipe away her tears.

"What was his name, your son?"

She cleared her throat and straightened herself a little. Her voice suddenly had a sense of stability and pride, the same she had displayed when she spoke of her older brother at war. I even thought I detected the under workings of a grin upon her face. "His name was Collin," she said, "and he was the best son a mother coulda asked for."

I smiled. "I believe you."

Now her smile was apparent, almost radiant in fact. "Here," she said, "I wanna show you something." She pulled at the black string of a necklace wrapped around her neck. From under her scrubs, she produced the small, cylindrical silver piece that was momentarily resting at her chest, holding it up for me to see. Behind the intricate craftsmanship of silver, a glass vial could be seen. "His ashes are inside of it," she said. "That way, he is always close to my heart."

I studied it with great approval. "It's beautiful, Jimmie."

"I planted a tree in the New Orleans city park so that whenever I'm there I can think of him. I have the rest of his ashes at home. Sometimes I think about traveling the world again one day and spreading them in all our favorite places. He loved India as much as I did. I hoped I could bring him back there before my time came. He loved Mumbai and the high mountains of Dharamshala. I could go and meet the people that he befriended there. I could remember him and honor his memory." With a sigh, she gently tucked the silver piece back down into her scrubs. "That's the idea anyway. I don't know though. I'm getting too old now. I feel so young and sometimes I act young, but it's hard for me to get around like I used to, and this asthma has really taken a toll. The doctor wants to give me steroid shots and put me on all these other medications." She laughs for the first time in a while, her good humor giving a lighter air to the room. "You know, I told my two daughters, when I die, don't do nothin' elaborate for me. You cremate me and spread my ashes along the levee in New Orleans where the dogs shit and piss. That's where I've always walked my dogs and have so many beautiful memories there, so that will be just fine." She nodded to herself, pleased at her own words. "Yeah," she said, "that'll be real nice."

We sat in silence for only a few seconds but it seemed like much longer. I replayed many of the stories she had told me in my head. Her whole life from a little girl down on the streets of Canal in New Orleans, her cousin sharing with her the experiences as a nurse during World War II, a war that would eventually claim the life of her older brother. Her career as a medical professional, her world travels, especially to the one place I wanted to see more than anywhere else. It was suddenly like a spark of divine inspiration had caught fire inside me. Almost at once, I felt an overwhelming sense of both urgency and purpose, of clarity and excitement. Without taking so much as a few seconds to process these thoughts, I found myself blurting out the revelation that had been bestowed upon me.

"We should go to India together," I said with wide eyes.

Jimmie looked at me from her chair. "What's that?"

"You and me," I repeated, "we should go to India together. I've wanted to go there for years but I've always been admittedly hesitant. It's such a big country. I don't know anybody. I wouldn't know where to go or how to communicate with the people. I don't know the culture. I'd be totally lost. I could spend a month there and would barely be any better off than when I first started." I was beginning to talk faster now. "You say your health isn't so good. I could watch over you and make sure you're okay. You'll have bags to travel with right? You'll need someone to help with those. You could visit with some of your friends and visit all those places you love. You could honor your son's memory and spread his ashes."

She looked at me with questioning eyes, filled with doubt. "You serious?" she said. "You'd wanna go to India with me?"

"I'm serious," I said without a second thought.

She laughed. For a moment I thought she would shoot the idea down faster than I had conceived it. I could see all the wonders of the new world slipping from my grasp. "Well, that's some plan you got there," she said with a big smile. "But a trip to India, especially if you were to go all over the place, is going to take a lot of careful consideration and forethought. India's on the other side of the world. The country itself is cheap but the plane ticket to get there ain't. Will you be able to pay for travel like that?"

"Sure, sure," I said, having no idea just how much such an expense would be, but I didn't care. "That won't be a problem."

"If you want to go to India, you can't just go for a couple of days now. You need weeks just to see *some* of what the country has to offer."

"The more time the better."

"Like a month?" she questioned.

112

"A month would be great."

"Gets real hot India," she warned. "I'm talkin' hotter than down here in the south. I'm talkin' hot as Hades."

"I love the heat. Can't get enough of the stuff."

"Yeah, well, you may be singin' a different tune by the time you land."

"Does that mean we're going?" I asked with a sly grin.

She laughed again and slapped the desk. She looked off down the hall and sat quietly contemplating. Lost in thought, her hand drifted to the silver necklace hanging against her sky-blue scrubs and gently rolled the piece between her fingers methodically, as if drawing energy from the contents within. I sat on the edge of my seat watching her. Finally, she turned and looked at me.

"Okay," she said, "we'll go to India."

I clapped my hands together triumphantly. "Alright!" I nearly shouted in the early hours. "We have an adventure on our hands here people!"

"Slow your horses," Jimmie said. "We not leavin' tomorrow now. This is gonna take months to sort through and prepare for."

"Oh yeah, of course, I understand. We gotta do it right."

"That's right," she said, "but you just leave all the heavy lifting to me. I'll call my people and travel agents, plan out our route and handle all the logistics. You just gotta make sure you have a passport when the time comes. Save up your money too. Might have to get some immunizations and things like that."

"Whatever it takes, I'll get it done," I said confidently.

She scratched her chin then with a concerning look in her eyes. "Now that I think about it," she said, "we may have to practice a little bit of harmless deception while we're at it."

"What do you mean?"

"Well, you gotta understand people in other parts of the world have their ways of thinking. It's what makes up their worldview. They are big on family in India. It's normal for families to live together, get around together. So, to keep the eyebrows down and not cause a stink, we will pretend you are my grandson while we are abroad. Otherwise, they might think it unusual that an old fart like me is travelin' around with a young man. Might lead to a lot of weird looks in the taxi cabs and hotel front desks. If folks don't understand the situation, they think something is amiss and might start poking their noses around. We don't want that. Not that we have anything to hide or worry about, it's just better that Americans stay under the radar and we keep our business private. Makes things a lot simpler." I gave that some thought and nodded. "Sure, that makes sense. It'll be like a movie. We will be incognito. Besides, me and half the staff already know you as grandma anyway, so it won't be much of a stretch."

"Right."

"So where would we go while we're there?" I asked.

She gave a thoughtful look. "I will go several weeks ahead of you. That way I can meet with some of my friends before you arrive. I'll go to Mumbai for a little while, then probably to New Delhi and the surrounding cities. When you come, you'll land in Mumbai and I could meet you there at the airport and then we would go directly to New Delhi. I'll make reservations for hotels and the like. You'll want to see the Taj Mahal, of course. It's one of the most stunning monuments and it would only be a few hours from Delhi. Then we could go somewhere up north. I've had Dharamshala in mind."

"What is Dharamshala exactly?" I asked.

"It's the district headquarters of Kangra up in the Himalayan Mountains. It used to be part of the British province of Punjab. There's a little town up there known as McLeod Ganj. That's where the Dalai Lama lives. He and some of his followers fled Tibet in the late '50s, afraid that communist China would have him imprisoned or killed. Tibet was an independent and sovereign country until China forced them under their rule. Tibet was a peaceful place full of people who wanted nothing more than to live life in harmony with their fellow man and develop their spiritual practice. China changed all that and they've been raging a genocide against those people ever since. If the people of Tibet so much as sing for independence or put up a picture of the Dalai Lama, China puts them in jail, tortures or kills them. Tens of thousands of peaceful people have been slain and hardly any of the world's governments step in to do anything about it."

"Why? How can no world leaders take a stance against such an injustice?"

"Because Tibet doesn't have any resources. Nobody has anything to gain from helping them, not to mention, they'd have to go up against the powerhouse that China has become." She shook her head. "Nobody will stand up to it because it's not worth the trouble. Doesn't fit their agenda. It's sad but true. Luckily, India was brave enough to offer the Lama the city of McLeod Ganj to establish their own government in exile."

I sat back and reflected on her words. "I've always held great admiration for Buddhism and the Dalai Lama. If we could visit his temple there in Dharamshala, I think that would be wonderful."

She gave a concerned look. "We will see. In the past, there has been a lot of terrorism in the north. I wouldn't dream of going back to my own home further up in Kashmir and, in truth, I don't know what the conditions are like in Dharamshala these days. I've never been myself, but my son visited at least three times when we lived in the north. He loved it there. He used to stay at this hotel. The Kunga Guest House, which was right above Nick's Italian Kitchen. Nick owned the place and my son befriended him many years ago during his first stay and that's always where he went when he was in the area."

"Oh, this is so exciting," I beamed. "India! I hope the time flies by until then."

"Well, don't wish too hard. If all you think and dream about is a time in the future then all the great things in your present will slip past you and that goes totally against everything that India stands for. The pace of life is different. We have a lot of planning and waiting to do, so just live in the moment and enjoy life. Do that and you'll appreciate the time all that much more."

I took heed of what she said and trusted her words. As excited as I was, I knew she spoke the truth.

******

The months marched on.

Jimmie and I grew closer as the nights continued to pass between the stories of her childhood, her nursing career and the years she spent in India. With each account of the distant land, my fascination grew along with my anticipation. We continued to treat the patients of the Winded Willow, making new memories with the many outlandish characters that came to our door. Between the stories of past patrons and the never-ending supply of new material that was constantly being admitted, we never had a dip in excitement.

The summer turned to fall. October came and, with it, Jimmie's eighty-second birthday. Caitlin, Natasha, John, Fox, Brandon, and I all secretly bought her gifts that we presented on our shift that night. When it was my turn, I presented her with a bag covered in brightly colored flowers containing a bottle of fine Italian olive oil, dark chocolate truffles, gourmet cookies, pomegranate hard candy and, of course, a bag of %100 Kona coffee with a new mug to go with it. Inside I had placed a card with a handwritten note. *You may not be the youngest nurse in the game, but you are definitely one of the best. Happy birthday Jimmie.*

As winter gave birth to spring, I celebrated my own birthday. I was twenty-five and was just about to clear my one-year anniversary at the Winded Willow. I could hardly believe that time had marched forward at such speed. I had never been much for celebrating my birthday, but that didn't stop my co-workers from surprising me with a chocolate cake, a card and a few small tokens of affection.

Perhaps the greatest gift came later that month from one of the techs on the day rotation. Lashandra, who I had shadowed during my first days as a psych tech, came to me and asked for my academic qualifications. I confirmed that I had studied psychology and received my bachelor's degree from the University of Southern Mississippi. She told me a nearby military base was looking for a psych tech with a year minimum of experience in the field and a bachelor's degree to fill one of their own positions in a behavioral health outpatient setting.

The out-patient environment would mean a far less chaotic workplace, with patients simply coming in for one-hour sessions with their providers. The hours were from seven in the morning to three in the afternoon with weekends off and paid holidays. I applied for the job and I was ultimately granted the position. I was going to be a psychiatric technician for the U.S. military as a civilian contractor. I was thrilled and took great pride in announcing this to my family over dinner. By the end of April, I was giving my farewells to the staff at the Winded Willow.

On the morning of my last night at the hospital, most of the staff I had shared so many shifts with were present to bid me goodbye. As the turnover report between teams came to an end, I made my rounds about the nursing station in preparation for my departure, starting with Caitlin and Natasha. I gave them both a hug, promising to stay in touch after my departure. Next to Jimmie, they were the two people I worked alongside the most. Next, I shook hands with the techs, starting with Brandon. He wished me luck in my future endeavors and I trusted he would make good use of his passions for health and fitness, most likely in some coaching capacity in the world of strength and conditioning.

Fox was next. I didn't work with him as much as the others, but I would never forget the first takedown that I had to perform with him by my side. His colorful personality and booming voice were something I would never forget. With his energy and larger-than-life attitude, I could easily envision him going on to be wildly successful in whatever he pursued.

John was the last tech to whom I would give my parting farewells. "We're gonna miss you kid," he said in the Boston accent I would surely miss hearing. Many of John's life stories and times as a technician had kept me engaged and entertained in the long nights we shared. He was easy to work with and had a sense of humor I found agreeable. His street smarts from a previously rugged lifestyle were always musings that I took delight in. He seemed almost right out of a Martin Scorsese film and his absence from my day-to-day work life came as one of the harder disappointments in leaving.

"If you find the pace at your new position isn't quite as exciting, you can always come back," he said with a gold-toothed smile that brought the lines out across his bald head. I shook his hand. "I'll certainly keep that in mind, John. Try to stay safe on the job, okay?"

"Of course I will," he exclaimed. "I've got Mrs. Jimmie to protect me."

Sitting at her chair, Jimmie gave a curt laugh and waved her hand dismissively.

"I guess that just leaves you," I said to her.

"Yeah, just me left," she said. "And just look at you. We made a good technician out of you after all. Uncle Sam just had to have you for himself." I beamed at her words and my heart was humbled. I felt a wave of gratitude as I pictured all our time together and the friendship we had developed. While I was excited for this next chapter in my life, I was also concerned about our future plans. "I sure hope this won't affect our trip to India in any way," I said. "Once I leave here, I'll have to start from scratch to save up vacation hours. Might take some time."

"Nothin' will change," she assured me. "My time is coming to a close here as well. I'm ready to retire again, this time for good. I still have a couple of months left in me, so that will give you plenty of time to get your vacation hours up. Not to mention, I gotta get this asthma under control. It's worse with age, but dealing with my son's death has made it harder this past year. It's almost May now. By November my health should be improved and you should have enough money and vacation leave to make the journey. It will be wonderful. In the meantime, we will talk now and again. You come to New Orleans sometime. There is a wonderful Indian restaurant not far from my house. Me and my son use to go there all the time together. I'd love to take you there for lunch and we can discuss the details of our trip."

"I'd like that very much."

"Yeah, you and me both."

We smiled at one another. She was wearing light purple scrubs today, the color I most associated her with and we embraced as the hospital around us began to stir with the new day's activities.

"Love you, Darlin'. Take care of yourself," she said.

"I love you too, Jimmie."

We pulled apart and she patted me on my arm. "You go on now," she said. "I still got to give the rest of my report to the oncoming nurse, plus, you know how I drag ass rollin' that damn suitcase everywhere I go. Go get some rest. You've got a lot of big things ahead of you."

"Yes, ma'am, Nurse Jimmie."

At the nursing station door, I turned and gave one last goodbye to those still present in the room and received generous waves and salutations from all. I went out into the patient commons area and the door behind me emitted a crisp, satisfying click as the latch found its mark. The sun was streaming in from a nearby window and I thought to myself how wonderful it would be to have a strictly day-based schedule soon. No more unnatural, long night shifts. No more flopping back and forth on my days off to gain somewhat normal waking and sleeping hours to participate with the rest of the world. I turned to go.

"Farewell, good doctor."

I stopped and looked back to the soft, feminine voice seated at the patient table. Lost in the streaming sunlight and my sea of thoughts, I had failed to see her sitting there. The infamous patient 317717. After all this time, she was still here with us. She had left to other facilities for small stretches over the year, but it was just a waiting game for the Jane Doe until a bed at the state hospital could be spared. However, the nursing staff was never troubled by her presence, as she was a mostly quiet and friendly soul, despite her fragile mind. She was dressed in blue scrubs, hospital attire provided to patients who had nothing else. Over the months, staff and other patients would give her clothes from the Goodwill but, often she would resort to the same hospital gown. Maybe she did this out of simplicity for her daily routine. Or maybe, she sought an attire that would mirror the monotonous nature of her own mysterious identity. A living, breathing enigma that quietly defied all constructs of social norms. No dates. No locations. No history. The only thing that kept her from being a ghost entirely was her own breath.

I slowly made my way to the table where she sat. I took off my book bag, set it on the ground and took a seat directly across from her. She was the first patient awake as usual. Her life seemed to move the speed of a slow, broken clock, lagging by fractions of a second, building up over time to become more and more out of sync with the rest of the world. Despite this, she never seemed off time for the important things in her day. Waking up, making mealtimes, therapy groups and going to bed were all things that were imprinted into her being. Along with her well-regimented waking routine came her usual cup of coffee from the hospital galley. With so many addicts on the floor, coffee was a monumental affair every time it was dispensed during the day. Coffee not made available on time or, God forbid we ran out, would result in a half dozen hostile and moody patients. But the woman in front of me didn't wake up and beat the crowds to feed an addiction. You could tell by the way she slowly sipped at her Styrofoam cup. The way it was still half full after nearly thirty minutes. It wasn't a biological demand she reactively sought to satisfy. She drank because it gave her simple pleasure. It made her happy.

"Your efforts are always appreciated here," she said with her long, unblinking stare. "Please do come back soon." I wasn't sure if she was commenting about my permanent leave or if she expected me to return for another shift. I wasn't sure if she had any knowledge of my plans to depart from the Winded Willow. Speaking with her was always like conversing in riddles. Dialogue was slippery and timeless, innocent and simple. Her long hair had grayed over the year, but her smile still held its childish radiance.

"You know, I've taken a job at another hospital. This is my last shift."

"That's nice," she said. "You always spoke so fondly of Singapore. I hear the sunsets are wonderful this time of year."

"I didn't know Singapore was known for its natural beauty."

"Oh, yes, the natural beauty of the world is everywhere if you know where to look," she said softly.

I leaned in slightly and dropped my voice to a low whisper. "You know, if you wanted to tell me your real name, I wouldn't tell a soul about it. Wouldn't that be fun?"

She gave a short, hushed laugh as if my pact truly tickled her. I thought there was no harm in trying again.

"Honest. Once I leave here, I probably won't be back for a long time. I'd have no reason to share it with anyone else." She didn't laugh this time, only continued to smile. I couldn't tell if her eyes were dull and lazy or if they were piercing through my mischievous antics, searching my soul for its true intentions. "You have my word," I said in a final effort. "I'm bound by doctor-patient confidentiality rules you know." I put on my best smile and waited. She continued to stare, her coffee cup between her hands. Despite her calm, gentle nature, she always seemed on the edge of exhaustion. Her whole demeanor a conflicting pool of personality attributes. I thought I had lost her and was about to stand when she spoke again.

"Do you have a piece of paper?" she asked.

My heart gave a jump as I processed the request before my hands began working through the pockets of my scrubs. I produced a sheet from my pant leg that contained my nightly to-do list. I put it down on the table with a blank side facing her. She stared down at it for a moment with the grin still on her face, then brought her eyes back to me. I understood and instinctively reached to my breast pocket to retrieve the pen there. I placed it gently next to the paper and waited. She was so slow to act that I assumed she was just trying to get a rouse out of me, but her hand finally took the pen, her other pulling the paper closer to her. I held my breath as her pen hand slowly began to take motion. I quietly leaned forward as she worked, too curious to wait for her to finish her methodical, delicate movements.

After witnessing the first three written characters, I slumped back into my chair, my excitement deflated. Numbers. She was writing the numbers. I waited patiently as she finished her "chosen" name. I could see it all from my seat – *317717*. The woman placed the pen on the table, gazing down at the numbers as if she was thoroughly pleased with her work. As she looked across the table at me, she slowly slid the piece of paper towards me. I held her gaze, trying to hide my disappointment. If it was visible, she showed no awareness of it. With a grin, she slowly brought her index finger up to cover her lips in a *don't tell* gesture. Then, taking her coffee, she scooted her chair back, stood up and shuffled away.

I exhaled and watched her go, feeling somewhat foolish about my futile attempts. I began to collect my pen from the table and reached for the paper. As I did, my hand stopped. After a moment, I retracted my hand and sat back in my chair studying what lay before me. I laughed quietly and began to follow a trail of personal thoughts.

So much in life is only what we see on the surface. People surprise you with their character, their personalities blossoming and revealing new insight into their true identity. You find yourself in new places, in unfamiliar situations. Maybe you think one way about it but, over time, you find yourself looking at that same situation with a different perspective. Sometimes, it's just the lens through which you view the world around you that affects what you take away from it.

Other times, maybe you just needed to be more present, more mindful of what was right in front of you all along. This seemed most appropriate given my initial feelings when I first came to the Winded Willow. Even more so when I reflected on my perception of Mrs. Jimmie. Sitting at that table for the last time at the hospital, I told myself I would go forward with fresh eyes and a more open mind. I knew if I did that, I would take away so much more from India and whatever else life presented to me.

I brought my eyes back down to the piece of paper, the smile still on my face. The sun streamed through the window onto the table and it was like I was seeing the woman's name in a new light. She had slid the paper in my direction but had not turned it to face me. Instead, the numbers were presented to me upside down. I read it one last time with quiet satisfaction, knowing that it was the new angle she had given me to view her puzzle that made all difference in the world.

L I L L I E

India

I woke up at 8 am.

I had already gathered together most of my things over the last two nights. I was headed to a third-world country with only what I could fit in a carry-on gym bag. I had acquired a pair of cotton hiking pants and a long sleeve of likewise quality, intending to wear this outfit almost exclusively in my three weeks, as both items would be very breathable and quick to dry. This was important, as I would likely be cleaning them every day in a sink or small bucket with limited resources.

My greatest concern developed two days prior when I began to sneeze and experience a loss of my voice. I had rejected the idea of receiving any recommended vaccinations for the trip. They were unnecessary in my view. I figured if an eighty-three-year-old woman could go without them, so could I.

Still, I was worried, and my current condition was not making things better. On top of that, Jimmie had recently sent an email instructing me to bring mosquito repellent, as the country was seeing a significant uptick in Malaria cases that month. I considered this and resolved to purchase a net to sleep with as well, a contraption I would never actually use.

I expected to take great precautions in everything I did while on my journey. I would not consume any water outside of pre-bottled waters and even these would have to be inspected, as Indian merchants would sometimes reuse bottles and sell tap water from the sink. This could make foreigners very sick. I packed a purification straw and charcoal pills in case of an emergency. I only had three weeks and I could not afford any downtime.

I had to work all year round to save up the time off I would need for the trip at my job. It didn't matter if I was sleep-deprived or feeling ill. I made myself go to work every day for fear I would lose even a single day from the adventure. In the weeks leading up to my departure, with all my leave hours secured, I began to experience occasionally stressful dreams in which I awoke late to my job due to some failure of my primary alarm. I would wake up in a sweat and quickly grab my phone in the dark, checking the time and making sure that I had not missed my seven o'clock punch-in.

After securing my belongings, I scooped my keys off the dresser. My eyes fell on the small piece of paper, a business card given to me by Jimmie almost two year ago. It was a simple card she often gave to the people she met all around the world as a means to stay connected with her. *I enjoy traveling the world, learning new cultures, meeting and making friends*, it read. The background, a pure pasture green with two elegant flowers of purple and orange. There was a picture of Jimmie herself, taken some ten years ago at an Indian wedding, holding a bushel of purple flowers from a low-hanging tree, the same species used for the card's eastern-inspired design. Above this it read, *Animal Rights Activist & World War II History*. On the back, an exotic sky-blue bird with multicolored wings perched delicately on a narrow branch. *Nice meeting you*, it said. *Let's keep in touch*. The card had the email Jimmie used when she first got online back in the early nineties. She had told the story at the hospital once over a meal of chicken masala from a local Indian restaurant in town. She had shown me a picture of a group of young people in front of a house with mountains in the distance.

"This is up in the Himalayan Mountains of the Pakistan border in Kashmir, about twenty-five years ago," she had said. "This little young girl came up," she points to one of the girls in the picture. "I have no idea who any of these other people are, but anyway, the girl says to me, 'you gotta get setup with electric mail.' I thought it sounded dangerous but she assured me I wouldn't get shocked by it or anything like that. So I went to a small internet café in New Delhi and told this young man, 'I wanna get one of these electric mail things.' He brought me to this room that was only big enough for one or two people. It was just a dirt floor. They had one desktop computer with one light bulb suspended over it. I sat down at this computer and the guy there, his name was AJ Shahare.

"He said, 'You gotta have a name. What you want your name to be?' I got to thinking, well, I like traveling and I'm a gypsy at heart. He asked if I wanted anything else apart of it. Make it more unique of a name, ya know? And I said, 'I love India's national flower, the lotus. I think they are some of the most beautiful flowers in the world. I'm not religious, but I do have a special place in my heart for Buddhism and I know they regard the lotus as sacred, so that's what I'll be, a Gypsy Lotus.'"

Almost two decades later, she still used that email. Furthermore, she was still traveling like the wandering gypsy that she was and, in a day's time, I would be there to smell the flowers of India with her. My parents picked me up shortly after the sun rose over above the Gulf of Mexico. I walked out into the crisp November morning, my single blue gym bag slung over my shoulder. My dad opened up the back of the van as I approached, not realizing I wouldn't need the space. I set it down and gave him the okay to close up. I went back to the house to secure the front door.

"Did you see what he brought?" My dad asked my mom. "He has nothing. I mean, *nothing.*"

******

My first flight began to board around the same time my nose began to run. I was cold. Upon entering the airport, I had immediately dawned a light jacket and a beanie. I rubbed my nose with the back of my hand, a gesture every socially concerned mother scolds but is the hallmark of a truly liberated man.

Best prep my day pack, I thought. I removed a medium-sized Jansport book bag that I used for hikes and other similar trips from my larger gym bag and began stuffing it with these items: a small pillow, my notebook, earplugs, a headlamp for extra reading light, a sleep mask, an external battery, my 2nd generation original iPod, two almond bars, two packs of raisins, my water canteen and a copy of *No Country for Old Men*. I approached my gate and the crew scanned my papers for flight 1646. I'm told I will have to turn over my gym bag as no more room is available on the plane. I won't see it again until I reach my destination in Mumbai, but it will be one less thing to carry around. At 4:20 pm the sun was falling as the plane from New Orleans took to the far eastern skies.

I did my best to rest on the Chicago flight but found I could only sit with my eyes closed. My next flight was on a blue and white 777 and I found my seat next to a couple who were also en route to New Delhi for the first time.

"Did you get any vaccinations for your trip?" I asked curiously.

"Of course," they said, "wouldn't go without them."

"Oh, good."

Awesome.

In the back of my mind, I sincerely hoped my confiscated luggage would find me in Mumbai and not become lost somewhere in Timbuktu.

The second flight to Munich was just around eight hours.

I tried getting some sleep as it approached midnight in Central Time. No such luck. I mostly rested my eyes for a few hours, hoping my body gained something from this lackluster attempt at suspended animation. It was 10:15 am in Munich, a six-hour difference from my home time.

I walked quickly to the gate where I discovered my plane was delayed. I went walking for a few minutes. I stopped at a caviar and fine wine shop. I didn't know much about caviar but skimmed over the wine section. It did indeed look very fine. I went off walking again. I strolled past an electronic sign that was broadcasting flight arrivals and delays.

Frankfurt…London…Budapest…

I made my way back to my gate and found a line forming to board. I took my seat and, within a few hours, I arrived at the Mumbai airport of India.

******

It was easy to find Jimmie Wakefield once I made it to the main lobby, as she was the only white woman among the sea of Indian men and women. All of five foot two, she was dressed simply in purple cotton pants and a white floral shirt. She stood before a muscular guard with a menacing-looking matte black machine gun that rested casually at his chest. She lit up with a huge grin when she saw me approaching, her eyes beaming behind her glasses. I threw my hands up and gave a laugh of victory.

"Okay then," Jimmie said laughing along with me, "you made it after all!" We hugged and then she gestured toward the guard. "He let me stand here so I could find you. He was very nice. I must thank him. Thank you, sir! We got him."

The guard smiled and waved at me. "Wonderful," he said in his accent, "you take care of your grandma, okay?"

We got Jimmie's belongings and stopped at a tea and coffee vendor. It was one in the morning, Mumbai time. We had almost nine hours to kill in the airport. Sitting at a table, we talked for half an hour about how things were going here in India as well as back home. She told me she had mostly kept to her room in the YWCA where she was staying in New Delhi. She said she wanted to be fully rested when I arrived.

"The air quality in New Delhi is terrible right now," she scowled. "Severe is 250 by the UN's standards. In the last couple of days it's been 500. The index doesn't go any higher than that." She took a sip of her tea from a comically small paper cup that looked like the ones you used to rinse your mouth out at the dentist's office. "It's bullshit what they charge for this sorry cup of tea. I mean really. It barely fits in the palm of my hand." She quickly changed subjects with a passing thought. "Are you still okay with the idea of going to Dharamshala?"

It was a trip I had not expected us to make since certain places in northern India were seeing increased occurrences of terrorist activity. Weeks ago, an attack had killed some two-dozen people and was deemed the worst attack the country had seen in two decades.

"If you're up for it, I'm up for it," I said.

"Okay, it's settled then," she said. "How have you been since the last time I seen you?" she asked.

"I can't complain. Life's been good to me so far. How about you? Did you have a good time at the Marine Reunion?" Jimmie was an active member of several Marine groups that met to honor those who served during World War II. It was one of the many ways she paid tribute to the memory of her brother, Harry.

"Oh yes," she beamed enthusiastically, "and boy do I have a story to tell you." She set her drink down and leaned in closer across the table. The necklace containing her son's ashes hung openly around her neck. "So I joined this particular organization about a year ago in Illinois that was for Marines who served on Iwo Jima. I asked the organization's secretary if he had any names of men who served in A Company, my brother's unit. He sent me five names. Three of them, when I called, the line was disconnected so they were probably either dead or they had moved. He had addresses for these people, so I sent letters to them. One came back undelivered, two of them answered but one must have had Alzheimer's or something because I couldn't make any sense of him at all. Then I called another one and this guy was good and alert. His name was Louie. He was from San Diego. So we got to talkin'. He was part of the group that relieved the other men on Hill 362 when my brother was killed.

"I told Louie about the banquet that was being organized for the Iwo Jima vets and he was very reluctant to go. He said all his friends were dead and he had no desire to go to such things and I just about did everything but force him to come. I had a ticket that was gonna be wasted and I wanted him to have it. Eventually, he agreed to come. Before the banquet, he came and met me at the hotel we were staying at about ten minutes from Oceanside, California. He brought me a few pictures and I gave him the ticket. He came to the banquet and he enjoyed it so much. He met so many men that had served with him that he had never actually spoken to before. On the last day, he brought me a beautiful red rose. We had a wonderful time."

"*Ohhh*, a red rose Jimmie?" I asked playfully, but she waved her hand dismissively.

"Just as a nice gesture," she assured me. "He was just being a gentleman."

"If you say so," I smiled.

"I have been talking to him back and forth on the telephone from time to time. His wife died almost seven years ago. He goes four days a week and plays golf. He's ninety-three years old. Very healthy. So anyway, when I first contacted him, Louie said he might have some military documents that belonged to my brother because he had been involved with some of the record-keeping that took place during the war. Months went by after we met and I forgot that he had mentioned them. Then one day those documents just showed up in my mailbox. There were about a hundred pages. Well, that afternoon I went to bed and I started to read them.

I got to page seventy or so. It was an inventory of my brother's belongings after being killed in action. I looked down at the bottom and read the name of the man who had signed off on the inventory. I picked up my telephone and called Louie. I said, 'Louie, I have Harry's records here. I found your name on his personal belongings. You were the one who signed off the paperwork after he was killed.' He was quiet for a moment. I thought maybe had hadn't heard me because his hearing wasn't so good. Then he said he needed to call me back and hung up.

"It was almost an hour before he rang me back. He said, 'Jimmie, I had a good cry. I couldn't call you back right away. That was the saddest day of my life. I went through sixty-three seabags of personal items. The date was May 24th, 1945 and that was the same day as my 22nd birthday. That's how I spent it.'

"What are the odds of that?" Jimmie asked. "After seventy years, I meet this guy who lives thousands of miles away in San Diego and I'm reading his signature on my brother's belongings. He touched my brother's stuff. My brother had one penny, a couple of catholic medals and some family pictures. Unbelievable."

"That is something," I confirmed. "Life never seems to stop providing you with good material."

We talked about politics. The Trump and Clinton election was two days away. At the moment I didn't want to put any brain power into figuring it out. Both of their campaigns eventually became to be nothing more than an entertaining, if not slightly nauseating, spectacle. We went to check-in, hoping to find food and rest before our flight. There was a help desk with a man speaking to two male customers. Jimmie walked right in between the two, her head barely clearing the marble countertop. "Excuse me," she said to the man standing behind the counter. "Can you tell us where to check-in?"

At the check-in, the young woman at the desk asked if Jimmie would need a wheelchair. "Oh no," Jimmie said. "I have this cart with my luggage. I'll just lean on that if I get tired." But once we reached a set of roped barricades with a posted guard, we were told we had to leave the cart behind. This worried Jimmie, who would no longer have the support she expected. We were just past the ropes when she stopped.

"Don't think I'm gonna make it. I can already tell. My hip is hurting." We were only twenty yards without the cart before we had to call for a wheelchair. I thought of the three weeks of travel ahead of us all around the country. How would she be able to do anything in such a condition?

"Come sit here," I told her. "I'll go back and get a rolling chair." I put her next to the guard. She could give him an ear full while I backed tracked. I found a chair sitting off to the side. When I began wheeling it away, a worker stopped me.

"What you doing with dis?" he asked.

"My grandma," I said. "She is having trouble walking." I lead him to the girl who had first suggested the chair to us. A few minutes later, this poor guy who had just been doing his job, keeping track of the chairs, was now wheeling Jimmie through the airport. When we arrived at the baggage check, Jimmie held up a hand. "Now hold up little fella," she told the boy pushing her along. "We have to get our baggage scanned here just like in the U.S. and then they are going to ask us to go through the x-ray machines, but I'm not doing it."

This surprised me. "What's wrong with the x-ray machines?" I asked.

"Don't trust em," she said. "When I was eighteen, I worked with x-ray machines in a hospital. This was in the fifties. They didn't give you radiation shields or anything. I mean, you look back at the pictures from World War II and the soldiers that needed x-rays for their injuries are just standing there, nothin' on, no protection. Well, in the seventies I got a postcard in the mail-" I glanced down at my watch, I hadn't expected to get one of Jimmie's stories at this juncture, but I waited patiently as she continued. "This postcard had come from the government. I thought it was junk mail! I almost threw it out, but my daughter saw it and read it. It talked about how I had worked on one of those machines all that time ago and I should immediately go and get my thyroid checked out.

"I went to the doctor and, don't you know, two days later they operated on me and took half my thyroid? I've been takin' Synthroid for forty years now. I don't need any doctor to tell me. I know when I need a little higher dose and some years, I need a little less. Anyway, I don't trust the damn contraptions."

After arranging for Jimmie to go through with an airport staff member for a private screening, we made our way to the belongings check. I slide my bag through the scanner. Jimmie went behind me. I got through okay, but apparently, the security officers found Jimmie to be a concern to national security and kept her there for almost twenty minutes. She and the determined agent looked around her main suitcase over and over again. The man kept pointing to an x-ray image of the suitcase's contents.

"No!" Jimmie protested, "That is not dangerous! It is of no concern to you!" This was followed by more digging. They took a small pair of scissors out of a tiny hand care kit.

"Now wait a minute, you take that away and you will have to put it in an envelope and send it to the States because I want it back. Again, they came across some sort of little tool. The man examined it while Jimmie protested. "No, that is no threat to you!" She reached for it and lightly tugged, but the man cautiously held it. Jimmie smacked the top of his hand. This seemed to settle the matter and he let it go. After a few minutes more of harassing the old woman, we were on our way and I took to pushing Jimmie's wheelchair. We made our way to the gate. Just outside number 52, we found some sofas and Jimmie went to sleep for almost two hours while I wrote in my notebook.

Shortly after she woke at 8 am, all the lights in the airport seemed to go out at once. An outage? I wondered. "Don't worry, this is normal," Jimmie said. "They shut the lights off like that because the sun is up. Saves power. It's common practice with the water too. The last time I was here, I was staying in a YMCA and everyone on my floor was given a time from midnight to 4 am to use the water that month. If you wanted to shower, you had to wake up and then beat the crowds before all the warm water was used." She laughed then. "The power going out like this reminds me of Hurricane Katrina. You remember John, the psych tech from the Winded Willow?"

"Of course I do." His familiar Boston accent coming to mind.

"Well, during Katrina he was using a generator to keep his power and air conditioner running. Don't know if you knew this, but John owns a few guns."

"Naturally." The idea of someone like John *not* owning guns would have been the real shocker.

"Anyway, so many people were stealing things from businesses and homes during all the chaos. He and his family would be asleep at night and the generator outside would suddenly stop runnin'. He'd run outside with a loaded shotgun and catch the thief just as he was trying to make off with his generator. John would then march them down to the Marshall's post. Twice that happened. One night he was lying in bed and he could hear the generator goin' outside like normal, but his house was becoming very warm. He couldn't understand it. After a few minutes, he finally got out of bed and went outside. Sure enough, his generator was gone and, in its place, there was a beat-up lawnmower with the handlebars duct tapped together to keep it runnin'. How about that?"

"I guess they got one over him after all."

"Yeah. Good old John. Sure do miss him sometimes."

Another hour or so later we were almost ready to board our flight. We moved to the closest seats to the door because Jimmie wanted to board first. "Put my bags here and turn my wheelchair so I'm facing the entrance. I want them to see me so we can get on before everyone else." We waited there for half an hour or so, her watching the door like a hawk and me sitting next to her in the chairs that faced the opposite direction. We talked from this angle all the while, her thoughts turning to other stories of the past.

"You remember that small Dachshund I told you I bought in India a while back?"

"The one you called Puppy?"

"That's the one. Well, when I first got him, I had to get on this plane in November and, up in the Himalayan Mountains, it's very cold and you are not supposed to bring dogs onto the planes. You have to put them in the luggage. Instead, I put him in my blouse to try to hide him so he would be able to stay with me on the plane. He was just a baby! I couldn't bear to leave him in the hands of somebody else. Well, this man in front of me, a Muslim, started protesting about the dog because he could hear it whimperin'. Muslims view dogs as filthy creatures you see, because that's what their holy book says.

"So he reported me and the airplane manager came and took my puppy and I said to her, 'If my dog dies, I'm comin' after you. Remember that.' Well, honey let me tell you after that man reported me, I gave him hell for the entire duration of that flight. As I would get up, I would hit the man in the back of the head with my elbow and pretend it was an accident. 'Oh, I'm sorry sir,' I would say. A little while later, I would get up for some water. *Whack*! The water spilled all over him. 'Oh my goodness, I'm so sorry sir, these seats are so close together.' I got up to get my purse and I'd hit him in the head with the purse. He'd look at me with those eyes. 'So sorry sir, so sorry. These seats are just too close.'

"Those seats weren't close at all! We were riding first class and there was all kinds of room between us. I had to practically lean out of my chair to give this guy a beating! Ya see, you can never get the best over an American. Ever! I let that man know it. That three and a half-hour run I was gonna smack him with everything I could find. I got the newspaper and opened it up and it was brushing all over the back of his head. *Wham*! Hit him with my purse again. That poor man got up and went to the very back of the plane and sat there for the rest of the flight.

"So I got to Srinagar and, of course, it's got a lot of Indian soldiers there because the Muslims wanna break away. They wanna go to Pakistan and the Indians won't let them. So there's thousands of Indian soldiers there and I saw a bunch of them standing outside. The snow is really coming down. I look out there and I see my little dog in this tiny box. No blanket or anything. So I get out of the plane and go down the steps and see him. He's sitting there, stacked up on top of the luggage like just another item in transit. It must have been twenty degrees and the wind was blowing. I run under the plane and *ohhhh* here comes the whole Indian army chasin' after me.

"'Madame! Madame! You can't do that! Stop! Stop!' they are all yelling and running after me with their machine guns. I told them they were gonna have to shoot me if they wanted to stop me. I ran and grabbed Puppy and put him in my shirt close to me. They hauled me into the airport and turned me loose. No animals were allowed in the airport either but I was beyond listening to what they had to say so they let me be. I put one of those soldiers to good use and had him get my bags for me. Do somethin' useful, ya know? As Puppy got older, I would travel and he would go with me everywhere and I would bring him through the airport and nobody would say anything to me because they all knew me at that point. We came and went as we pleased."

"That's quite a story, Jimmie," I said.

"Yeah, never a dull moment at the many airports of the world." She seemed to become distant for a moment as her thoughts began to drift to other places. "My son traveled with me a great deal as well," she said. "We use to always have trips planned during the holidays. We had a ritual during Christmas time. Whenever we were in the air headed to our next destination, we would always exchange one gift while in the air. One time he gave me a beautiful Swiss watch. Oh, but whatever happened to that watch? I wonder. Then again, where do any material things we lose track of go? They just slip away and it's like they never existed at all. That watch? It was probably taken in the raging waters of Katrina like all the photographs of my life. But, yeah, that was our special little tradition." I sense the grief building in her words as we sit there awaiting our flight. "Hard to believe I can't do that with him anymore," she said softly. I took a long look at the necklace that hung at her shirt and pat her reassuringly on her shoulder.

"Just keep in mind why we're here," I said encouragingly. "We're here to honor his memory and visit the places you both loved."

She nodded and wiped a stray tear from her eye. "You're right." She smiled and took my hand. "Thank you."

After what seemed like a very long time, we boarded the plane and took off to New Delhi.

******

When we stepped out of the Delhi airport it felt like my respiratory system was under attack.

"My God!" I exclaimed.

Jimmie merely laughed, but doing so caused her to cough as unnatural levels of filth filled her airways. "Shit," she said soberly. I offered her one of the masks I had taken from the medical clinic back home. She used it briefly before condemning it as too stifling and promptly removed it, preferring to use a cotton handkerchief.

We followed our driver to the parking lot just outside the main terminal. I heard the echoing cries of several horns reverberating from the many concrete floors of the airport garage. It seemed like it was coming from the nearby streets too. "And what's going on with all that noise?" I asked.

"Oh, that? It's always like that," Jimmie said. "Before long you won't even know it's happening." We climbed into a black SUV. I was in the back wearing my blue face mask, my wayfarer glasses beating back the sun that was still bright despite being hidden behind the hazy sky. When we pulled out of the complex and got out into the open, I recognized this haze as part of the pollution. The air was thick with it. It was like a fog that hung over the city, suffocating anyone foolish enough to stand around outdoors. When we pulled out into the highway traffic flow, I was treated to the most chaotic display of vehicular mishappenings.

Indian traffic was a far cry departure from what I was used to in the States. As we drove around the hectic streets, the analogy that came to mind was that it was much like taking a handful of marbles and flinging them across the floor. That is the mental image that comes to mind, thinking of all those cars fighting for the road, using horns more than turn signals as they sped about maddeningly.

"Why do they even have road lines around here?" I joked.

"Those are just for decoration," Jimmie responded without missing a beat. "Indian style." She turned around to face me then. "You know, the first time I came to live here, they wouldn't let me drive because they said I wouldn't be able to make sense of it all. The man I bought my car from said he would get me a driver to take me through the country, over the mountain and into Kashmir. So I agreed to that. My son followed us on a motorcycle I had purchased when we got there. Honey, that driver made me a nervous Nancy. He was as reckless as anyone on those streets. I kept tellin' him 'slow down! You're gonna get us killed driving like a God damn looney!' Well, he just couldn't keep it together so I eventually had to yell, 'pull over, get out of this car at once!' He was so confused. Kept asking what the problem was. I said, 'I'm firing you. Here, take your money and get outta here.' So he took the cash and walked away.

My son came pulling up on the motorcycle just as I climbed behind the wheel. He said, 'Momma, what are you doing? Where is that man going?' I yelled back, 'Get out of the way, Son! I'm driving now!' He rolled his eyes at me but he knew better to object. And I drove all the way over the mountain and straight into Kashmir. I sure did. In the towns we frequented; I was the only woman driver. I was the only white woman for that matter and I traveled around with all my dogs. You think I didn't draw a lot of attention? I tell you, everyone knew who I was."

I looked out my window again and noticed many vehicles had badly damaged side-view mirrors if they were present at all. Here, a three-lane road was treated like a five-lane. People would drive on the shoulder lanes for no other reason than it was an open space to be occupied. Despite the craziness of it all, I never witnessed an accident take place the entire time I was there. This is, of course, excluding an incident that would happen several days later in an open tut-tut that I happened to be occupying.

******

It was early in the morning when I woke to find Jimmie sitting in her bed across the room. She looked at her watch, which prompted me to do the same. 2:31 am. She threw the light on and saw me.

"You awake?"

"I am."

"I always wake up this time of night," she said. "When you're old you gotta pee at all hours, but right now, I need to take a treatment."

I lay there a few minutes more, knowing I wouldn't be falling back asleep again. It had been almost five o'clock yesterday evening when I had gone to bed at the Blue Triangle Family YWCA in New Delhi. I had slept almost ten hours now. Somewhere between the time we took off on the last flight and laying down yesterday evening my brain had begun to fail. My energy had drained completely.

I think things really took a toll when we stepped out of the New Delhi airport. As we landed, the smog was so thick we could barely see the tarmac until we were right on top of it. Stepping into this fog of death was intense at first. Just that day, *The Hindi* newspaper front page detailed measures to curb the pollution which forced officials to close down schools for three days due to excessive crop burnings in neighboring states. All construction and demolition work in the city was banned for five days and the coal-based power plant in Badarpur was shut down for ten days. One could only guess what the energy supply would be like as a result of this.

Now Jimmie had all the lights going in our small room and began unpacking her bags. "I just wanna go ahead and do this now, otherwise I'll be thinkin' about it and it will make me anxious, ya know?" she said.

I took off my eye mask and checked my phone. There was a full charge on the battery. I would need it for our trip to the Taj Mahal this morning where Jimmie planned to release some of her son's ashes. We had spoken with our travel agent Rajesh the day before to have a car pick us up at 8 am to drive us to Agra. I snacked on a bag of cashews, the bed comforter wrapped around me as I sat on the edge of the mattress. When we decided to save some money by sharing a room at the YWCA for the next thirteen days, I had completely forgotten that Jimmie kept whatever room she was in at temperatures that would chill a penguin. I only had two outfits that were long-length for chiller conditions and I had been forced to wear one of them to bed to keep warm. I now realized I would have to do this for the rest of the trip, wearing one outfit during the day, washing it at night, hanging it to dry and using the spare set in between.

Washing brought my mind back to last night when all the traveling was done. After eating a delicious meal of rice, chapatti, beans and vegetables, I had retired to the room with the intent to shower. I flipped on the geyser that heated the water and got my things together. The bathroom was unusual to me. Tile floors, tile walls. There was a sink and a mirror in the corner opposite the door. Off to the left, there was a toilet. A few feet to the right of the toilet was a shower. No dividers were separating any of these things. They were all just there in the room. You would use the shower and the water would fall onto the floor where a drain pipe was located. Afterward, you would have to squeegee the rest of the excess water into this drain pipe.

I ran the hot tap. It was room temperature at best. I was too tired to wait. I grabbed the two buckets on the floor and filled one with a small amount of water. I stripped off my clothes I had been wearing for almost two days now and put them aside. I picked up the sponge I had brought and began dabbing the water over me. I poured a handful of hemp castor oil into my palm. Using the smaller of the two buckets, I began to pour water over my shoulders. I made an initial gasp as the cold water ran down my back and then began to work quickly. When I finished, I stuck my head under the faucet to clean my hair.

Having cleaned myself as best I could, I placed more soap in the big bucket and threw my shirt in, sloshing it around the mixture. I took the soaking clothes under the faucet and wrung them out with my hands. I did this for my pants, socks and boxers, then hung them up to dry on the shower nozzle. Just like camping, I thought.

******

Our departure to the Taj Mahal was around 8:15 am. Agra was about four hours away by car. After we got out of the denser parts of the city it became mostly long, rural stretches of farmland, miles and miles of open ground with little buildings or shacks, roaming animals, and fires. Fires everywhere. I witnessed one of the greatest contributors to the intense pollution that plagued the region. It was crop burning season, and the many farmers we saw, who were still setting flame to the Earth, had either not gotten word that the government had called for a cease of such activity or simply did not care.

When we arrived in Agra, our driver, a quiet Muslim man, took us on a slight detour to see the surrounding area. There was even more poverty and congestion here than outside of the Delhi airport. It was oftentimes an overload of the senses. Filth everywhere. The smog and the smell. Dirty animals and soiled people. Here a fruit stand, there a clothing store. One shop on top of another. The ceaseless horns. Bumper to bumper, door to door traffic. A driver leans from a public bus and spits black goo. A group of mangled dogs lay in the rubble of a demolished building next to a trio of wandering cows. An underfed donkey pulls a cart with an equally underfed man at the reigns. A group of children riding bicycles two at a time suddenly veer into traffic and weave among the chaos. A woman holding a baby sits side-saddle behind a masked driver on a speeding moped, squeezing into four-foot gaps between cars that switch lanes without warning. A taxi that missed its turn cuts sharply and shoots back against the flow of traffic. An young boy goes from window to window asking passengers for money. Emergency vehicles with no lights use sirens to clear a path, but traffic is so congested that the response team has nowhere to maneuver. Motorcycles ride out of the street and onto sidewalks when there is free space to take. A rickshaw that fits six is crammed with a family of twelve, three of which hang out on the vehicle's sides, brushing against other cars as they pass. Black soot pours out of the exhaust pipe of a motorbike that is making sounds indicating severe mechanical failure. Several times I notice men urinating on the side of the road, stopping wherever the urge strikes. Garbage litters the ground for miles at a time. A clan of monkeys picks from an overflowing disposal bin. A demolished building lays several years untouched. Like many major cities in Indian, this is the normal commuting lifestyle and it is constant.

Having reached the city, the smog was somewhat reduced, but the smells were as strong as ever. I took a small bottle of pure peppermint oil, rubbed a few drops under my nose, and replaced my face mask. It burned for the first few minutes but did help to control the odor. Between the mask, my sunglasses and my white skin, I drew many stares from the outside world.

We arrived at the ticket office that managed entry to the Taj. Our driver tells told us what to leave behind in the car. No food, no chargers and a few other items. "What about the book bags?" I asked as Jimmie and I both had one in our possession.

"Bookbags okay," he reassured us.

"You're sure," Jimmie pressed.

"Sure, sure, no problem. I wait here till you return."

Exiting the vehicle, a young boy began to pester us with merchandise. He waved a Taj Mahal book in the air, even after my repeated declines. He continued to follow despite my lack of interest. It wasn't until we went inside for our tickets that he retreated to the parking lot. Outside again, we loaded a shuttle that would take us to the Taj's entrance. An Indian man with a royal blue cap with the words *Racing Machine* in big, white letters, climbed behind the wheel. As we cruised down the street, I let my mind drift in a short-lived daydream, letting my thoughts go to nowhere and nothing in particular. Racing Machine drove us and the group of a dozen people on board to the main entrance but stopped short of the gate. Jimmie seemed confused that we were not closer.

"What's this," she tapped the driver. "Why did you stop? The entrance is way up there." The man tried to encourage her off with what little English he possessed. "No," Jimmie said, "you're not doing your job. Take us the rest of the way." But everyone else piled out the vehicle and we were left sitting there by ourselves. "Come on, Jimmie, let's just go," I said to her. "It's not far."

We began walking down the long strip towards the entrance. More tiny shop owners and street vendors descended upon us. "Don't talk to them. Don't even say no. They won't stop if you acknowledge them," Jimmie said hotly, in no mood to be bothered. In the line to get in, guards separated us. Men on one side, women on the other. We went through scanners and a guard pat me down.

"I sorry sir, no bags," the man said, pointing at my bookbag. I could already hear Jimmie's voice over the large crowd rising to a shrill as she received the same talk a few yards away. We had to argue in broken English with the guards for several minutes but to no avail. Finally, I told Jimmie I would just take our bags back to the driver, even if I had to walk there. I didn't admit it, but I wasn't sure how far our shuttle ride had been, but I knew it hadn't been too long. Meanwhile, the guards stated we could leave our bags, "in the lockers".

"With who?" I said. "You?"

"No, no, shopkeeper," they said, pointing at one of the local stands nearby.

"No. No way," I shook my head. Young men were already drawing closer to us from the streets, overhearing the exchange and sensing an opportunity to capitalize on our situation.

"Locker? You need locker?"

"No! No locker," I said. Eventually, we worked out that I would shuttle back or walk to the car. Jimmie was already complaining about a pain in her hip and we had barely started. She waited there at the entrance until I got back. I saw Racing Machine turning around to go back. I hopped on in the seat behind him without a word. I didn't understand what he said, but his gestures made it clear that I was not welcome to sit.

"I need to get back to the ticket booth!" I pleaded. "I just rode here with you not a few minutes ago." But he would not hear of it. After a series of gestures and incomprehensible words I reluctantly got off the shuttle and immediately began walking. It was noon and I was already developing a slight film of sweat. I walked ten minutes to the first barricade and kept going. I knew it was a straight shot, wherever I was going. I just needed to keep my eyes peeled.

I looked behind me. One of the shuttles was passing by, fully loaded down with fair-skinned tourists. Racing Machine was at the wheel. He saw me and I spread both my arms in a *"what the hell man"* kind of gesture. He nodded hesitantly but did not stop. I kept walking...and walking and walking. We must have been driving awfully fast, I thought. Every distance ahead seemed like it would be the end, but it never was. People from both sides of the long road approached me for a ride. One man pulled up and followed me for a time.

"Where you going? Come, come," he pressed.

"No money," I said, which was true. I had yet to exchange a single dollar for rupees.

"No money?" He said in a surprised voice. "India is *greeeat!*" He exclaimed enthusiastically and then sped away. To this day I am still confused by his words.

I pressed on. I could feel sweat collecting under my brow, so I removed my baseball cap with its large Biloxi "B" and wiped my forehead with a long backhand. After almost a half-hour of walking, I stopped. The landscape was changing. Signs of the city were starting to become more prominent as if I was leaving the safety of the tourist area behind. A sinking feeling developed. I felt exposed and unprotected as shady-looking buildings started to crop up around me.

"I don't know where the hell I am," I said to myself in frustration. I could not believe I had not yet spotted the welcome center. Had it been off to the side somewhere? Had I missed a turn? I was roaming blind. There was only one thing to do. Go back.

A rickshaw pulled up next to me.

"I give you ride my friend?"

"No money. This is why I walk." The driver waved the statement away. "No money, no problem. I take you for free."

"Nothing is for free. I can't pay you."

"It's no problem, no problem."

I was growing weary of such interactions. "No, that's okay. I can walk."

"Come, come, you are tourist, yes? You help me out by coming to my country. I will help you out now. Where you from, huh? California? New York? Florida?"

"I'm from Mississippi," I said.

"Oh..." and with that, he quickly sped off.

A few minutes later another rickshaw pulled up with two men in it. Again, they followed alongside me as I walked.

"I'm sorry, I have no money."

"It okay. We take you anyway." I looked at my watch. I still had a ways to go. Maybe twenty minutes.

"I don't have rupees...but my grandmother...I need to get to her. She has been alone for a long time now. If you take me to her, she can pay you," After another minute of discussion, I found myself in the back seat of the tiny vehicle. The two men upfront drove quickly down the road, the man at the wheel as silent as a statue and the other talking continuously. At first, I had been cautious about boarding their vehicle, as Jimmie had warned me about them in past stories of her Indian travels. "You gotta be careful with who you pick to drive you around," she had said back at the Winded Willow. "Shady characters are everywhere. One time, I got into a rickshaw and as we were heading down the road, the driver turned and put something in my hand. I thought it was a piece of shit. It was hashish. The man was tryin' to sell me dope." As I reflected on this story, we came to a stop momentarily behind another vehicle in front of us. I was looking out the right side of the vehicle when I was suddenly jolted as the small vehicle lurched forward. Another Rickshaw had just hit us from behind. Being in the back, I felt a great deal of the impact as my body jerked and slammed against the hard seat.

The man driving us slowly got out and walked a few steps to inspect the damage of his vehicle. He looked up at the man behind us and, with a detectable sense of agitation, said something in Hindi before climbing back into his seat and driving on as if nothing had happened. "So sorry about that," the other man riding shotgun said. "Some people in India you know. They don't drive so good. Not pay attention."

At the drop-off, I shook the man's hand and made a slight bow to the silent driver who had never said a word. They couldn't go any further the man said, and he suggested I meet him back there 'a few hours from now' to pay up for the ride. Sure, buddy, I thought to myself. I let the notion slip from my mind as soon as I walked away.

As I began the last stretch toward the entrance again, I turned to see a familiar shuttle fast approaching. I threw up my hands again and had to stop the urge to jump in front of Racing Machine's vehicle. "*Heeeeey!*" I said as he shot past. "Come on! Really!" A sea of confused white people stared back at me as the shuttle puttered on. "Asshole," I said long after the insult would have been considered effective.

I found Jimmie sitting among the guards in the same place I left her. "Jimmie, I don't know where the hell I'm going. I've been walking the last hour and couldn't find the damn ticket center. I'm sorry. I'm pretty road tired and I guess I lost track of my surroundings on the ride here."

She was surprisingly in good spirits. "That's okay," she said getting up. "I've been giving them an ear full. They're gonna let us through. Come on."

Jimmie waved sweetly to the handsome senior officer on duty who she had spoken with while waiting. An older man in a sharp tan uniform and a thick black mustache. He shook her hand sweetly and they smiled together. After over two hours in the sun-soaked smog, we proceeded toward the Taj Mahal. We stopped short before passing through the large entrance to the courtyard. Jimmie, needing rest, sat down on a brick encasing surrounding a nearby tree. She expressed feelings of doubt regarding her ability to continue and we had still not yet laid eyes on the Taj. After a few minutes of rest, she resolved to fight through the pain in her hip and continued.

We stood in awe at the magnificent construction. Its marble walls towering at the feet of a beautiful green courtyard with fountains running through its center. This was Jimmie's fourth time bearing witness to the incredible monument. We could see just how large the crowd was from the main archway. Seemingly thousands of people flooded the area in what Jimmie called "record numbers".

"This is more than I've ever seen here," she said. "First time I came, there were maybe ten people total. The last time was a couple hundred. This is something else altogether. We must take a picture from the archway here." She took out her camera and strained her five-foot stature over the many heads on the crowded path. "Too many damn people. Can't get a good shot." There was a wheelchair ramp where a guard stood posted, his arms crossed sharply as he surveyed the incoming foot traffic. Because of the man's presence, it was the only place where people were not actively trying to take pictures. The Taj Mahal appeared distant behind him on the long walkway that ran through the courtyard.

"He'll move," Jimmie said, walking directly over to him. "Excuse me." He turned sternly, but she merely waved her hand and asserted her position in the same place he was occupying. She faced the Taj directly and lifted her camera to show there was no room for discussion. The guard gave a long look at her and then slowly stepped aside.

"Okay, he's gone now. You stand there and I'll take some shots of you, then you can take some of me." We entered the courtyard and continued walking toward the Taj but had to stop halfway so Jimmie could rest on a bench. Taking a seat next to her, we stared together at the sight before us.

"It's beautiful, isn't it," she asked.

"Yes. It certainly is. Can you tell me about it?"

"I know a few things," she said. "I'm sure you're aware a mighty emperor built it. His name was Shah Jahan. He constructed the Taj for his favorite wife, Mumtaz Mahal, who died giving birth to their 14th child. Construction started in the 1630s and took over twenty years with something like twenty-two thousand workers and artists. It's made of all kinds of precious stones. The white marble is from Rajasthan. Jade and crystal from China. Jasper from Punjab. Turquoise from Tibet. Sapphire from Sri Lanka and dozens of other materials from as far away as Arabia. The entire project would have cost somewhere around a billion U.S. dollars in today's money. Some say the emperor cut the hands off of the key workers so that no other structure could be built to surpass its beauty."

"Do you think that's true?"

"I don't know…Probably I don't."

She thought for a time and then continued. "Shah Jahan went on to rule for many years before appointing one of his sons to rule, but the remaining brothers bickered and protested his decision. A family feud ensued and eventually, one of the sons took over and imprisoned his father in the Agra Fort where he remained locked in a tower for eight years under the care of one of his daughters. When he died, his body was laid to rest in the Taj Mahal's tomb alongside his wife."

I gave a low whistle. "If what we are seeing is so magnificent, I can only imagine how incredible the tomb is. It must be overflowing with exquisite treasures."

"No, it isn't. Islamic tradition forbids the decoration of graves. The emperor and Mumtaz Mahal's tombs are as plain and ordinary as a peasants."

"Interesting."

"You take a good look at what you see," she warned. "I fear what stands before us will not survive the test of time for long."

I turned towards her. "What do you mean?"

"It's been of great concern to the Indian government for many years now. Do you see how yellow the marble is? Can you see its discoloration?" I looked out to the structure. The discoloration she spoke of was most apparent, even from where we sat. "It's from all the pollution," she said. "Acid rain is stripping the Taj of its natural look. The Yamuna River runs directly behind the structure. You'll see it when we ascend the steps to go inside. The integrity of the building was designed to be dependent on the moisture provided by the river. The lack of groundwater is causing cracks beneath the Taj Mahal's foundation. They say the waters are receding several feet every year and in the summer months it dries up completely. There aren't even any fish left in it, so the insects are breeding exponentially and damaging the building too. It's a big problem. Do you see the four tower-looking things that surround the main structure? Those are called minarets. The one closest to us has slowly begun to tilt several centimeters from its original position. They are all designed so that, if they should ever fall, they will do so away from the main building."

"Fascinating," I whispered. "I had no idea."

"It's ironic. The Taj Mahal has survived almost four hundred years against all manner of natural disasters. During World War II, officials built elaborate scaffolds and decoy structures to hide the site from aerial bombers. Now, the whole damn thing could fall apart anytime now because of a lack of water and poor regulations on pollution." She shook her head in dismay. "Like I said, store it securely in your mind's eye. What you see now before you may not be here in decades to come."

We sat in silence for several moments. The people around us filed past as the heat continued to beat down on our shoulders. We couldn't stay out under the sun like this for long. Again, Jimmie spoke. "We're gonna go around the backside of the Taj where it overlooks the river," she said, "and that's where I'll release some of Collin's ashes."

We walked on a little further but Jimmie's hip started bothering her almost immediately. "Damn it," she panted, "this is gonna be a hell of a chore. I can tell you that right now."

"We've got plenty of time," I assured her. "We can stop as often as you need."

"Let's push on a little bit further. Which way do we go from here?"

The crowds were moving everywhere. It was hard to tell the layout of it all. Some were pulling to the left and others to the far right away from us. I noticed a staircase directly ahead that people were gathering around. It would be our quickest entry point, so I suggested we give it a try. As we got closer and we saw past the large crowd, I realized this staircase was blocked off with a locked barricade of some type. From the way things looked, it didn't make much sense. Over to our left, we had seen a sign that simply said, *Entry*, with an arrow pointing to the far right.

"Okay, let's go that way," I said. When we made it over, there was another staircase, but all of the people were going down it.

"Wait a second...what?" I said getting frustrated. Jimmie dropped a few F-bombs between heavy breaths. Some guards were standing around, watching what was clearly an exit, not an entrance. "The hell with this, I'm going up this way," she said, moving past the barricades with a large *Exit* sign and pushing up against the flow of people on the narrow steps. A guard rushed over to me as I leaned against the rail, indifferent to her decision and watching her go. The man began pointing at her.

"Sir, she cannot go that way, sir."

I felt bad for the guy. I knew his cause was hopeless.

At the top of the stairs, another guard stopped her. "Madam! You must use the entrance. Over there!" He pointed a hundred yards in the direction we had come from. Now it was my turn. I came around the barricade and ascended the stairs, cutting into their argument.

"The sign said, *Entrance this way*," I interrupted.

"No, no, you must go that way."

"She can hardly walk. She can't make that distance and the sign said the entrance was *this* way," I retorted.

"I'm tired," Jimmie squawked at the guard, "Just let me come up."

I could tell the guard was getting flustered by our double-teaming, especially with the mass of people flowing about us in the soggy heat.

"No, no, you must go-"

"But why do you have a sign telling people-" I started.

"Please! Please!" he exclaimed in frustration, "you can go to the side entrance to-"

"I know *I* can, but *she* can't. This woman is ninety years old. You're going to deny her the Taj Mahal?" I exaggerated—a little.

"She came from America for this."

The man looked around for a moment.

"Okay. You go to side. She will come this way." I turned to Jimmie, "Is that okay with you?"

I turned to Jimmie, "Is that okay with you?"

"Yes, go on. I'll meet you up top."

I climbed the opposite stairs and reached the front of the Taj's center structure. Jimmie was just now reaching the top herself, pushing against the stream of exiting people descending the steps. "Okay," she said, "let me find somewhere to rest." She headed directly toward the nearest seat and sat, totally indifferent to the young man who was trying to take a picture of his girlfriend that was three feet away from her. We made our way to the back after she recovered.

The view over the Yamuna River was stunning as a group of birds flew overhead. A series of ropes were strung up a few feet from the edge. It was a measly two feet off the ground. A comically weak deterrent to keep people from crossing over to the dangerous edge, the other side of it a straight drop off. Nearby, another guard was eyeing us suspiciously as we stood inches away from the roped-off area. Jimmie studied her surroundings. "These ropes weren't here last time. Somebody probably wasn't watching their kids or something." I could detect a hint of frustration in her voice. "How am I supposed to send his ashes out towards the water if I can't get near the ledge?"

"Maybe you could just try. Perhaps the wind will carry him down to the waters below."

She considered this for a few seconds. "Well, I guess we don't have a choice." She dug into her pocket and pulled out a small container with her son's remains inside. "I'll just stand at the rope there and shake out a little bit and we'll see what happens."

She walked a short distance away and stood at the ropes, looking over the water once more. She dropped her gaze at the vile in her hand and quickly gave it a gentle shake. The wind picked up but blew at an unusual angle and the ashes settled on the ground before her feet. That scene from *The Big Lebowski* came to mind, though our predicament was far less comedic. She stood a moment, capped the vile and came back.

"I'm not gonna do anymore. The wind is too much. It's not going anywhere and I don't want his remains on the ground like that." I could hear a note of sorrow in her voice now. I looked down on her pitifully. "I'm sorry, Jimmie, I know this wasn't the way you had expected it."

"No. He deserves better." She began looking around. The guard kept a watchful eye on the crowds and I imagine Jimmie and I were his main focus. She looked the man over for a short while and then suddenly turned to me and shoved the vile in my hand before I knew what was happening.

"You do it. You go over the edge with the vile and release some of it out over the water. I'll distract the sentry."

"Do what?" I exclaimed.

"Yeah, just a little bit, not all of it. We still have to bring him to Dharamshala and Mumbai."

153

"Jimmie, I don't know that we-"

"Wait till you see he's not looking," she said shuffling away from me quickly. "And don't fall over the goddamn ledge cause I'm too old to go after you."

I opened my mouth to call out to her but instead just stood there holding her son's ashes. I looked around and then back out towards the river. I looked down at the vile in my hands and back up to Jimmie who was almost to the guard now. I popped the cap of the vile and stood waiting. After a few seconds, I turned my head to find her again. It was too far away to hear what she was saying, but I could see her pulling forcefully on the man's arm. She held up a piece of paper, a brochure or something in her other hand. She pointed and waved towards something out in the distance in another direction. I looked towards the river, quickly stepped over the rope and took several paces in the direction of the ledge.

I poured a handful of ashes into my hand and stretched it over the winds which caught me at just the right moment. The gray powder was carried out and away towards the water below. I hastily capped the vile and spun on my heels. In the distance, I could see Jimmie continuing to pull at the guard's arm as he made attempts to dislodge her grasp, no doubt wishing to return to his duty. In seconds, I was back across the rope and made my way over to the base of one of the minarets. As I did this, Jimmie released the man's arm. With a grin and a wave to the irritated sentry, she began to slowly make her way back.

"I saw," she said breathlessly. "That's good. You did real good. Thank you." I handed the vile back to her and she tucked it away into one of her pockets. "Okay," she said. "Now I want to just stand here a moment and look out to the river and think a while."

"Sure." We both stood looking out to the water. Birds flew overhead and the sun continued its rampage through the sky.

"*O Soul, thou art at rest. Return to the Lord at peace with Him and He at peace with you,*" Jimmie said.

I looked down at her. "What is that?"

"It's written on the Great Gateway we came through to get into the courtyard behind us. The emperor had it inscribed in the walls for his wife. It's pretty, isn't it?"

"Yes, beautiful," I said.

After a time she spoke up again. "Why don't you go on and leave me here a while? Go see whatever you want to see of this place. I've been here before so I already know. I could use the rest and...a little time to myself."

"Sure, I'll only be a minute. I just want to see the inside. You'll be right here?"

"Yes, I'll be fine."

I moved around to the front again, where people squeezed through the main door. A guard was pushing and shoving against the two-way stream of people to keep things flowing. In the main chamber, a beautiful light fixture hung over two replica tombs surrounded by a large circular marble enclosing. The people circled the chamber in a disordered fashion, its walls emitting a hushed acoustic resonance that sounded like a distant ocean. I found this low hum very unusual but loved its calming effect. It seemed to quiet the crowd around me despite the commotion. I circled back around and exited the chamber then took a branching hallway to the left. I ran my hands against the marble walls.

Completely smooth. Not a bump or crack to be found.

I could only imagine how flawless it had been at the time of its original completion, a monument to love beyond compare. I came out the back, exited the last dark hallway and reemerged into the light of day. Across the way I could see Jimmie, her loose-fitting white and pink shirt and baggie purple pants ruffling in the wind, still sitting in the corner where I had left her. Her gaze had remained fixed over the river all the while.

"It's something else, isn't it?" She asked upon my return.

"Yes, it certainly is."

"You'll remember this all your life. Maybe one day you'll even come back. Well, the sun will be going down soon," she said. "Are you ready?"

As we turned to go, two Indian teenage boys approached me. "S'cuse me," the first one said. "You take?" I saw a smartphone in the second one's hand. I didn't mind taking the picture so I said yes. I was surprised when the one holding the phone stepped back and the other boy positioned himself alongside me.

Oh, this is what we're doing, I thought.

Not sure exactly what to do, I put my left arm around the boy's shoulder and smiled at the camera. They said thank you and left. "What just happened?" I asked Jimmie.

She laughed. "You were born a white American, that's what happened."

Ten minutes later, we passed the guards who had stopped us for our book bags. Jimmie waved at the senior officer who was still on duty. He brought his hands together and made a slight bow. We exchanged words of thanks and then exited to find a returning shuttle. At that moment, one was pulling up with the notorious Racing Machine at the wheel.

The man. The legend.

"Hey," I said, "there's that guy."

"Is that him?" Jimmie's voice already rising. "Is that the mother fucker?" She quickly moved toward him just as he was stepping off the shuttle. "You!" she yelled, pointing her finger. "I'm filing a complaint against you! Do you hear me? You did not drive me up the whole way up to the entrance! And where do you come off not giving my grandson a ride when he needed one! You take us back right now!"

The man put his hands up in an attempt to calm the fiery woman. "Please, please, is okay! No problem, please. You get on now and we go okay? I take you."

"You're damn right you'll take us! You are not doin' your job proper!" He hurried us on the shuttle and jumped behind the wheel repeating his apologies.

I helped her up as she continued to mutter choice words. We arrived back at the ticket office which turned out to only take a minute to drive to in the shuttle, confirming that my earlier aimless wanderings were overshot by at least a factor of five. This proved that my ability to daydream recklessly must surely be unmatched. At this point, Jimmie's temper had subsided enough that she abandoned the idea of filing a complaint, much to the driver's relief. We walked a short way and then I sat her down under a tree. "Okay," she said, "Now you go and find the driver. I'll wait here."

I went over to where the driver had originally parked when we first arrived. His car was nowhere in sight. Several cars with drivers waiting close by but none of them was our man. I walked around a while hoping one of us would see the other. My search was fruitless. Oh boy, I thought and turned back to find Jimmie. I was confronted once more by the same young kid who had tried to sell us a book about the Taj when we first got there. "Sir, sir, you need book? Lots of information. Good information! Only 600 rupees."

I was in no mood. "No."

"Good book, many pictures!"

"No." I walked past him but he kept at my side. "No. No money. I don't want it." But he would not hear it or, perhaps couldn't, and pestered me all the way back to where Jimmie sat.

"He's not there," I said plainly. She rolled her eyes and sighed deeply. "Jesus H. Christ," she muttered. "He's gotta be around here somewhere." The boy spoke up from behind me.

"Driver? I know where driver!" He exclaimed enthusiastically.

"You know where the driver is," she asked.

"Yes, yes," he was already running back the way we came. Jimmie shouted after him. "Okay, yeah, you get the driver and I'll buy one of

157

your little books."

"Watch him come back with some other guy," I laughed skeptically.

"No, he knows where he is. Indian style." Sure enough, the boy returned with the taxi cab trailing behind him. Our driver stepped out and walked around to open our doors. Jimmie, scoffing at the inflated price of the books the boy was totting, resorted to giving him a handsome tip for his good deed instead.

We stopped not far from the Taj to dine at a restaurant called *A Pinch of Salt*. We shared portions of fried rice, mixed sweet and sour vegetables and some form of pasta with buttered naan. As usual, once we finished our meal, Jimmie had the leftovers placed in to-go boxes to feed the stray dogs in the city. The bill was paid and off we went, back to the hustle and bustle of New Delhi.

******

The next day we woke around 5:30 am. It was Election Day in the U.S., expected to be one for the books as Donald Trump and Hilary Clinton waited on the people of America to decide who would-be leader of the free world for the next four years. I won't dwell on the backstory or the significance of the race leading up to the occasion because, much like Indian traffic, it was a complete cluster fuck most of the time.

Some of the early votes were likely just coming in. I pulled my smartphone from the table and switched on the YWCA's WiFi, which was the only way I could get internet or have any form of communication. There were only a few votes in so far. Trump had the lead. It was far too soon to make any judgments. All we could do was wait. I pulled the curtains back. The sun was just beginning to rise. We sat up in our beds and Jimmie told stories of her previous years in India. An hour later we ordered some chi tea and I made a video call to my parents back home on the Gulf Coast. They too were watching things develop and reported that an unprecedented number of voters were being recorded at the polls. The intensity was rising all over the country. I rechecked the numbers. Trump still in the lead and climbing. Surprise had yet to register as it was still early in the game. Major battlegrounds had yet to be won.

"I just spoke with my daughter in New Orleans. Would you believe she told me she found a homeless black man taking a bath in the washing machine I keep in my garage?"

I thought about that for a second. "What?" I asked.

"Yes! You know she lives next door and she saw the garage door open. She went over and found the man sitting naked on top of the machine and he was soaking his feet while it was running. She said, 'What are you doing?! You can't be here!' and then she called the police. There's a psychiatric care facility a couple of blocks down. If he didn't come from there already then that's probably where they sent him. That's New Orleans for you. The crazies don't just live around the Winded Willow."

A few minutes later I was reading into projected results for the many marijuana legislation set to drastically alter the country when Jimmie made a shocking discovery herself. "I don't believe this," she said looking at her tablet from her bed. "Oh, this is just like India. What madness!"

"What's wrong? What are you so worked up about?"

"The Indian government has just declared that both the 500 and 1,000 rupee notes are *no longer valid tender!* They did away with them overnight! Says here, they are doing it to fight black-market counterfeits and to encourage currency hoarders to invest money back into the banking system. The money can be exchanged for the full value, but it has to be done within the month."

My mouth hung open for a moment while I processed what she was saying. The 500 and 1,000 rupee notes were India's most valuable currencies, making up approximately 86% of the country's cash. How serious was this going to be to us? "How much of our money is made up of those denominations?" I asked.

"Almost all of it! I had planned to go to the bank today to have money for Dharamshala tomorrow. Hell, I barely have any money left excluding those bills."

I, of course, had no Indian money at all to my name yet. "Damn...well..." I sat thinking, "I suppose we better get down there and make the exchange."

"We can't!" she exclaimed, "They've shut down all the banks too!"

"What?"

"Yes! Even the ATMs it says. They are taking the day to prepare new currencies and tax receipts."

"Shit," I muttered aloud. "This place is crazy...and we've only been here three days. Uncontrollable air pollution shuts down schools and power plants, traffic from hell and now this?" I hit refresh on the election feed. Trump soaring ahead with early predictions favoring him for the win. Maybe there were crazier things in the world, I thought.

We went down to the dining hall for breakfast—buttered toast with jam, hard-boiled eggs, potato curry, naan, cornflakes and chi tea. We ate among other visitors and then returned to our room to prepare for an outing in the surrounding area. I checked the election again. Trump moving up still.

How surreal it was watching this battle rage in my own country from the other side of the world. Social media was running wild; news outlets were posting new updates constantly. It felt so odd not to be a part of it all as it happened in the States. Yet here I was, seeing it unfold all the same. The internet providing a gateway to the rest of the world as I looked on from an alien country, made only stranger by the fact that Donald Trump appeared to be on the cusp of winning. Could it really happen? Was this our next president? I could imagine so many others in my position swearing they would stay right here in India and never return to the States if one or the other nominees succeeded. It was a unique vantage point, to say the least.

We went out into the lobby and waited for our cab. Jimmie sat next to me on a small sofa. We were leaving for lunch out in town when I decided to do one last check before we departed. That's when I read it for the first time.

Donald Trump has won the presidency.

I leaned over to show Jimmie. She stared at the screen with a crooked face. We looked at each other in a half-shocked, half stupefied manner, then we both began to laugh. "Well then," she said with a wave of her hand, "I guess that's that." And it was.

We left the lobby and went out into the New Delhi streets searching for our afternoon meal.

Into the Himalayas

Jimmie was awake at 3:30 am the next day and, consequently, so was I. Our taxi was not due to arrive until six. We ordered chai tea from room service but could not tip the men, as we still had no money. Jimmie assured them they would be remembered and they were very understanding of our situation. I expected no less as I had witnessed nothing but enduring hospitality and kindness from the Indian people so far. Everything here was "no problem", even when it *was* a problem.

We made it to the airport with minimal traffic. It was nice to see New Delhi without all the usual daytime congestion. Even better, countermeasures to curb the stifling pollution seemed to be paying off, as visibility was noticeably improved. We decided to get Jimmie another wheelchair at the airport, which resulted in us moving very quickly through security and all the other lines.

There were benefits to traveling with an eighty-three-year-old woman, I thought.

We sat near our gate drinking Masala tea that Jimmie bought with her Visa card, one of our few sparing ways to buy things and only effective in places modern enough to support their use. I was surprised when we were asked to proceed but, instead of stepping out to board a plane, we boarded a bus instead. We then drove out across the tarmac to a waiting plane. This was a first for me.

The flight was a short one at an hour and a half. I had been writing in my notebook when I glanced out the window. The smog of Delhi had been left far behind and replaced with a light mist as the

Himalayan Mountains rose into view. As we flew on, it expanded and swelled, dominating the landscape as far as the eye could see. It was easily the most impressive mountain range I had ever observed and certainly one of the most stunning geographical features. It dwarfed and surpassed the Colorado Rockies seemingly tenfold. Small villages dotted the foothills and roadways curved through its broadsides.

"Amazing, isn't it?" Jimmie asked from the seat across the aisle.

"I've never seen anything like it," I returned.

"You know the Himalayas is the only mountain range that runs through six different countries. You have China, Bhutan, Nepal, India, Pakistan and Afghanistan from east to west. They measure its distance around 1,500 miles and it's home to dozens of the world's highest peaks, including Everest and K2. Despite all that, you might be surprised to know that these mountains are actually some of the youngest in the world. Scientists put them around twenty-five million years old and they are still rising. The Indo-Australian plate moves several millimeters every year. Way up high like this, you'd think it was one the most uninhabitable places anywhere on the planet, but over fifty million people live in the Himalayas, along with some of the rarest animal species on Earth. The Hindus say Shiva herself resides in these mountains, not to mention the great white ape they call the Yeti."

I grinned and turned towards her. "Have you ever seen a Yeti out here, Jimmie?"

"Nah, but your eyes are younger than mine, so if you see the big monkey, let me know would ya?"

"Sure." I turned back to the view before me. "But in any case, I think the mountains themselves are more impressive than any ape could ever be."

"You probably right about that." We watched the range slowly slide across our plain of view, one continues stretch of jagged, ascending Earth. "The Himalayas," Jimmie said. "The Nepalese are known to refer to it as *Sagarmatha*. The Goddess of the Universe."

We landed in a laughably small airport. It couldn't have been more than a few acres, but it was beautiful. "Now this is all new to me," Jimmie said. "My son came here three times but I've never been to this part of India. Dharamshala is derived from the Hindu Sanskrit. It doesn't translate well in English but it means something like a spiritual sanctuary. Let's not hang around though. We got a lot of ground to cover."

A bank was first on our agenda, then Mcleod Gaj, home of the Dalai Lama and the Tibetan government in exile. In the days leading up to this leg of our adventure, Jimmie had told everyone that we were going to Dharamshala to have tea with His Holiness. It gave me a laugh every time.

We found a group of taxi drivers out the front door and made arrangements with one of the men. Our driver took us to a small village along the way where the National Bank of Unpronounceable was located. It looked like it was just as much a whole in the wall as every other run-down shack and street vendor we passed. The driver pulled over as we approached the building.

"Okay," Jimmie said unbuckling her seatbelt, "I'll go in and you stay here with the driver. Keep an eye on the bags."

In she went.

The driver pulled up a little further on the street and parked. He pulled out a smartphone and began watching a cricket game, India's most popular sport. I sat in the back seat and watched the action on the streets. I saw a man squatting low on the floor of a shop, hammering at a metal bin. Another sat reading paper outside his small automotive goods store. A donkey, hauling what looked like a large bag of dirt, shat in an alleyway. A clerk nearby brushed away the animal droppings without expression. A group of kids shouted and ran up the street in their bare feet.

Ten minutes went by, then twenty, then thirty. The driver got out suddenly and walked to the other side of the road. He came back for a moment to lean against the car and then took off again toward the bank.

Great.

I sat there alone in the car as the minutes continued to tick away. The driver returned.

"What's going on? Is she okay?" I asked.

His face was uncertain. "Uh, no so much. Big problem. Money exchange?"

"Yes," I said, "the money exchange. What's the problem?"

"No five hundred rupees. No one thousand rupees. "

"Yes, we already know. We thought this bank could help. Do they have the good money?"

His response seemed unsure. "Is she arguing with them," I asked, already knowing the answer. He nodded fiercely.

Great.

Another twenty minutes went by. I wanted badly to go in but I couldn't leave our luggage here. After a while, the driver got out again.

"You wait here, ya?"

I nodded. He went inside. Five minutes later he was back. He climbed into the driver's seat and started up the car immediately. "Ah, no good, no good," he said and began turning the car around after driving a short distance down the street.

"What's happening? Where are we going?"

He muttered something and waved his hand. We approached the bank again but continued past it down the street instead of stopping. "Where are we going," I asked again, wondering if I was in the process of being kidnapped. Before he responded he came to a slow halt and jumped out of the vehicle. "Come, come," he signaled to me.

Oh geez, I thought as I wondered what drama lay ahead of me. For a brief moment, I started to wish maybe the guy had just kidnapped me instead.

I got out and followed him as he waved towards one of the tiny shops. Inside, Jimmie was sitting across from a man at a computer desk. She gave a laugh when I walked in, a confused look on my face. "Are you cleaning them out or what?" I asked.

"Honey, it's all a big shit show in India. I was in the bank down the street. They wanted to give me the black money. They thought I didn't know anything because I'm a foreigner. I said, 'No! I can't take these five hundred rupees! Your government won't accept these anymore. I need the one hundreds!' The bank manager called this fellow so now I'm doin' business with him. This is how things go in India. Nothing is straightforward."

The man behind the counter was noticeably agitated, but after arranging to have electronically signed copies of our passports as proof of transaction (required for foreigners) his mood changed and the hospitable Indian demeanor quickly resurfaced. We stepped back out onto the street to the relief of our driver.

"Come, come. I am very late."

From the small village, we began to ascend into the Himalayas. The roads twisted as other vehicles honked their horns before they were even visible, a warning as they rounded the steep curves which offered no protective railings and often plummeted a dizzying distance down to the canyons below.

"Oh Jesus, be careful," Jimmie laughed nervously, grabbing the driver's arm. "You gotta go slowly because I get scared." The further up we went the more apprehensive she became. "God, I'm gonna have to close my eyes. If I had known it was this high up, I might not have come."

"It's not too bad Jimmie. This isn't even a mile up yet."

"Ah, shit," she said.

Along the way, we saw vegetation both impressive and unusual. Tall pine, Deodar cedar and Himalayan oak, which sounded like great material to have furniture built from to impress party guests.

Rounding a bend, we encountered a clan of monkeys, at least two dozen or more, who positioned themselves along the road in a long line. Several small babies clung to the backs of their mothers while other more mischievous-looking males paced in the dirt and clung to fruits they had scavenged. "Oh, pull over," Jimmie told the driver, "I want to give them some of this bread." The man glanced over at her and then reluctantly pulled to the side of the road. One of the monkeys, perched atop a nearby rock some twenty feet away, began eyeing us curiously. Jimmie, who was on the same side of the car as me, rolled down her window and stuck out a handful of bread.

"Oh, it's got a baby on its back. Let me see if I have some more bread." She looked down at the plastic bag from which she had produced the food and began to rummage through its contents. As soon as she looked away, the monkey darted forward at an alarming speed and was instantly perched on a rock that was level with Jimmie's window. It looked like it would jump right into the car when she noticed. "Oh, God!" she said in surprise, quickly pulling her arm back into the car. "Roll the window up!" she yelled at the driver, but in his panic, somehow *my* window started coming down. Now I was frantic as several other monkeys shot toward the taxi. "No, no, just drive!" I shouted. The man stopped fiddling with the windows and the car made a jerking leap forward, leaving the disappointed primates behind in the dust. "That was a close one," Jimmie said. "Maybe we'll have better luck next time."

After half an hour we finally reached our destination, the small town of McLeod Ganj nestled in the Himalayan Mountains. "Okay," Jimmie said, "every time my son came here, he always stayed at Nick's Italian Restaurant. It's a restaurant but it's a hotel too."

Finding Nick's proved to be no easy task. We pulled over several times, Jimmie waving down pedestrians and asking about the Italian restaurant. We arrived in the town's central square, a tiny slab of road that was the connecting point for all other routes of traffic on the narrow streets. Taking a cue from one of the townsfolk, Jimmie abandoned the taxi, began walking up a side street and disappeared around the corner. A few minutes went by before she returned. When she got back to the car, she was noticeably tired.

"Wow," she breathed. "I forgot how high up we are. I shouldn't have gone off like that. I keep forgetting I'm eighty-three years old." She took several deep breaths and fanned herself. "Okay," she finally said. "It's up there. Not far at all. Drive us the rest of the way, will you?" The man took us around the corner and up another side street where we found a sign next to a three-story building with large windows facing the street.

KUNGA GUEST HOUSE & NICK'S ITALIAN KITCHEN

"That's it there," Jimmie said. We paid our driver who quickly turned around in the impossibly narrow road and began the long descent out of town. Inside, Jimmie immediately began asking for Nick. The waiter said he was out but offered us a menu while we waited. Again, Jimmie commented on her lack of breath and I suggested we take a seat and have something to eat in the meantime.

We took a table on the back patio overlooking the mountains. It was the best seat in the whole restaurant. The little town appeared to be completely enclosed by the towering landscape and Nick's felt like the center of it all. We ordered salads, pasta in tomato sauce, homemade Tibetan bread and I ordered a hot ginger lemon tea with honey. Right away I developed a love affair with this drink and requested it several times a day to help combat the sinus infection that had plagued me before I had even arrived in the country. We sat and ate, marveling at the view and watching as large birds glided through the clear sky. We stayed there for some time once we were through with our meal. After a while, Jimmie decided to climb the stairs that led back into the main room to ask about sleeping quarters. I remained outside for several minutes, facing my chair over the balcony, enjoying the more hushed atmosphere of McLeod Ganj.

"Excuse me, sir," I turned to find our waiter behind me. "Your grandmother," he pointed upstairs.

I collected my things and followed him up. Jimmie was sitting at the back corner table. Another worker was standing next to her and gave me a concerned look as I approached. Jimmi's face was flushed. "Listen," she said, finding her breath, "the waiter says they only have one room left that isn't too high up. I'm not feeling well and I can't climb so many stairs. We're going to take the room, and I want to go up to it right away to lay down. Take my bags and let's go."

I reached for her bags as she found her balance to get up. "Should we pay for the food and lodging now?"

"No, I'm not worried about that. Call those men over. I'll need help to get up the stairs." I signaled the two waiters over who were standing by to assist us. We walked to the other side of the main room to a sliding door right next to the front entrance. On the other side was a narrow concrete staircase of a dozen steps. One of the men went up ahead of us, the other held Jimmie up as they slowly ascended. Halfway up she came to a stop. I stood behind them with my hand on her back.

"Are you okay?"

"Just give me a second." She breathed heavily for a moment. "Alright. Let's go." We started up again. At the top the first man unlocked our door. The other still held on to Jimmie. We stepped inside a lovely room with large windows looking out to the Himalayas. The first man ran to the nearest bed of the two in the room and began moving sheets aside for her.

"Two pillows," she wheezed. I grabbed the one off the other bed and put it on top of hers. "That's good. Now set a water on the nightstand. And my medicine. It's in the book bag." I collected her things while the men eased her down onto the side of the bed.

169

"Help me take my shoes off please." I bent down and unlaced them for her. We eased her onto her back slowly. "Thank you. Thank you all," she said closing her eyes. "What else do you need," I asked.

"Nothing, that will be fine for now. You go on and see the town. I'll be okay here. I just need to rest. Have the men check on me every hour or two."

There was a knock on the door. One of the workers entered. He had brought another pillow for me. "Nick is here," he said, "shall I send him up." Much to my surprise, Jimmie was excited at this news and gestured from her bed without getting up. "Oh, yes, that would be great. Have him come up please!" A few seconds later there was another knock and Nick entered the room. He seemed young, maybe in his mid-thirties with clean features and closely cut black hair. Jimmie addressed him from her bed, still laying there on her back.

"Nick! How you doin', Honey? My name is Jimmie Wakefield and this is my grandson. I've come a long way to find you. My son was a friend of yours. He came here several times, years ago when we lived in Kashmir. His name was Collin."

"Collin," the man repeated slowly with his native accent.

"Yes, he had red hair and a great big smile. Always laughing and carryin' on. He spoke very highly of you and your business here." She produced a small picture book from her bag and waved him over, her head never lifting from the pillow. He came around to her side and took a seat on the bed. She handed it to him and he began looking through the collection of shots dated from the early 2000s to 2014.

"He passed away," she continued, "and I've brought his ashes with me here to India. He once took a motorcycle from where we stayed in Srinagar and fell in love with your place, so we have now come from New Delhi to find you." Nick studied the photos carefully. "I recognize him," he finally said. "He had a very distinct character. Very different from other visitors."

"Yes," she said delighted, "he was the outgoing type. A true embodiment of the New Orleans spirit."

"Yeah, yeah," Nick confirmed, "he was a very positive person. Very fun. Very happy guy."

Jimmie palmed her eyes with one of her hands. I could see the memories were already beginning to take their toll on her as they always did. As much as I loved hearing her stories of him, it pained me to see her suffer. They talked back and forth like that for a few minutes more. Dabbing at her eyes with a handkerchief, she thanked him for his hospitality and all that his staff had done for us.

After Nick had departed and I made sure Jimmie had everything she would need, I set off for my first walk into town. I headed toward the main square, the tiny area where the two main streets running through town intersected. I examined a small map of the city that I had taken from an information book. The Dalai Lama's Temple was only about a kilometer away. I walked through the narrow street taking in the sights. Vendors and small shops were jammed together, the crowds moving past, squeezing into a single file as cars and motorcycles came by.

I passed souvenir shops, convenience stores, money exchanges, small cookeries, temples, café's and bakeries. Foreigners were plentiful, many with long hair or dreadlocks, overgrown beards, sandals or hiking shoes. Buddhist monks in red and gold robes walked alone or in small groups with their peers. Others conversed alongside the locals. It gave the feeling that there was a strong sense of unity among the people as dozens of Tibetan exiles walked with the northern Indians native to the land.

I explored the Dalai Lama's temple. There were cushioned mats on one side where devotees and practitioners could be seen engaging in a prayer that involved the entire use of the body. I adopted the peaceful measured walking pace of the monks and, thoughtfully, with my hands in my pocket, did my best to appreciate the details of the temple. I found the entrance of the inner sanctum and investigated it briefly in my sock feet, as shoes were not permitted. Outside again, I found several people walking by a row of Mani Wheels, spinning the cylindrical devices with their hands as they walked. A sign was posted:

This is a MANI Prayer Wheel. It is filled with thousands of Avalokiteshvara mantras "OM MANI PADME HUM". By turning this wheel once, one earns merit equal to the recitation of the mantras filled inside the wheel. Kindly turn it clockwise.

I walked along and spun the wheels to my karma's delight.

******

At the hotel, Jimmie was awake in bed, her condition having improved. She was still tired and refused to go down the stairs for fear of triggering another episode. We ordered food and had it sent up to the room, a light snack of apple walnut cake, toast and milk tea. We opened all the windows as we ate. As the sun began to set, a chill fell over the little mountain town and the evening air circulated through our room. I sat on the back porch and watched as the great ball of light fell behind the village and disappeared from the sky.

A group of monkeys ran across a neighboring rooftop, horns honked softly and people conversed on the restaurant terrace below. Lights of all colors came to life in the nearby houses. The town appeared to have no shortage of stunning visuals, but tomorrow I would have to put the sites on hold to fulfill the laborious task of standing in line at the bank in hopes of retrieving more cash for our journey, as we had hardly a rupee to our name to pay for our food and lodging. I went inside, having enjoyed the night air free of the crippling smog I had become accustomed to in New Delhi. Jimmie was already asleep in her bed. I climbed into my own at the other side of the room and was dozing off in no time.

The next day Jimmie was well enough to venture downstairs for breakfast. We grabbed our book bags and money packs and stepped out into the hallway. Our door was secured using a latch and a padlock fastened with a large, old-fashioned key. I had to go down the steps first with Jimmie gripping my arm as we slowly descended one step at a time. There were no railings, windows or lights in the staircase, so we proceeded carefully to avoid accident. We took a seat next to a window in the back that overlooked the mountains. It was still chilly outside but the sun had cleared the peeks and began to warm us. Once we finished our breakfast, Jimmie was ready to go back upstairs. I went to the counter and paid our bill with the rupees that Jimmie had. Our money concerns were fresh in my mind as each precious bill left my hand. As I was doing so, a red-headed woman with a hiker's pack came into the restaurant and we exchanged smiles.

"Enjoying the sights?" I asked.

"I am," she said. "It was beautiful out this morning."

We struck up a casual conversation. One in which she expressed the same money troubles as everyone else. From the sound of it, she too was going to attempt exchanging her currency that morning at a nearby location. From across the room, I could see that Jimmie would be needing help getting upstairs again, so I wished the woman luck and bid her farewell. Little did I know, I would cross paths with her again very soon. Jimmie and I went to the sliding door that led to our room on the second floor. I helped her up from the first step and turned to slide the door back. As I turned to take her arm, I was surprised to see she had already begun ascending the steps on all fours.

"If I can't go like the people, then I'm gonna go like the animals," she said.

"Oh God, Jimmie, don't hurt yourself."

I pulled the curtains back inside our room and opened the windows to the new day's light. Jimmie lay on her bed again and took out her tablet. "You go on now. I've done enough for one day just

173

going up that staircase," she said.

"I was thinking of hiking up the rest of the mountain," I joked, "You sure you don't want to come with me?"

She laughed. "You get your ass outta here."

"Well, I guess I better get some money first. Bank opens in forty-five minutes. I want to be one of the first in line if I can."

"That's good. I'll be right here."

Out in the streets, any smell of pollution or trash was overpowered by the fresh scents of baked goods, breakfast dishes and assorted unknowns. People preparing to open their shops walked by with giant bags of rice on their heads, carried bushels of tree branches on their back or pushed carts loaded with fresh produce. I reached the main square within a minute. Already it was beginning to fill with people and passing cars at a quarter after nine o'clock. I found the bank around the corner where I had seen people standing the day before. Already a line had formed. I took up a position behind what appeared to be a group of Tibetan men, one of them a monk. I took out my notebook and began to write to pass the time.

In the forty-five minutes that passed, other people weaved themselves into the line where ever they pleased—no real organization. Eventually, two men came from inside the locked gate which secured the bank's entrance. They unlatched and slid it open and the first few people poured through. The men immediately began to shut the gate and even pushed an old man back into the streets during the scramble. The locals in line began to shout and protest.

Things died down and we waited for the doors to open again. After almost two hours, my time came to finally enter the bank where I was promptly turned away. "No tourists!" The agitated manager said with a dismissive wave. "Sorry."

"What do you mean? I have U.S. dollars here. I want to exchange."

"No, no exchange. We no do that here. Only locals."

"I don't understand. They told me I could come here for Rupees."

"I'm sorry, can't help you. You must go to other location."

"But I've been waiting in line for two hours! There's got to be something you can do. Help me out here." I thought this was just another way of doing business in India, but my pleas fell on deaf ears. I left the bank with no sensible information on where I was to go. Still broke, I marched back to the hotel and went up into the room to tell Jimmie.

"How'd it go?" She asked from her bed.

"I stood in that line all that time and don't have a damn thing to show for it."

"What do you mean?"

"They wouldn't deal with me! I don't know why. I tried arguing with him but it was no use." I dropped my backpack on the floor and sat on my bed. "This is so frustrating," I stewed. "This is really a beautiful place and we've only got two days to be here and I just spent all that time for nothing when I could have been exploring."

Jimmie interjected quickly at my words. "Well, this is what we'll do then," she said. "We'll stay a few more nights. I'm growing very fond of this place myself. I feel a strong connection to it and I'm sure my son felt the same way when he first came all those years ago. We'll stay another two days. I'll call Rajesh and make arrangements. How's that?

"That would be great. I'm not sure exactly why, but I feel as though the best part of the trip for me is going to be right here in Dharamshala, so a few extra days would be awesome." Little did I know how true that statement would become for me in the days ahead.

"Okay, then let's get it squared away now. Persistence in the face of adversity. I want you to go find Nick for me, okay?"

I went down to the restaurant below. It didn't take me long to find Nick. Hearing that Jimmie wished to speak with him, he left his task at once, signaling for an employee to take over for him in his absence. He followed me up the stairs and into the room where Jimmie waited.

"Hey, Nick. Yes, I'm feeling much better today, thank you. Everything is wonderful here. This room is just incredible! But listen, we got a problem. My grandson went down to the bank and they wouldn't deal. We're runnin' low on money and we would like to stay a few more nights. Can we work something out?" After a few minutes of talk, we quickly arranged for a way to get money through Nick's connections as well as book a few more nights at the hotel. After settling up with Nick, I went out into the streets heading north to explore the town.

******

I arrived back at the hotel as evening came about. I found Jimmie in travel attire and stuffing items into her mesh backpack. "Come on," she said. "I'm ready to go have tea with the Dalai Lama." A short cab ride later we were at the front of the holy temple. Jimmie had already begun to cough again. She glanced up at the walkway ahead, the vehicle unable to go any further down the narrow street.

"What is it like from here?" she asked from the front seat, clutching a tissue over her mouth. "From here there is a staircase we'll have to climb to reach the main sanctuary," I replied.

"Oh no," she wheezed, "I'm not going. This will have to be good enough for me. I'll take some pictures next to this beautiful statue and I can say I came to see his Holiness." The statue she referred to was a large, black granite structure with Tibetan writing and pink flowers on either side. Behind this, figures of people exiled from their homes were carved into the stone. After asking the driver to turn around and wait at the end of the lane, we got out. We took a couple of pictures near the monument and Jimmie poured some of her son's ashes into the soil with the pink flowers she loved so much. She stood back admiring the statue and the flower garden that would now grow in harmony with her son's remains.

"My son and I were not religious people," she said, "but everyone has a spirit. For me, God is nature. To put my son into the river at the Taj Mahal, or here among the flowers of the Dalai Lama's garden, is to release his spirit into nature. We were not devotees of Buddhism, but the teachings of the Buddha meant something to us."

I nodded silently, listening to the sounds stirring from the sacred temple. "It makes me very happy to have made it all this way," she said. I would have loved to have seen this place with him at my side, but I'm thankful that you're here, because who knows if I would have been able to make it without your help." She turned and patted me on my arm with a kind smile. "Thank you."

"Of course, Jimmie. I have just as much to be thankful for."

She turned and her eyes searched the area. "Okay, enough of the mushy stuff," she said. "Let's see what else is around this joint."

A staircase led up to a Tibetan museum that detailed the harsh reality of the Chinese government's ongoing persecution, forcing over 150,000 Tibetans into exile since 1959. Every year thousands more attempt to escape this oppression, often crossing the Himalayan Mountains during the most treacherous times of the year to avoid pursuit.

An elderly man behind a counter nodded to me as I walked in. Not a single other soul around. Dead quiet, save for a television screen that displayed old pictures of Tibetans being paraded in shackles through city streets, beaten by Chinese law enforcement or marching across some vast, snowy wasteland. Cut in between these still images were videos of present-day locals and monks who gave long, piercing stares, as if trying to break through a barrier to remind me that their struggles were not confined to these images in history.

The sounds that accompanied these shots were not music, but ominous hums and noises that hung with deep resonating bass. Somber tones that found their way inside the viewer and chilled the bone. I strolled past artifacts on display, most of them several decades old, a story behind each one. A white, long sleeve shirt behind a glass case detailed the horrors experienced by its owner. The entire length of the shirt was dotted with crusty, dull yellow stains. Blood splatters that had hardened with time. A card next to the display reported that the T-shirt and shorts issued to this prisoner could not be shown here because of their exceedingly poor condition.

Another case showed instruments of war used by the Chinese. A knife formed as a small pistol, handcuffs designed to tighten if the prisoner struggled. Smoke bombs. An electric baton caught my attention. A card next to it written by a woman: "*The Chinese police would sometimes insert these into our private parts...*"

My skin crawled. Another card lay next to an assortment of knives: "*Used by the Chinese police during a demonstration in Lhasa, 1980. The Chinese concealed the knives and wore civilian dress to mingle with the crowd of Tibetan people.*"

One portion of the exhibit catches my eye. A short article titled, "*Why Are Tibetans Turning to Self-Immolation?*" The iconic image of Thich Quang Durc in flames on the first Rage Against the Machine album cover comes to mind. I stepped closer to read the small print. "*From February 2009 till April 2015, a total number of one-hundred thirty-eight Tibetans have self-immolated. Tibetans, mostly young and healthy, soak themselves in flammable liquids and shout slogans demanding freedom for Tibetans and the return of His Holiness the Dalai Lama to Tibet, as flames consume them.*

"*Sixty years of Chinese occupation and rule have failed to address the grievances of the Tibetan aspirations for basic freedoms and the preservation of Tibetan culture and identity have been met with repressive measures, which have led to political repression, economic marginalization, cultural assimilation and environmental destruction in Tibet. Hence, in the absence of space for conventional forms of protests, Tibetans have resorted to the drastic action of setting themselves on fire to bring the world's attention to the plight of the Tibetan people.*"

Faces of the dead hung from the walls. My footsteps echoed across marble and brick. Short tales of sorrow describing hardships endured.

I went to the second floor. More images of broken and defiled humans. Expressions of a misused society. What grief encased behind these tired white walls. The lives of men, women and children systematically subjected to the horrors of unspeakable evil.

A new sight. A faded earth color stone or some type of marble etched with people in either torment or protest. Three figures at the top cry out in anger, or perhaps defiance, one clutching his fist in rage. Under them, a pile of the dead is carved into the same block. Men laying on top of one another in eternal sleep, one seeming to erupt out the side of a horse who shares the same similar expression of pain as the humans it parishes alongside. A baby reaches for its mother's breast, her left arm flailed out behind her drooping head. The faces at the bottom only get younger, their expressions filled with uncertainty. At the base sits a toddler, its face covered in black soot, cries out amid the destruction. How can our world bear such tragedy?

A child's question gone cold in the wake of death.

Why?

I look away, but for how long?

******

I stepped out of the museum feeling exhausted. Descending the short flight of stairs, I bump into the same red-haired woman I met at Nick's previously that day. In an attempt to make conversation, I did my best to tuck away the horrors I had just witnessed. How does one resume normal life after such an experience? How to shift the thoughts that plagued my mind?

"Hey, how's the money situation going?" I asked casually, but secretly feeling gross to inquire about money, given what I had just seen. She confirmed that she was still searching, though she appeared optimistic.

She said her name was Marijke. She was from the Netherlands and stayed at Nick's Italian Restaurant. "No kidding? Would you like to ride back with us," I asked, pointing to the parked taxi on the street corner. "My friend wanted to see the Dalai Lama's temple, but she has had enough for the day. To be honest, I think I've had enough myself."

"You must have been inside the museum," she said.

"Yeah. Pretty intense."

She gripped tightly to the straps of her black and blue backpack and returned a nod of her own with wide, understanding eyes. "I know the feeling. After I saw it, I felt like I could use a beer. Why don't we head back to Nick's and then go out to one of the rooftop terraces?"

Marijke and I ended up getting to know each other over Kingfisher beers on a rooftop terrace overlooking the southern running mountains. She was a theater teacher who had temporarily suspended her workload to travel for a few months. Like me, she was somewhat new to solo traveling, but her recent adventures to various parts of Asia put her far and above my rogue wanderings.

She told me the most incredible story of how her brother had moved to California from the Netherlands and fell in love with a girl in the Golden State. "For the next few months, I had heard all about this girl," she said. "He would send me pictures and tell me what she was like. After a while, I felt like I actually knew her personally. That said, I never got the chance to meet her because of how far away we lived from one another, but I was certain he was in love with her and that this girl would become my sister-in-law before long.

"So, fast forward to now, I'm traveling through Asia and decide to come to India to see Dharamshala. It was a fifteen-hour bus ride from where I was last hanging around. I get here. I'm walking around town and don't know anybody, but suddenly, I see this girl in the street and get the feeling that I've seen her somewhere before...so I go up and ask her name. It was *her!* My brother's girlfriend! She decided to travel overseas to come out to India, having *no* idea that I was here and having *never* met me before, I just happen to run into her here in Dharamshala. What are the odds? After calming down from our hysteria, we exchanged numbers and made plans to get acquainted over coffee sometime. Isn't that crazy? I hardly know what to think of it."

"They call this place a spiritual sanctuary," I said. "Maybe it wanted to bring you together."

She smiled and brushed back a strand of her long red hair. "Who's to say?"

I would have been very content to go on talking with Marijke, sipping a beer and watching the night sky take its color, but it seemed the more I spoke, the more the unfamiliar air sent me into fits of coughing. The virus or whatever it was that afflicted me before my departure was still an occasional hindrance to my adventures, particularly at night. While we were far from the metropolis machine of New Delhi, there were still large-scale construction projects underway through the town and a degree of filth still littered the streets and clogged the surrounding air.

I told Marijke I would have to excuse myself for the evening. She understood and knew that Jimmie was tormented by similar symptoms back at the hotel. I popped a cough lozenge that Jimmie and I had purchased in the Delhi airport, along with a box of GNC probiotic capsules, as I was actively trying to avoid dairy products for the sake of my sinuses. I took to hiding the probiotics from Jimmie who, at the sight of it, would begin to fume, "Read the ingredients on it," she would say. "All the important stuff you can get in yogurt. All the other stuff is bullshit."

Marijke confessed she would be going to bed soon as well. She intended to locate a money exchange and possibly look into renting a motorcycle to drive up into the mountains for the day, an idea that she had spoken about several times that night. She was looking for someone to travel with her, an opportunity that seemed too good to pass on. Alas, even the slightest consideration of such an expedition sent my calculating mind into overdrive.

For starters, I was very much ill-prepared for such a trip. I had no gear to protect from the wind or the snow we would encounter. I had never ridden with someone on a motorcycle and barely knew how to operate one myself. My first experience with trying to back up on my cousin's sports bike resulted in me laying down in a ditch, the motorcycle having wheelied and shot out from under me. Then there was the fact that people around here drove like lunatics and I could envision the all too real scenario of being forced off the road into a three-thousand-foot free fall to our death. Contending with icy roads would be a certainty. I stifled another cough as I considered what the cold air higher up in the mountains would do to my lungs. Furthermore, I had no idea how capable Marijke was on a motorcycle herself. "How many times have you ridden one of those things?" I asked.

"I've ridden motorcycles about three times. The *second time* I had a pretty nasty spill. You could see the bone sticking clear outta my arm!"

I politely declined.

We passed the still busy main square. Despite its size, it was still a bustling hub of activity, the lights of the multi-floored eateries and bars rising and falling with the terrain, the open mountains peeking through distant shadows in the southern sky. We reached the restaurant and agreed to meet for breakfast the following day. Marijke said good night and departed to her side of the hotel.

******

The next morning Jimmie and I took a seat at what would become our favorite indoor table at Nick's, right along with the windows that looked down the street toward Main Square. We did this to avoid the blazing heat from the rising sun which we had experienced the day before and came to appreciate the view our current vantage point afforded us. The same merchants began lining the street and placing their goods out on tables outside. One was a man of late thirties with short black hair who sat passively in a chair after setting up. Along with the traders were a group of dogs that always congregated around the window. This little strip of road was their territory and they remained vigilant of the roaming monkeys that passed above on rooftops and railings.

Unlike the many others we crossed in the streets of India, these dogs appeared somewhat fed and groomed, leading us to believe they belonged to somebody. They were a funny group of animals and the littlest of them, a white, fuzzy thing that he was, seemed particularly eager to play with the other dogs when there was no threat of a roaming monkey about. When a troop of primates did arrive, however, all the bigger dogs would run up the side staircase to the upper street to give chase, while the smallest remained behind to shout encouragement and protect their home turf. Sitting by his goods, the man pet one of the dogs as it rested its head across his knee. He gently lifted its head and began cleaning around the animal's eyes. The dog appeared at ease in his hands.

Another man in a straw hat carried his goods with some contraption upon his back. Lush, green branches of some plant I could not identify. He walked slowly with a meditative stare at the ground before him. The effect gave him the appearance of some sort of tree creature lumbering through the chilly pass. We watched all of this while being served an American-style breakfast of eggs, toast, hash browns, banana pancakes and chi tea. I ordered yet another tall glass of freshly squeezed apple, beet, carrot juice which I had ordered previously and found quite enjoyable. "You go and do what you want today," Jimmie told me. "I expect I'll stay right here at this table and make postcards and talk with friends back home."

After breakfast, I walked down to the Main Square. The first thing I noticed was an over-amplified advertisement for a cheesy Bollywood comedy-drama. I scanned the Square further. The town was fully alive now. The sun rested its early rays upon me. I took the southernmost path parallel to the opposite street, only separated by the small buildings between the two roadways. Two monks sat on the corner of a convenience store. One gently pet the head of a young dog, its tail down below its hind legs. Opposite this, two large black cows stuck their heads in a store, the clerk behind the counter no more concerned than he would be over a person window shopping. He produced some kind of food and one of the animals ate from his hand.

A trail of foreigners walked by. One had an unkempt brown beard, another with dreadlocks that swayed as he turned and laughed with his companion. Another man followed with two girls, one wearing blue jean shorts. I walked past a range of souvenir tables. Merchants dealing in handmade quilts, prayer beads, the occasional western-influenced T-shirt and more. I eyed the beads and made a note to purchase one before departing. An English man haggled with a clerk on the authenticity of his supposed Cashmere wears. Another block down, a man holding a remote, encouraged passers to take a seat in an egg-shaped virtual reality experience, which struck me as the most unusual and out-of-place business in the entire town.

The smells changed with every few steps. Street foods were being prepared at every turn. Chicken, mutton and various forms of the popular *momo* dish. Their scent would linger about momentarily and then be replaced by the odor of warm trash, pungent incense or the musk of wandering hippies and street drifters.

I walked past a building under construction. Around the outside, people with baskets dug up dirt and shuffled about in their bare feet, moving debris or sweeping away rubble. I saw two young boys lying on the ground nearby. They were staring up at the sky and I was surprised to hear them speaking in English. Their skin was a shade darker than my own, but I couldn't tell if they were Indian. One of them had slick black hair and the other was a bit on the chubby side with a buzzed head.

"What do you think it's like to die?" The black-haired child asked his friend.

"I don't know. It's probably like this," said his chubby companion. "You just see all the clouds and you're just swimming around in them and it goes on forever."

"Let's try to pretend like we're dead now," the other said. "Close your eyes and don't think about anything. Just let your body lay there. Imagine everything is gone and you don't have a body anymore."

"Okay."

They both closed their eyes and lay motionless on the dirt. After a few seconds, the chubby kid opened his eyes with an uncomfortable look on his face. "Can I pretend to die with my eyes open?"

"No, it won't work as good."

The nervous boy closed his eyes again reluctantly. "Dying is kind of scary," he said.

"It's not even that bad," the other insisted. "You're overthinking it."

I smiled as they became motionless again, beginning to move along just as the larger of the two boys inquired with his companion about what kinds of food would be served in the afterlife. I walked further and rounded a bend and stopped at the sight of some peripheral movement in an overhead tree between two apartment buildings. A monkey shifted its weight on a branch while a second perched atop a balcony rail. Another joined them and then another. The clan crept together in the same direction and descended to the street below. I knew they were likely going for the overflowing dumpster just a few feet away from me and wanted to ensure I didn't influence their course. They swarmed the bin and picked at its contents while I took some pictures made blurry by their constant, agile movements. When I was satisfied, I strolled past them and they dove for the apartment stairs, water drains and railings to avoid my presence.

I came across three cows laying in the fresh ruins of a demolished house a little further on. They eyed me in passive regard, unconcerned. I went around a monastery and found a staircase that descended to a building with rooftops that gave me a view across to my room at Nick's. I found posters advertising free yoga sessions on weekday mornings. Graffiti could be found all about the buildings here. I admired the details in the more psychedelic representations of nature and a blooming third eye erupting from the brow of a half-man, half-animal being. I suppressed another burst of coughs. Any further down the road from here and I would be out of the town altogether. I cursed a new series of coughs. Satisfied with my wanderings, I resolved to go back to the hotel to attend to my climbing pile of clothes that badly needed to be laundered.

******

I was back at Nick's in thirty minutes. Jimmie was still downstairs in the restaurant typing on her tablet, which she kept protected in a cushy pink case. I checked in with her briefly and then headed upstairs to tend to my clothes. I had done several hand washings at the YWCA in Delhi, but the conditions here were much more suited for the work, thanks to our back balcony with its all-day sun exposure.

I locked the main door and checked the geyser for hot water. Deciding to take advantage of the water's pleasant temperature, I took a quick shower and then got to work cleaning my clothes using a bucket and some soap. I got dressed and brushed my teeth, feeling the cool noon air coming in from the open balcony door. There was a knock at the door. I went to find Jimmie being led by the arm into the room, one of Nick's employees moving slowly with her towards the bed. "Hey," she said out of breath, "I thought I'd come up so I had this nice young man take me. Boy those stairs are hell. Thank you for the help, couldn't have done it without you. I mean, I could have, but who knows if I would have been able to do anything else for the rest of the week. Okay, let me just sit down here for a second." At the edge of the bed, she sat with great care. I thanked the man and he retreated back down the steps. "What do you plan to do next," she asked.

"Not sure. Maybe go down and have something for lunch."

"That's good. I got a lot of postcards made. Sent some messages online while I drank my tea and watched the people out in the street. It's so nice here, isn't it? Very peaceful. At my age, it's uncertain if I could ever come back to India with all the pollution. And there are so many people now, and the population has exploded since I was here last. It's just too much. But Mcleod Ganj...I could see myself coming back to Nick's and getting this room again. Not going off to do things like you, but just relax. I now understand why my son loved this place.

"But anyway, that's all in the future. Who knows what will happen. You see, my real problem is that I've got to start realizing at some point that I *am* getting older. I go, and I go, but I never stop to think how time has slowly overtaken me. The first day we got here, I got out of the cab in the main square and walked up here to find Nick's, and as soon as I got halfway I realized I had made a mistake. I just took off without even considering it. Next thing you know, that dizzy spell came over me and I was incapacitated for the rest of the day. That's no good. I've got to be better about pacing myself. My mind works fine. I just forget that I'm livin' inside this old woman."

"Well, I hope I have as sound a mind and can see the world like you when I'm your age," I commented. "I think any living person would hope for as much."

"Oh!" She shrieked and pointed behind me. "There go the monkeys!"

I spun around just missing the creature through the open door.

"He went across the rail of our balcony! Quick, close the door!" she shouted, but I had to see and stepped out onto the balcony looking in the direction it had gone. There it stood, not far from my hiking shirt. I pulled my phone out and took a quick shot, getting mostly monkey ass for my efforts.

"*Ahhh! Look out!*"

I turned my head and the other monkeys were following behind their leader, walking across the railing toward me not five feet away. I swore and jumped back into the room, slamming the door behind me as they passed. "Those things are mean as shit," Jimmie said as she stood up from the bed and hobbled her way over to the window. "They will give you a bite you will not soon forget!" The group quickly moved on, thankfully. Jimmie gave a little laugh as she peered through the blinds, the tiniest sliver of light falling on her face. We waited and watched as they ran back across our balcony again, no doubt chased off by someone or something in their original path. When we were sure they had gone, I quickly grabbed one of my shirts and a pair of pants from the railing. I would need them to explore the town this afternoon.

******

I went and took a seat in Nick's restaurant. I ordered my usual honey-ginger lemon, as well as a Greek salad. After the small but satisfying lunch, one of the waiters took my plate with a wide smile. I sat back and observed the inhabitants of the café as I reflected on my thoughts.

I pulled out my notebook and began to write. A young couple walked in and sat two tables over as I did. They spoke to one another enthusiastically while looking over menus. As soon as the couple finished placing their orders, I leaned over my notebook. "Hi there. How is your day going?" I asked.

"Pretty good so far," the guy said in his unmistakable accent.

"Australian?" I asked.

"Yeah," they announced together with a smile.

We continued to talk as their food was prepared. The guy's name was Alex and the beaming girl sitting across from him was his girlfriend, Jay. They had come to India after saving up for several years working jobs back home on the Central Coast of Australia, about an hour and a half north of Sydney.

Jay, got her first desire to see the country after some time working in an Indian restaurant back home. "My boss, an Indian man," she was saying, "would ask me, 'Why do you want to go to India? It's a shit hole! There is a reason I moved here to Australia.' But Jay and Alex loved the country's cuisine and mysticism. They had both just completed their degrees in June and found the time ripe for extended exploration afar. In the first couple of years of their young adulthood, they wanted to travel to as many parts of the world as possible.

The duration of their trip was undetermined. "We're kind of going until the money runs out," Alex laughed. "We arranged for our three-month Indian tourist visa, a requirement to purchase a plane ticket here. We scheduled a flight out of Australia on the 19th of September and then another three months later to Nepal on the 19th of December." They both had backpacks and nothing more than the contents within them. They had almost no set itinerary and could come and go as they pleased within the country. "We thought, screw it, we have open hearts and that should be enough," Jay said.

Like me, they had first seen the city of New Delhi upon arrival. Their only necessary action was checking into a hotel booked before leaving Australia. They knew they wanted to see North and South India and spend a little time in Rishikesh to practice yoga. The rest they trusted would find them through word of mouth and serendipitous exploration.

"Peoples' reactions back home were so interesting when we talked about coming here," Jay said. Most of our friends and family were extremely supportive, but we did get the occasional, 'You are both so brave,' and 'make sure you're *very* careful'. Others couldn't believe we would even want to come to such a place. My step-father is a policeman. He started sending me videos on how to escape from hostage situations," she rolls her eyes. We continued talking and I extended them an invite to trek down to St. John's Church in the Wilderness, which was only a kilometer outside of town. They cheerfully agreed and we departed in unison shortly after the bills were settled.

We quickly moved to the main square and began walking down the road leading to St. John's Church. They talked about their journey, especially the initial arrival to New Delhi. "I remember first touching down," Jay said as we walked single file up the mountain road. She was at the head of the line as we hugged the sides to avoid oncoming cars. "That thick, hot air just smacks you straight in the face. Even going through the airport and flying on the plane felt like an experience in its own right. We had been told stories about them. One of our friends back home had been here for a time. He bought a souvenir in Mumbai, a melon-sized statue of an elephant and he needed to take a flight to New Delhi. They wouldn't let him carry the statue onto the plane but he was living out of a backpack and had no checked baggage to store it in. The Indian workers at the check-in just took his souvenir and put it into a random person's bag and told him to retrieve it at his destination. When he got to New Delhi, our friend had to explain to an Indian woman who couldn't speak English why he was going through her belongings. He said the look on her face when he pulled out the elephant statue and walked away was priceless."

They went on to talk about being picked up from the airport at midnight and taken to their previously booked hotel. They admitted it wasn't in the best part of Delhi. It only took one night in the shady establishment to know they needed to swap it for a safer location.

"We still hadn't had any food or any real idea of where we were going," Alex said, brushing blonde hair from his face. "I remember paying for our room and walking straight out the door into a massive crowd. The noise from all the cars and the city life was overwhelming. We walked for what felt like hours to the train station in the heat. I don't know if it was lack of food, sleep or both, but our adrenaline had kicked in and it was like having blinders on. I just knew I wanted to get to the train station as fast as possible.

"We had been told before that the train stations were places where the homeless would go to die. That was unsettling. We were also very much aware that the station was a notorious hangout for pickpocketers and thieves. It was hard to trust people. We had to be vigilant constantly. The whole time we were in the Golden Triangle the first seven days, we didn't trust anyone." The Golden Triangle being the heavily traveled tourist area between Delhi, Agra and Jaipur. "Looking back, I think we were right to be cautious in that situation. A man came up to us in the Delhi train station saying our tickets were invalid and we needed to pay again if we wanted seats. I had read this type of deception was common and we were able to avoid his scam. While there, we also met a French couple that flew in the night before. You could see it in their faces. They couldn't handle it. They both said they wanted to get out of the country as fast as they could."

"And that's what India is like," Jay added as she led us around another bend in the road. "It's so full-on, so intense, but you need to stick it out. You need to push through because it shows you its true beauty over time and it changes you in the process."

"What was it like for you the day the currency chaos started?" I asked.

"We were in Rishikesh," Jay said. "We were getting our favorite coconut masala chai when we heard the news from the store owner. Alex and I both had eight thousand rupees each in five hundred bills.

They became impossible to use. No one had change or was willing to exchange with us. Most places were starting tabs with customers. No one could pay. It has hit the Indian people hard. This is Indian's wedding season and the financial setbacks could ruin many hopeful couples' ceremonial plans."

Alex and Jay wouldn't begin to feel the strain of their money situation until several days later, a day marked by the first sentence in Jay's travel diary.

Today came with a big lesson in patience.

After eating breakfast at Nick's, they had run down to their last eighty rupees. The ATMs were only restocking bills once a day and the couple waited in line from nine in the morning until five that evening. They were incredibly fortunate, as the money supply ran out shortly after them. Everyone else was out of luck. The crowd dispersed. They would all have to come back again and endure the day-long lines.

"I think we had it pretty good, all things considered," Jay told me. As another car came around the corner up ahead, she stepped to the farthest side of the road and we followed her lead. We still couldn't see St. John's Church as we continued, but I was certain we were getting closer. They told me of their first week in The Golden Triangle.

"The Taj Mahal was one of the most breath-taking experiences," Jay was saying. "Spending six weeks in Rishikesh was a highlight too. When we arrived, we had no accommodations booked and walked around for three hours trying to find a good place to stay. Funny how India works. We ended up back at the place we had our first tea that morning and that was where we got our room. We met so many incredible people in Rishikesh and learned a great deal about yoga."

"What made you want to come here to Dharamshala," I asked.

"We had honestly never heard of it," Alex admitted. "When we were at the Ashram in Rishikesh we met a wonderful woman named Gabriela. She spoke so highly of Dharamshala and the Tibetan people, so we decided to head here next when we felt like our time in

Rishikesh was complete. Just as we had hoped, word of mouth led us to our next destination."

They arrived in McLeod Ganj on November 11th, the day before Jimmie and I. It was a fourteen-hour bus ride from Rishikesh and they made a curious comment about meeting a redheaded girl from the Netherlands with who they had coffee after arriving in the town. "It sounds like we have a mutual friend," I said. "I just met Marijke yesterday. She is staying at Nick's hotel also." The small world connection tickled us.

"So far we've loved everything about Dharamshala, this town particularly," Alex continued. "It is incredibly clean and full of the most genuine people. We're a bit surprised at the amount of meat they serve here though, especially after being in Rishikesh where there is barely any meat to be seen. We decided to go strictly vegetarian while we were in India and, in Rishikesh, that is pretty much how they live as far as we could tell."

We arrived at the church that lay silently waiting in the woods. A few people talked in hushed voices atop a small wall on the side of the church and another group was taking off their shoes to enter the structure itself. I took some pictures of the landscape with its scattered tombstones, most of which remained in the constant shade of the many Deodar Cedars that covered the grounds with their wiry branches that began low at the base and stretched high into the sky. Jimmie had told me about these trees. She said they were a cedar native to the western Himalayas in Afghanistan, Pakistan, India, Tibet and Nepal, typically growing at altitudes of 1,500 meters. Worshiped among Hindus as a divine tree, its botanical name, which derives from the Sanskrit term evader, translates to "wood of the gods". A large sign near the entrance made of stone was fixed nearby:

ST. JOHN'S IN THE WILDERNESS: Episcopal Church, built in 1834 as a private chapel. Given to Diocese of North Carolina, 1836.

I spoke to a guy from Sweden who had been working in McLeod Ganj for several months with some of the Tibetan refugee organizations. He told me there was another more populated graveyard in a separate lot next to the church. I went back around toward the front of the structure and found my Aussie companions. We approached the quiet church with its huge doors swung open to us. We removed our shoes and walked in, the silence from the forest fading behind us. The interior was beautiful. It had a certain presence to it, as if it was still clinging to the spirits that erected it, along with the souls that once congregated to it. The architecture was primarily neo-Gothic with impressive Belgian stained-glass windows that were given to the church by Lady Elgin, wife of Lord Elgin, the British colonial administrator and diplomat who, at different times in his career, served as the Governor of Jamaica, the Governor-General of the Province of Canada and the Viceroy of India beginning in 1862. His body was buried in the graveyard just outside the building.

Down at my feet, the tile floors kept their shine. The wooden ceilings rose high above us. The pews and fixtures on the alter were a deep mahogany that contrasted the gray stones the church was constructed from. From the ceilings, long ropes ran down to hold small light fixtures suspended over the aisles. My eyes studied over the words of a mounted plaque:

In loving memory of Thomas William who met his death at Dharamshala by an attack from a bear on the 25th October 1883. Aged 50 years.
"In the midst of life, we are in death."

"That's so metal," I whispered to myself.

The church had not only been well kept over its one hundred fifty-plus years but had also survived the devastating Kangra earthquake of 1905 that killed nearly twenty-thousand people and destroyed most of the buildings in Dharamshala. Outside we put our shoes back on and I told the couple about the graveyard nearby that the Swedish wanderer had mentioned. Finding a path away from the church, we walked to the neighboring site that could be seen through the trees and bushes— a beautiful plot of British colonial graves, situated on a sloping hill. Looking out in the direction that the tombstones faced, one could see clear over the tree line of the woods to town, the mountains propped up majestically in the background.

******

Later that night Alex, Jay, Marijke and I dined at the Common Grounds Café. The building was small and had mixed seating arrangements including standard table tops with box chairs, a sofa on one of the far walls and a floor table with cushions and pillows. We enthusiastically took the ground table, sitting crossed-legged on the floor while looking over the laminated menus. Arguably the most interesting characteristic of the café was the taste in music the owners possessed. At first, it was simple, traditional Indian music. Then, as time went on, it changed to western pop tunes. A few minutes later we found ourselves eating while being assaulted by a ten-minute Eminem freestyle absent of any music at all.

As far as the food went, it was some of the best I had had in the town. I would come to eat there several more times, but that first meal would become my most remembered. Our group shared three or four plates of stir-fried vegetables with marinated tofu, pan-fried green beans, carrot slivers, snow peas and a type of Asian noodle. After the meal we enjoyed white hot chocolate sprinkled liberally with ground cardamom.

Marijke had made plans to see a well-known local bar on the other side of town and soon departed. As I sat trying to enjoy the last of my hot chocolate, the night air began to play on my lungs and a series of coughs escaped me. By the end of the dinner, I could hardly suppress them. I told Alex and Jay they would have to go on without me. We made plans to hike down the mountain into the town the next day to catch a movie and then I retired to my room for the night.

The following day, I was roused by the sound of dogs barking as they chased away a clan of monkeys in the street and reflected on how odd it was to be regularly woken up by such a thing. I took a quick shower and squeegeed the floor. I went down for a breakfast of cold cereal and juice on the back patio with my three foreign companions. As we ate, we discussed our descent from McLeod Ganj and what we would watch at the movie theater. At the time, *Dr. Strange* had just come out in theaters and was receiving a lot of hype, so we agreed on that. Marijke wished to make another attempt at getting her currency exchanged at the banks. She would then meet us at the theater afterward.

The walk down would be almost an hour-long, so we left with great haste after our breakfast. The hike provided some of the best photography of the area and we made good time getting to the theater. Even Marijke was able to make the film, coming in to take a seat at the row in front of us. Afterward, Marijke took a bus back to Mcleod Ganj and Jay, Alex and I hailed a taxi. All three of us crammed into the back of the vehicle, as the front seat looked like it was occupied by a chicken cage. Along the way, I turned my head to the window to find Alex and Jay unusually silent.

"Everything okay you guys?"

Alex was at the opposite window seat. "Yeah. We were both just chatting on the walkout about the movie."

"Did you not like it?"

"It's not that," Jay chimed in. She was still staring ahead as she spoke. A crowd of young boys had managed to wander in front of our taxi and took their time clearing the street. Our driver seemed unconcerned. "We're both fans of the Dr. Strange comic books," she went on, "but it was a little concerning a particular choice they made in this film."

"Probably just artistic direction," I offered. "They can't recreate everything and some producer always wants to put a new spin on the story."

Jay made a face. "I don't think that's what happened in this case," she said. "I just think it's ironic that we saw this movie *here*. I felt like in this movie, Hollywood chose to save face with China for political and monetary reasons. It doesn't surprise me, but it is sad."

I gave an uncertain look. "You've lost me," I said. "What exactly are you talking about?"

Alex picked up the conversation. "She's talking about the role of the Ancient One in the movie, the character who teaches Dr. Strange how to use his powers. In the movie, they cast a British actress, but in the original comic books, it was written as a very different person."

"Who was the Ancient One in the comic books?" I asked.

Jay was the one to answer.

"He was a Tibetan man."

******

Later that night, our crew of travelers had dinner at the Common Grounds again. We were finishing up another round of unique dishes that included cubed eggplant in a sauce that turned a wild color of orange and purple through the combination of spices. I ventured to try the café's version of the honey ginger lemon, which I found was good but held second in my mind to the one served at Nick's. At our table, I found a flyer for a live performance of Tibetan folk music showcasing at a nearby café called the Seed. I suggested the event to my companions who seemed pleased with the idea.

We walked down the declining slope into the Main Square and headed east toward the Seed Café. I noticed that one of the bars we passed, a narrow two-story structure, was advertising an open-mic night that evening. "Who's up for karaoke," I asked enthusiastically. "Any singers among you?" Marijke, who worked in the world of live theater, certainly supported my suggestion.

We descended a long series of wide steps between residential abodes and businesses. Then, after walking along the side of a pale apartment complex, we came to the Seed Café, which was on the edge of the rise. There was a fair amount of graffiti on the walls around us and this café, in particular, seemed to embrace it with a mural of Jim Morrison on the entrance. In front of the wall in a small, square concrete space, a group of four men of Tibetan decent sat tuning a series of instruments and warming their voices. We all smiled at one another in passing and stepped through the door.

I was first inside and was immediately taken by the café's atmosphere. In one quick motion, I pulled my phone from my pocket, took a mostly aimless shot of the layout and slipped it back into my pant leg. I scanned the place as my friends piled in behind me. The Seed Café was a blend of eastern culture mixed with the American rock era of the '60s and '70s. A Jimi Hendrix painting shared the walls with electric guitars, music notes and a large, black microphone.

The floor was a simple concrete slab, but my gaze drifted across the colorful decor of furniture and ceiling fixtures. Above us, long fabrics of maroon and blue hung parallel to the ceiling which sloped upward. Prayer flags of all colors. Hanging box lights illuminated the tables below while horizontal metal beams fixed with additional lights shined against the blue interior walls. The north side of the building, which faced the mountains and the town, were tall windows encased in wooden frames, providing an excellent view of the surrounding area. Most of the patrons sat in plastic chairs at wooden tops, but in the far back corner against the windows, there was a floor table with cushions and pillows. It was there I saw a young Indian woman who sat crossed-legged on the floor reading a book.

"Let's go sit over there," I pointed. As we approached, she lowered her book. "Can we join you?" I asked. The girl smiled. "Of course," she said sweetly. We all gathered around the table and removed our shoes before sitting. Menus were brought to us and we began looking over the food. I talked to the girl. She had smooth, long black hair. Bright eyes behind big glasses that complimented her friendly smile. A laugh that testified to a sense of genuine character. She told me her name was Anika but she went by Ramana, a nickname she used with family and friends. She was on holiday and decided to come up to Dharamshala for the three-day weekend. It was the first time she had ever traveled alone. Like my companions, she too had taken a lengthy bus ride to get here. She was originally from Punjab but had gone to university and now worked in New Delhi.

We talked about travels. I told her about the U.S. and she told me about her recent visit to Nepal. She asked why Americans had such elitist attitudes. I told her with a sly smile that it was because we were the shit. She smiled and rolled her eyes, the reaction I was looking for. I inquired about traditional Indian heritage and customs. Then we discussed her country's varied dishes and I used the opportunity to scoot around the table to sit closer to her, pointing at items on the menu and asking for descriptions of the different entrees. Not a moment after I closed the distance, a dog that had been sitting next to one of the other patrons came walking behind me and promptly laid down in the gap between us.

"Oh, what a cute little furball," she gushed.

It was the first time a dog had ever prevented me from getting closer to a woman.

We continued to talk as she gently petted the snoozing mut with care and spoke of her affection for animals. Despite the barrier my four-legged friend had put up, I managed to break the touch barrier a handful of times with Ramana over the next half hour, which she in turn reciprocated. She asked about the sights I had seen in the town and I told her I hoped to go to the nearby meditation center, a short hike up the mountain. "Oh yes," she beamed. "I know the place well."

Before long, the musicians took to the floor and began playing various Tibetan folk songs with great enthusiasm. There were four of them in total, but they would switch to different instruments or appoint a new lead vocalist with each new song. Some songs they chanted in unison, some songs they danced on the open floor while they played, kicking their feet in time and giving the occasional spirited shout. The musicians would banter comically in between tunes, explaining a composition's origin or commenting on the ongoing atrocities that have been taking place in their homeland for more than half a century.

"These songs and dances are an important part of our culture," the lead musician said, "but the Chinese government works to oppress these art forms and keep our people from their roots. This is why we perform for you, to keep these traditions alive because when we lose sight of where we come from, it is harder to know where we are going.

"We love to play. We hope to continue to do so for many years to come, but always with the Tibetan people in our hearts. Here, we are safe. We are free. But it is important to remember that not so far away in the world, injustice is being done to a peaceful people and war is being waged on a culture rich in heritage. A people that can teach much to their brothers and sisters of the world. We ask that you remember the Tibetan people too and pray for their liberation."

The café' was quiet as he concluded his statements. One of the players handed him a mandolin which he slung over his shoulder. "But, this all said," he continued, "we are very thankful that you would come out tonight to be with us and we are here to be happy and have fun, so we ask you all to join us to dance to our final song!" A murmur of delight from the audience. "Come on," I said, gently shaking Ramana, "let's join them". I went barefoot onto the cold floor with her following behind. Alex and Jay stayed behind, but Marijke took up next to us with the other patrons forming a circle at the café's center.

We were given instructions and the premise seemed simple enough. They began to play slowly, the circle of people beginning to rotate clockwise, following the player's motions as they stomped out a pattern of movement. We smiled, trying to memorize the sequence, a collective group of missteps and chuckles. The musicians became more animated, almost swinging their instruments in an upbeat fashion as the tune began to speed up in unison. The circle moved quicker with them. The laughs became more pronounced as we attempted to adjust to the new tempo. Some patrons kicked their legs while others missed the beat and kept circling, causing humorous bump-ins with their neighbors.

We were caught off guard when the players suddenly changed course, taking a counter-clockwise rotation. I caught Ramana in my arms briefly, as I was quicker to change direction than she was. She laughed, then quickly went the other way with the crowd. The music quickened. We could barely make heads or tails of when our feet should have been stomping and when they should have been shuffling.

The laughs were now group-wide as the circle fell into chaos, the sequence becoming like a blur of drunken motor skills as the rotation began to shift more frequently. We bumped into each other again and again, our hands playfully pushing against one another in search of the right direction as the circle sped into a dizzying dance. At last, the musicians gave their last breath and final strums to their instruments and threw their hands up to signal the end of the song with a united shout of joy. We threw our hands up and shouted too, a round of laughter and applause.

I turned to Ramana and found her giggling in delight, her eyes lit up. I took her hand and walked her back to our table. Our group conversed for a time before deciding the next course of action.

"Karaoke!" Marijke suggested.

"Oh yeah, the open mic. Let's do it!" I turned to Ramana. "You should come with us."

Shoes back on and jackets zipped up we passed the folk players outside the front door, giving our thanks as we went. Jay and Alex decided to return to their hostel for the night. It was now just Marijke, Ramana and I as we moved along the stone streets.

"You're going to sing for us right," I nudged Ramana's arm with my elbow. "Maybe one of your country's hit songs from the radio?"

"I'm not very good at singing," she said brushing her hair behind her ear.

"Your voice is so beautiful. I find that hard to believe."

I enjoyed talking to her. She was a smart girl. There was very little language barrier between us. I occasionally had to ask her to repeat something if it was noisy or if I misunderstood her pronunciation, but she could always spot when I was grasping for the full picture and would repeat or rephrase her words.

The three of us walked along, talking. Our hands tucked away in our pockets, our breath almost visible in the developing chill. "So, what is it you do exactly?" Marijke asked as we rounded a bend in the road.

"I work for a company doing risk management." Ramana looked at us with a half-hearted smile. "I don't really enjoy it, to be honest, but that's why I'm hoping to begin a master's program soon."

"What kind of masters?"

"I want to go for business administration. I'd like to find time to travel and then, if I can do so, I believe I will study and work briefly in America."

"Do you plan on traveling while in the States?" I asked.

"No," she said with a sense of finality, "I don't care to see America and I have no real desire to live there. I would just go to study and work, then move back to be near my family." This gave me the impression she was not very fond of my country, but I didn't inquire further.

Our roaming trio talked and shared stories until we reached the small bar hosting the open mic. We went up a narrow staircase to the second floor. The seating was very tight. A tiny bar was manned by the owner who had to squeeze past the refrigerator to get out. Next to the bar was a door to a balcony that overlooked the moon-soaked street with room for maybe a half dozen people. Next to the balcony door was a table which other men rose from when they heard we were paying customers. A band of five was in full swing in the corner directly on the other side of our table. There were three men playing bongos. The two guitar players each had a microphone, one with an acoustic, the other with what looked like an electric Fender. At the moment, the entire group was in mid-stride of singing *Rains of Africa*, the man equipped with the Fender using an effects pedal to supply a healthy tone mixed with reverb and delay. I played a similar Stratocaster back home and longed to feel my fingers across its frets again.

We watched the men perform various other songs, talking among ourselves between each number. We tried to persuade one another into going up for the spotlight but, as the music went on, I noticed no one else came up and the same group of men continued to play. I was content with this and was happy to sit and drink. I finished off a second King Fisher, feeling the alcohol beginning to loosen me up. Ramana was sitting to my right finishing her first drink. To my left, Marijke happily sipped at her bottle. It was then that I resolved to try and go home with Ramana.

The band began to sing a song in Hindi. Ramana seemed to melt a little bit at this new performance and smiled. "I love this song. It is one of my favorites. He is talking to his girl, telling her how much he cares for her. They like to smoke together and get high."

"Oh yeah?" I said with raised eyebrows. "You know, not that you mention it, it is a pretty good song."

The more her layers peeled back in our short time together the more I grew attracted to her. At the end of the next song, the girls excused themselves to smoke on the balcony. I told them I would hold the table and watch their belongings. While they were away, I realized a most inconvenient truth. Before I left our room at Nick's, I had given the key to Jimmie, for reasons I couldn't recall. I was sure we would be back before the outside doors were locked at nine o'clock but it was a quarter after eight now. If I stayed here, it might take time to work things out with Ramana. If I couldn't get it together, then I might be locked out of my hotel.

I could go right then, get the key and come back, but it would take close to twenty minutes, valuable time considering my newfound resolution. We had only been here a short time and I was worried my sudden leave might cause a halt to the night's activities. I could also put it all on red and hope to convince Ramana to take me back with her. I decided to carry on and cease worrying about the key. The girls came back and we ordered another round of drinks.

"What's the plan after this?" Marijke said in my ear from one side. I leaned in. "I forgot the key at the hotel. They're locking the doors at nine."

"I have my key, but my room is on the other side and uses a different entryway, so I guess I wouldn't be able to help you there. So, we will just head back to the hotel after this then?"

"Well, I was thinking of trying to go home with this girl."

"I noticed that," she said, "Better try to lock it in soon or you may be sleeping on my floor!"

The minutes continued to go by and before long it was a quarter till nine. "I really should be going," Ramana said over the music. "The place I'm staying at is further up the mountain and the taxis won't run much longer. Since I am by myself, I don't want to stay out too late."

"You should take me with you," I tried.

"What?" She said, leaning closer over the noise.

204

"I said, you should take me with you," I repeated directly into her ear. She pulled back to look at me. "No," she said with an innocent smile. "No."

"Why not?" I asked sincerely.

"I just…I don't know."

"Why don't you know?"

She grinned, took hold of my arm and, as I was leaning in trying to be heard over the noise, she gave me a quick peck on the cheek and retreated. "I'm sorry, I don't think so." I turned my hands up to press her, but then let them fall.

"Okay," I said. "Well, let's go ahead then."

I turned to Marijke and nodded toward the door. She had been waiting on the move and saw it was time to go. Ramana was gathering her things too. Marijke went out first and I followed. We descended the steps and went out into the street. I put my beanie on and placed my hands in my jacket. I was not bitter or upset. She had every reason to say no to a foreign stranger who wanted to sleep with her, but I had been hopeful all the same. I figured that was that. But my interest was sparked again as we conversed on the return walk. The girls talked of a shared mutual interest in a Bollywood movie star they both admired.

"He has glasses," Ramana was saying, "but they are sexy glasses…kind of like Stefan's…"

"Oh, I can see what you mean," Marijke said turning to me and giving me a knowing look. I undoubtedly said something to be charming, but it was mostly to hide my bruised ego. We were at the Main Square shortly after, the streets as lively as ever. This is where Ramana would catch her ride.

"Goodbye, Ramana," Marijke said, "It was great to meet you."

Marijke stepped away and I smiled at Ramana, but before I could speak, she said, "There is a meditation center not far from where I'm staying. They do morning sessions. I know you said it's on your to-do list while you're here. Maybe I'll see you there."

"Maybe you will," I returned. "How can I keep up with you while you're here?"

"Use my phone number online. That's the best way." She gave it to me but I told her I didn't have the app to make calls here and asked if there was another way. "Sure, just look me up online," she said.

"Yeah," I said, not thinking much of it. "I will."

"I had a good time with you tonight," she said. "I'm glad we met."

"Me too. Be safe going home." She flashed a farewell smile and I watched her as she climbed into a passing taxi. I rejoined Marijke and we pressed on up the road.

When we got back to Nick's the main entrance was locked.

"Shit," I said to the door. It said nothing back.

Luckily, an employee cleaning up in the kitchen overheard our attempts and managed to let me into the side of the hotel I was in.

"Lucky you," Marijke smiled.

I reflected on my failed plans with Ramana. "Yeah, would have been a shame to be unlucky twice in one night."

She smiled. "Don't worry, she still digs you, I can tell. Just stay in touch with her and maybe you'll meet again tomorrow. You said she wanted to go to the meditation temple up the mountain? Well, I'm heading up that way tomorrow for an all-day hike, so maybe we can go together halfway."

"Yeah, that'd be cool. She told me to look her up so I'll have to find out when and what is exactly going on. I'll try to connect with her tonight before I go to sleep."

"Sounds good. See you at breakfast then!"

I went upstairs and pressed my ear to the door out in the hallway. Nothing. I tapped lightly against the door but still didn't hear anything. I knocked this time.

"Who is it?" I heard Jimmie from inside.

"It's me."

A pause, then slight shuffling. The door unlatched and cracked open.

"*Heeey*, you're back. Did you have a good time?" I told her about our activities and the lovely girl I had met while she climbed back into her bed. The room was dark, illuminated only by the lights that shone in the town. Jimmie loved hearing my stories of fun and was not bothered about my waking her. In a way, I felt like she was reliving memories of the travels with her son who would go out to have a good time after sundown and would sometimes not return till early morning. I loved that she operated at all hours. She was free of time in a sense. A night worker by trade and a lifelong traveler unrestrained by typical day rhythms. Not quite a hippie but certainly a gypsy lotus.

After I had changed in the bathroom and climbed into my bed by the window, I began looking for Ramana on social media but quickly became dismayed at the number of Indian girls with the same first and last name. I kept searching but could find nothing. Small square profile pictures deceived my eye as hundreds of young Indian women with dark black hair crowded my search. I quickly realized it was a losing battle. I would never find Ramana like this. I sent messages to the Aussie couple and Marijke.

"*Can't find this girl,*" I typed, "*Here is her name...can you see if you can find anything?*"

I put my phone down, rolled over and soon fell asleep.

I looked at my phone the next day before taking my morning bucket rinse. A part of me had hoped Ramana would have gone looking for me online since I was having a hard time finding her, but there was nothing new. No messages, no requests. I took a shower and went down to breakfast with Jimmie and Marijke.

"I looked up Ramana last night," Marijke was telling me. "but I couldn't find anything on her. It's a pretty common name."

"Yeah, you're telling me," I said. "Not to mention all the black hair."

I took a sip of my tea and stared out the window. The street dogs were playing with each other while the vendors began the morning ritual of setting up their tiny shops. "Maybe you should just come with me up the mountain and go to that temple. She might be there," Marijke suggested.

"I suppose I have nothing to lose. It's a beautiful morning anyways. Let's do it."

We finished our food and said goodbye to Jimmie who was looking forward to another day of relaxation with the glorious view the back balcony offered. We left the restaurant and headed north up the mountain road.

It took us about forty-five minutes to make it to the temple. There came a split where you could continue up the mountain or go along the side to the temple. Marijke and I parted here. I began the short solo walk onto the meditation grounds and she carried on for a hike I expected would take up most of her day. The place was more like a school than anything. Small buildings for various lodging, meditating, yoga and cooking were tightly packed on this little piece of land that looked out over the dense trees.

The concrete walkway swirled with beautifully painted designs and a quiet hush held over the grounds. To my right, a small flight of steps lead to a modest roof patio with chairs and tables that overlooked the mountains. A sign requested a refrain from speaking, as many individuals were undergoing vows of silence. Devices were to be turned off on the property. I walked around aimlessly, taking it all in, looking for some indication of where I was supposed to go. Nowhere could I find the long-haired girl I was actively searching for.

I walked around the outer edges of the main temple at the center of the grounds. A little dining area with over a dozen circular tables, four chairs at each, were positioned next to the railing that overlooked the side. A monkey was sitting on the railing and jumped to a nearby tree as I approached and quickly descended to the base and was lost in the thick vegetation. I peered into a window and briefly observed an unmoving group of people sitting silently in zazen. I walked around the back and found a lovely sitting garden, decorated with expertly carved stones. A pale young girl passed me with a nod and went up the steps to the back entrance of the main temple. She took off her shoes, placed them among a row of others and went inside through a large wooden double door that looked like it belonged to a medieval castle. Coming full circle on the grounds, I found a small ten by ten glass room on the opposite end of the garden. At the center was a gold-colored statue of the Buddha. It was adorned with fine jewels and surrounded by candles and other offerings, the smell of burning incense in the air.

Walking around to the front again, I saw a small group of people collecting at the door of one of the buildings on the second floor. I walked up the stairs as several of them began to go inside. One man was sitting on a bench removing his shoes. The others had already done the same. I followed his lead, removed my footwear and placed them among the other shoes. The inside was a large, open layout with dozens of cushions and pillows placed about the hardwood flooring. Everyone was seated with their back to me. At the front of the room was a short-legged table, presumably for the teacher.

I tip-toed in my sock feet down the middle aisle, taking a cushion near the front. As I took my seat, I scanned the room but didn't see Ramana anywhere. I felt as though the game was up. Sure, McLeod Ganj was a small town, but what were the odds that I would run into her again in the course of the last day that she would be here? I crossed my legs in half lotus, my usual seated position and found alignment in my spine. I envisioned a string gently pulling up from the center of my head toward the ceiling. My breath came naturally, accustomed to the practice and my mind began to relax.

The door opened quietly from behind us as another practitioner walked in. With my eyes closed my hearing was most attuned to the noise, but I was not bothered by it. The door closed behind me.

Focus...focus...

I tried to center my consciousness to the blank state, free from the many sensory inputs that surrounded me. Then I heard the same person walking. A rustle of cushions directly behind me and I found I couldn't help myself. I opened my eyes and turned my head to find Ramana settling on the floor just behind me.

"Hi," she mouthed silently.

"Hey," I returned in an equally inaudible manner, then brought my gaze forward again. A French woman entered and took her seat at the front of the group, giving hushed instructions as she led us into our meditation. The session ended after an hour and we were told we could remain as we were or take our leave. Many people began to silently rise from their pillows and moved towards the exit. I took my time stirring from my meditation. When the feeling had returned and I was convinced I would not look like a fool trying to stand on nerveless legs, I got up and looked behind me.

She was gone! I had not even heard her leave. Where did she get off to so quickly? I was not even sure she had stayed for the whole session. I picked up my book bag from the floor and followed the crowd out to the shoe rack. Outside, I looked around for the ever-elusive woman. When I didn't see her there, I peered over the steps below to see if she had already gone down. I couldn't believe it. She was nowhere in sight.

I quickly put my shoes on and readjusted my bookbag. I walked down, taking my time, not wanting to feel rushed after such an experience. Just as I was exiting the grounds I looked off to my left and saw the rooftop patio.

There she was at the far end, walking as slowly as she pleased, her hand gliding across the railing. The sun was just now overtaking the trees and found her in a poetic kind of way that needed no words. The scene of the sprawling mountains behind her was a sight to behold, but it was her presence that completed the picture. I stood there admiring everything nature had given me at that moment. She found my eyes and began walking toward me. I walked up the steps and meet her at the center, my hands clasped to the straps of my bookbag.

"It's beautiful here, isn't it?" She said.

"Yes. So beautiful," I responded. She smiled at me and we began to walk side by side back down the steps toward town.

******

Ramana invited me for tea on the mountainside just outside her hostile. It was a ten-minute walk from the temple grounds through a small town not far from the meditation center. When we arrived, the owner brought us out a few cheap plastic chairs to sit on, facing out over the range, the sun working for its noon position in the sky. There were other guests there as well, sitting in chairs like ours with little glass mugs in their hands. They greeted us as we approached. She introduced me as we settled into our seats.

We talked to the other guests while waiting for our tea to brew. Yosif was from Israel and had a wild beard of thick hair. Neither his English nor his Hindi was particularly good, but it never kept him from smiling at almost anything discussed. Daniel was an English teacher from New Zealand who had come to India six weeks ago to see his country play against India in Cricket.

"I just never left," he said in conclusion of his story, holding a cigarette and squinting in the bright sun. A black goat came from behind a clump of bushes and began grazing, paying no mind to our assembly. "I figured I'd just continue my instruction using video chats, but getting internet here has been a bit problematic," he went on. "I'm trying to make the best of it. This place has a way of putting you at ease. A way of keeping you grounded. Guess that's what happens when you don't have a good connection on your phone all the time. You find yourself sitting on the side of a mountain, having a smoke and a tea, watching the wild animals rummage around and say to yourself, 'Yeah, this is alright then.'"

A worker came out with two saucers and cups, handing one to each of us. Ramana stirred hers with a spoon in a smooth clockwise motion. We drank and watched the wind play at the trees as the afternoon light brought warmth to the once chilly morning air. A cow joined in with the nearby goat and enjoyed what small amount of grass the lot of land provided.

After our tea, Ramana said something to Yosif who produced a small tin can and a pack of cigarettes. He took one out of the pack and began gently rolling it between his fingers, the tobacco falling onto the empty saucer he held beneath it. "Would you like a smoke?" Ramana asked. "Yosif has some hash he is willing to share with us."

I examined his work with new interest. "You mix it in with the tobacco and re-roll it?"

"Yes, it is the common way here. Hash is much easier to find than the flower itself. Nobody ever has just flower." I watched Yosif delicately play with the paper, watching the tobacco fall away rhythmically. "I've never done this before," I said.

"What? Smoke weed?" she asked uncertainly.

"No. A cigarette," I smiled mischievously. "My friend Jimmie warned me of these things, but I guess I could make an exception." We sat quietly for the next few minutes watching him work. After all the tobacco was removed, he opened the tin can and scooped out little pieces of broken hash and mixed it into the tobacco. Once blended, he carefully repacked the cigarette sleeve, twisting the end to signal the job's conclusion. Ramana pulled out her phone and began to play slow, traditional Indian music. Yosif produced a lighter and took the first drag.

Yosif, barefooted and smiling, exhaled a long, thick stream. One of the workers came out and witnessed our congregation. He said something to Yosif that I couldn't understand and made his way over to us. Yosif gave the spliff to the man who inhaled from it, handed it back and returned to his work inside.

Ramana took a few puffs and handed it to me. I savored my first drag, analyzing how the foreign tobacco tasted with the equally unfamiliar hash. The result was smooth at first but, as it made its second and third rotation to me, my throat began to tickle from the substance that I was so unaccustomed to. I held the cigarette and tried exhaling a little slower in hopes the irritation would be reduced.

The hash was mild, producing a calming euphoria. The mountains came alive to our ritual. The pink and purple petals of a nearby Bauhinia broke free by the dozens and showered down around us. Save for the gentle flutes and chimes from Ramana's music, all else was hushed on the mountainside. Still rummaging in our vicinity, the black goat could be heard chewing leaves with earnest. The cow stopped and watched us curiously. She gave a soft *moo* of indifference and continued her unhurried search for edible vegetation.

Eventually, Yosif quietly stood and went inside, leaving Ramana and me to finish the joint. We began quietly speaking to one another as we sat side by side, sinking further into the chairs, our feet propped up on the same stool. More than anything else, I remember how she looked sitting there, totally at ease and strikingly beautiful. She had a thin veil over her head that she would use to block the sun when it edged out from behind a stray cloud. Now, as I looked at her, she was half peering through it with her sunken eyes and a lazy smile. Her silk black hair fell about her tan features. Smooth arms you'd like to have around you. Hands you wanted to hold in your own.

We spent the next half hour there, getting to know each other more, discovering our personalities. She was easy to talk to. What language or cultural hiccups we did experience often gave us cause to laugh, finding that our stumbling words were more a source of humor than frustration. It was evident her upbringing was good as she spoke fondly of her family and her schooling while growing up. After a time, another silence fell over us. It seemed to bond us together in some unspoken way and we came to know each other even deeper through the spaces in between dialogue.

"It will be evening before long," she said in a near whisper, "and I have a few things to take care of before I leave tonight."

"Will you have dinner with me before you go?"

"Yes," she said, "I think that would be nice."

I made my departure not long afterwards and walked back down the mountain road toward town. The moving sun was lost behind all the massive trees, the temperature dropping quickly. I would go back to Nick's Restaurant to rest and prepare for the evening. I wanted to make more of what I had developed with Ramana, to whatever end it might lead. As I walked, my carefree disposition of a traveler with nothing to lose made me feel invincible and as weightless as the cool mountain air. I had been in India for just over a week and this empowering feeling was beginning to take root on a deeper level. I was nobody to anybody. I had almost no money but felt like I had all the time in the world. No pressing matters to attend to. No clock to adhere to. I looked out across the blossoming afternoon horizon. A hawk circled briefly nearby, the wind across its feathers rustling faintly as it glided over the open space between the forests. It surveyed the land with keen eyes for several moments before emitting a gentle call and then flying off to become one with the great mass of blue sky, the distant mountains appearing to stretch for eons into the origins of time.

******

I sat at a table not far from the windows, looking out where the mountains seemed to become a blurry haze of mist and played tricks on the senses in the first serene hours of evening. The smells of dinner in the tiny town compounded over fires and stoves, making their own impressions with gusts of wind carrying a buffet of tantalizing aromas past me. Sharp, but pleasant odors of foreign spices and herbs. Meats cooked all day to perfection, reaching their peak appeal as the sun fell from the sky.

I had my back to the window so I could watch the front door. She came in and navigated the floor quickly, but not without grace. She moved with a pleasant and cheerful demeanor that showed purpose and self-assurance. She had changed since this morning into evening attire that was simple and elegant. She sat across from me and ordered a ginger lemon honey. I had my steaming mug clasped between my hands. We kicked around dinner ideas and settled on the short walk to the Common Grounds Café.

In our remaining time at Nick's, we explored world religion topics with special emphasis on Indian culture and traditions. I was pleasantly surprised to find Ramana seemed to hold similar views on religion as I did, giving special care to the person as an individual instead of how they fit into an organization or system of thinking. She showed skepticism to religious dogma, mysticism and any information written way before our own time by authors whose identities and intentions could never be fully proven or understood. To me, this is always a refreshing quality in a person. She seemed very much her own person, but not without a sense of wonder and respect for the mysteries of the unknown. Her eyes said as much about her as her smile, both features I felt fortunate to witness every time she revealed them. I marveled at the way we easily sat so comfortably and talked. I thought how nice it would be to not sit across from her, a table and civilities between us, but side by side.

Eventually, our stomachs encouraged us to find our dinner. I left cash on the table. We smiled and waved to the worker behind the register as we departed. We reached the Common Grounds Café shortly after passing the town's Main Square. Two locals sat on the very small front patio playing a game of checkers, a dog lying obediently at their feet.

We went in and took a seat at one of the floor tables. We talked about the coming super moon that night. I had told my new group of traveling friends that I would meet them at Nick's to watch it peak over the sleeping Himalayas. Ramana and I ordered food, ate and talked. Our hands began to find one another in a flirtatious, playful way. As the hour passed, Ramana and I came closer together, both of us quietly considering her leave, another long bus ride that would take her through the night and straight into work the next morning. My hand was on the small of her back. We would talk and lean into each other, our legs touching. She could be silly as much as she was witty. She would tease me about my American ways and I would playfully take jabs at her in return. It was only an hour away from her 6:30 pm departure. We decided to finish up and take a walk through the town. I paid the bill and exited to the street. The night was beginning to form around the evening activities. We went about, looking at street vendors, waving to travelers we recognized, going nowhere in particular. Our hands interlocked as we weaved through the crowds together. Eventually, the time came and we found ourselves standing at the bus stop. A small group of travelers boarded the bus or stood nearby. We stopped in the street and I turned to face her.

"Well, this is my ride." She said somewhat deflated. "Thank you for dinner. I'm happy we've met like this."

"You're welcome," I said, matching her smile and taking her in my arms. "I'm starting to wish you'd skip the bus and just take a plane with me back to America."

"Oh, come on."

"I'm sorry," I said. "I'm just messing around. Sort of." She laughed and pulled from our embrace but I held her in front of me, looking down into her eyes. She seemed to hesitate.

"I'd let you kiss me but…with all these people around-" she started.

"What? These people? They're not concerned with us. Besides, with a little maneuvering like this…" I turned us so my back faced the nearest group of men standing around. She laughed again at my determination and finally gave in. We kissed as the sun's resting light made its last contribution to the evening canvas, the stage setting for the super moon that was shortly to follow. We remained engaged like that only for a brief time before her shyness got the better of her.

"Okay," she said quietly. "I have to get on now."

"I hope I see you in Delhi," I said. "I'd hate to think this is it."

"I know. I will have work during the week though. It is hard to say right now. And you will leave on a train for Mumbai on Friday, yes?"

"That's the plan."

"I guess we will just have to see then," she said.

"Yeah, we'll see."

"But, in case we don't…"

"No," I cut her off, "let's not say it. Let's have a reason to make it happen. To work it out. Then we can have our goodbyes."

"Okay."

"But, tell you what, just to be on the safe side…" I kissed her again, longer this time. We broke apart slowly and she began walking to the bus, turning to look over her shoulder and waving. I returned the farewell and then stood with my hands in the pockets of my jeans. I watched the bus pull away completely before turning to go back.

******

I found Alex, Jay and Marijke sitting at the restaurant's best table on the back balcony furthest from the building. The same one Jimmie and I first sat at when we arrived a few days prior. Somewhere nearby the sound of festive music was barely audible. The super moon had yet to show itself but its brilliant light was already radiating behind the Himalayas, rising and spreading up into the sky, giving the mountains an otherworldly character. The prayer flags rustled gently in the mostly tame winds as a mild chill began to find us.

"How did it go?" Jay asked, picking up a piece of Tibetan bread to dip in her pasta dish, topped with a creamy pumpkin sauce. "Dinner was good," I said. "We walked the town afterward for a bit. I've just come from dropping her off at the bus."

"Did you kiss her?" Marijke asked intrigued. I told her that I did, much to her delight. "I love it! Will you see her again?" She pressed.

"I don't know. I'd certainly like to. I have her number now but with me traveling like this and her working at her job it's hard to say."

"Oh, I so want this to work out," she beamed.

"Well, let's not get too ahead of ourselves," I said. "This is such a chance happening, you know? Who knows whether I'll actually see her again? No point in-"

"Oh, you'll see her again, I'm sure of it," Marijke interjected. "I'm putting it out into the universe."

"Well, your optimism is greatly appreciated." We all ordered drinks, either hot chocolate or ginger lemons, and sat awaiting the moon's arrival. We talked about our lifestyles back home and gravitated towards discussing food and diet. I admitted the starchy and carbohydrate-heavy meals I'd received in India were a far departure from my regular eating habits. I of course never let this deter me from stuffing my face at any point along the journey.

"Here it comes," Alex said, looking past my left shoulder. I turned to find the moon, its top half cresting the seemingly smooth surface of the distant mountain. The light, a marvel even before its full arrival, now began to show its true brilliance as it rose from behind the colossal inverted curtains of Earth. The four of us, along with the rest of the now hushed rooftop patrons, held our view as the moon ascended, its progress clearly visible as it worked to overcome the sprawling landmass before it.

We remained at the outdoor terrace for over an hour. Occasionally,

Marijke would glance my way if I appeared distant or hadn't said enough in the conversation. She asked if I was thinking about Ramana. Generally, I was, but I tried not to stray from the present, as there was nothing to be done besides be there and enjoy myself. I was here and she was on a bus, traveling hours over long stretches of empty valley roads, the same moon shining down on us both.

A surprising thing happened then. Jimmie had commented on multiple occasions about Indian's improvements, notably the lack of power outages we had experienced. Since we'd been here, there had not been a single one, something she classified as unusual. But, as luck would have it, in that very moment the entire town fell into the darkness of a power failure. The night sky suddenly came alive above us, revealing its deeper qualities in the distant stars. The town took on a new character, its machines and gears going silent and the presence of the often-forgotten qualities of a world in motion were made apparent. As I observed the mysterious mass that dominated us, I thought: *We are as much looking up into space as we are looking down into infinite nothingness.*

After a few minutes, the sound of generators could be heard and small lights around the town twinkled into existence. We resumed our conversation, but it wasn't long after that that the contaminants of the night air began to find me as they usually did around this time. I could still only manage an hour or two outside before my coughing was with such frequency that it became a bother to me. As I was announcing my leave, the rest of the group admitted their own submissions. I made my way up to bed, hoping to be well-rested for the last day in the mountains of Dharamshala.

Return to New Delhi

The next morning Jimmie and I prepared our luggage to return to New Delhi. I messaged Alex and Jay to join us for breakfast but they were slow to rise and missed our departure. Marijke ate with us and I hugged her goodbye in case I wouldn't see her again. As it turns out, we would be running the streets together again in a few days once more in Mumbai, more than a thousand miles from Dharamshala.

"What did you think of that moon last night," Jimmie said as we sat at a table sipping tea and waiting for our taxi. "I saw you sitting outside with all your little friends. You'll remember that as long as you live. Me, I had a nice table inside to watch. Reminded me of my home in the Kashmir mountains. You talk about dark at night. It was a shade of black you'd think came from another world. And the stars. Oh, the stars were like nothing else you ever saw. I had this telescope, a gift from an Indian friend, and I used to look out into that great light show every night. You couldn't help but marvel at it." She looked off to the mountain range and fanned herself, the morning sun having already found us. "It's fascinating, outer space. I've always loved everything about it. NASA and everything they do, I think it's great. Although, there was that one time they went and put that monkey into space." Her face changes to one of stern disapproval. "I didn't like that. Not at all."

Our taxi arrived. We began loading our baggage into the trunk and then climbed inside, Jimmie taking the front as usual. Our driver couldn't speak English very well, but it was far better than we could speak Hindi, so we had no grounds to complain. "Okay," Jimmie said, buckling a safety belt across her waist. "As lovely as it is, it's time to leave this town behind us."

Just then, a thought struck me. "Hey, Jimmie, what would you think of stopping by St. John's in the Woods before we go?"

"You mean that church you was tellin' me about?"

"Yeah. It's only about a mile from here. It has a great view that overlooks the town. Might have been a place Collin once visited," I said of her son.

"Oh, well yes," she said, intrigued. "We should stop by there then."

We made the short drive less than a kilometer from town to the holy site. I instructed the driver to take us to the far entrance where the stone walkway lead right up to the large, wooden front doors. Despite my intentions to take the most direct path to the church, Jimmie was unable to make the walk, even while gripping my arm for support along the way. She was still not well and the altitude continued to take a toll on her body. We stopped halfway down the walkway which was about forty meters in length.

"This will have to do," she panted. "I can see it good from here. I hate to say it, but I may not make it back on my own feet if I go much further. God damn this hip. Can't do the things I use to. Let me just have a look from here." She gripped my arm tightly and took long, labored breaths. I took some pictures for her on her tablet. "You should have a look at the graveyard I told you about. It's just over there," I said, pointing through the foliage.

"Oh no, I can't walk that far."

"You won't have to. There is an overlook off the main road."

We walked slowly back up the incline, stopping three times for her to rest. Something didn't seem right. I knew she was tired, but the coloring in her face seemed to be draining. She was coughing with a great deal of severity that began to concern me. "Are you feeling alright, Jimmie? You don't look so good."

"Honey, you wait till your eighty-three. You won't look so good yourself. At my age, you start contemplating taking all the mirrors out the house."

"No, I mean really. That cough. And you look exhausted."

"It's just the altitude. Just hold my hand while we walk back the rest of the way, will you?"

I helped her in the cab and went around to the front. A few seconds later we were parked in front of the overlook. Jimmie got out with the driver's help and shuffled to the railing. The sun fell over the grounds and illuminated the landscape of green plots with their various stones of remembrance sloping down the mountain to where the woods began to grow thick and unruly.

"Oh, it *is* beautiful," she said, holding the rail to support herself. A mile away, past the rising trees, the town was still waking up to the new day and the birds made music with their song. "My son has been here. I'm sure of it," she said. She dug into her pocket and produced the vile of her son's ashes. She let some fall into her open palm and then stood there looking out. After a moment, she released them into the gentle wind that carried him over the grounds. She turned to me. "Will you take this down and leave some in one of those nice plots? Do you see the one with the cross? That one. Try to be quick. I don't want anyone to see you."

"Why do you want me to put his ashes in that plot?" I asked.

"Well, I just like the way it looks. Go on now, before somebody comes."

I climbed down through an opening in the fence, vile in hand. I came to the plot with the cross and knelt before it. Uncapping the vile, I poured the ashes into my hand and studied the tombstone, reading the name and dates of a person I never knew, nor would I remember after this moment, but felt I should observe all the same.

Our brief partings on Earth will appear one day as nothing beside the joy of eternity together. And when the Earth shall claim your limbs, then shall you truly dance.

******

Before leaving the town for good, we decided to stop at one of the many street vendors to buy a keepsake. Jewelry, singing bowls, fine scarfs of silk, handwoven winter caps and quilts, rings of precious stone. We would have liked to buy them all, but our money situation was still delicate. I settled for the one thing I knew I wanted for myself—a single set of dark wood prayer beads. Jimmie herself took a liking to a necklace that appeared to contain stones of Ruby.

"Collin loved the prayer flags," Jimmie said. "He would hang them up everywhere and admire their colors. I'd hate to leave without some." We found a man on the street next to a spread of goods on the ground. "Slow down here," Jimmie told the driver. She rolled down her window. The man's face brightened at her appearance.

"Prayer flags?" Jimmie asked.

"Prayer flags? Yeah, yeah," he announced excitedly, pointing to some plastic packages on the ground which he quickly retrieved.

"That's good. We'll take three."

After we paid, we made one last stop at the Dalai Lama's temple. I wanted to get our beads blessed by one of the monks, even though I did not know if they did such a thing. We stopped one of the monks, a young Tibetan man en route towards town. We tried to explain what we wanted but his English was poor. He instead pointed to an older monk who was shuffling along in our direction.

"Oh, okay, thank you," Jimmie said patting his arm. He turned and continued on. "He must be in training or something. Maybe he can't do things like that yet. We will talk to this old-timer. He's probably got loads of holy blessings he can give us."

When the old man approached, we began explaining our visit. He too seemed a little spotty on our American speech, but appeared to grasp our request. He took the prayer flags and beads in his hands and held them. He appeared to concentrate on the items briefly, then smiled and returned them to us. "Thank you, Darlin'," Jimmie said and they clasped hands and smiled deeply to one another. The old man went on silently and we began down the road in the opposite direction. "No magic words, no extravagant gestures," Jimmie was saying. "Just the way I like my spirituality served."

We made our way back down the alley leading to the main road where our taxi driver waited. We passed a large sign and Jimmie asked to stop to take a look. I was shocked at its content and couldn't believe I had passed it twice while visiting the temple grounds and had never taken notice of it. On it, a small Tibetan boy was painted to one side. My eyes studied the words.

TIBET'S STOLEN CHILD – THE WORLDS YOUNGEST POLITICAL PRISONER

Born April 1989
May 14, 1995, His Holiness, The Dalai Lama, officially proclaimed him as the reincarnation of the 10th Panchan Lama.
May 17, 1995, He and his parents disappeared from their home after being taken into Chinese custody.
May 28, 1996, China admitted to having custody of the young boy and his parents.
He is deprived of his religious education and traditional upbringing essential at this age.
China fails to publicly declare the boy's whereabouts, despite international appeals
He is considered the world's youngest political prisoner

The temple with its heart-breaking museum and now this had both made an impression on me about matters I was mostly ignorant of. I remembered taking Buddhism courses in school, about learning about Tibet and its struggles, but it had never hit so close to home until now. Standing in the place that resulted from those struggles took on a whole new meaning. It pained me to think what fate had befallen this young child and his family. He would be twenty-seven now, if he was even still alive, just a year older than me. A grown man practically born into captivity at the hands of a communist regime. We walked back to the taxi and climbed in. The ride would take us down the mountain, through the town below and once again return us to the Dharamshala airport.

******

Back in Delhi, I made contact with Ramana again. She had managed to make it back home despite a severe breakdown that forced her bus off the road and extended the trip an additional three hours, almost fifteen hours in total. I told her I would reach her again when I had more time later that night. Jimmie and I were about to go out into the city and we were currently waiting on a taxi to arrive at the Blue Triangle YWCA. Just as we were leaving Dharamshala, Jimmie developed a cough so harsh that she insisted we seek medicine out in town at a local pharmacy. "It's owned by a couple of brothers in Connaught Place," she said. "They know me. I always do business with them when I am in New Delhi."

We took a taxi into the city that afternoon. Jimmie stared out the window from the front seat, watching the hectic streets that were so different from the ones she used to know.

"I wonder how far we are from Khan Market," Jimmie wondered aloud. "I haven't been there in years." She turned around to face me. "You know I met Bill and Chelsea Clinton in Khan Market back in the nineties."

"What?"

"You know, the President?"

"I know who Bill Clinton is Jimmie. You said you *met* him here in India?"

"That's right. I was going to Khan like I always did in those days and I noticed the whole damn place was shut down in one section. All these big guys wearin' black suits were standing everywhere. I started lookin' around and sure enough there he was off in the distance, looking at some clothes or something like that. I thought, oh, I've always wanted to meet a president and I voted for the guy so, why not? Next to Harry Truman, Clinton was the best president our country ever had. He was a road scholar." She becomes heated and lifts a finger as she spoke. "And he didn't do *anything* that any other hot-blooded man wouldn't do if you put a young woman in front of him. The whole scandal was over nothing if you ask me. He did right by this country. Hilary could have run it too, but they would never have let her because people would have been talkin' about her ankles bein' too fat or something like that.

"Anyway, I saw Bill standing there and I walked up to one of the service agents. He said, 'Ma'am, you can't go in there right now.' I said sure I can, I'm an American and that's my president. I wanna talk to him. He wouldn't let me but Chelsea saw us talking and she had the man stand down so I went over and said hello to her and told her who I was and what I was doing there in India. Bill came over and I met him too. They were shopping—just passin' time. We spoke for a few minutes and Chelsea was so sweet, very nice girl. I could tell Bill had something on his mind. He looked like he was ready to go. They asked me where I lived and I told them. 'You should both come by for tea sometime', I told them. They said that would be lovely, but of course, they never came. World figures like that, you can't expect them to go out of their way for tea with an old lady. But still, it was really somethin' to meet them."

When we arrived in Connaught Place, the streets were slammed with pedestrians and ceaseless traffic. Everywhere we turned there were lines at banks and money exchanges that stretched out the door and down the corner. It was then that we saw firsthand how badly the city's people were still struggling with the new money transition. It took us some time to get to the corner where the pharmacy was located. Our driver weaved through the crowd of vehicles with the same sense of urgency that everyone else in Delhi seemed to possess behind the wheel, honking his horn and making maneuvers that were jarring to the nerves.

Our driver dropped us off on the corner and then sped away as several other vehicles began to honk, displeased that they should have to stop just so we could exit our taxi. Jimmie said she would speak with the brothers directly and I could stay or go as I wanted. I walked around for a time but soon became disinterested in the unbearable mass of people and the continuous pestering of men who began to follow me, asking me questions, wondering what I wanted to spend my money on.

Roaming aimlessly about and dealing with both factors, I ultimately decided to return to the pharmacy and peaked in through the front doors. I could see Jimmie in a back office, sitting patiently at a desk and casually conversing with a staff member. Meanwhile, the main floor was packed shoulder to shoulder with customers who pointed at medicines on the walls or in the glass counters wrapped around the room. After a time, Jimmie looked my way and I gave her the okay sign and pointed out the front door. She gave a thumbs up and I turned and went back out onto the street.

I took a seat on a cement garden encasing and pulled out my notebook, passing the time by updating the journal with details of the trip. Several people walked by and slowed as they passed me. I looked up and a pair of girls turned away giggling and continued walking. Another man, homeless by the looks, came and sat down a few feet away from me. I returned my attention to my writings but I sensed the man's eyes on me. I carried on making notations. After a few minutes, the funk of the city smog (or was it the homeless man?) became so strong that I was forced to slip my face mask over my nose and mouth. Jimmie eventually came back out of the store, a small bag of medications in her hand. She asked me if there was anywhere else I wanted to go.

"No. I'm done with here," I reported dryly.

We phoned for a ride and waited near the corner for pick up.

The taxi eventually found us and stopped in the street while we climbed in, horns of frustration roaring behind us. "Just wait a damn minute!" Jimmie barked at the vehicle behind us. "Everyone's in a big friggin' hurry." Our next course of action was to locate a bank that could help us exchange our old money for the new currency. The supply we had acquired from Nick during our stay in Dharamshala was already running low. Jimmie continued to be in charge of all of our funds. I had yet to take a single rupee on my own accord, instead using a system with Jimmie to utilize what she had while we kept records of our housing, transportation and miscellaneous costs to be squared away at the end of our journey.

Unfortunately, finding a location where we could exchange our money was no simple matter. We resorted to calling our travel agent who gave us the best information he possessed on the situation. Even still, we often found ourselves asking people in the street near various banking institutions if we were on the right track. Often we had to modify our plans based on what information we gathered. We ended up going through two or three different buildings in various parts of town. Each one was jammed packed with people who Jimmie would shuffle past, flagging the attention of a security guard or clerk by announcing something to the effect of, "I'm an American!" followed by a brief explanation of what she needed. As always, this proved incredibly effective for us and we moved past the scores of people to the next available clerk.

We spent a whole day inside humid buildings with broken AC units, lines of people, filling out paperwork, counting and exchanging money, showing our passports, showing our IDs and haggling with people over the types and amounts of currencies we needed. In many cases, we got the feeling that some of the bankers were trying to keep the most valuable, in-demand denominations in stock for themselves, either for personal use or as a backup.

The implications of India's government to take such drastic measures with their currency would stretch on for months to come. By the end of it all, over a hundred deaths would be reported, linked to individuals who had become exhausted from waiting in line. Rural workers who did not have easy access to banking systems were hit particularly hard. Suicide numbers jumped drastically. I would read criticism in an online article about the decision. Former Prime Minister Manmohan Singh labeled the event with colorful phrases like, "organized loot" and "legalized plunder." Even a year after the fact, Singh continued to bash the move stating, "Nowhere in the world has any democracy taken such a coercive step. The damage it has caused has been multiple – economic, social, reputational and institutional." However, income tax returns filed for citizens jumped a reported 25% months afterward, which would indicate a larger tax net overall. A steep increase in digital payments and transactions was later reported in the country and substantial rises in self-assessment and advance tax collections. The final result on how that November 8th decision would play out for India's long-term economy could take years to justify. At the time, we were just two of the many unlucky people who were caught in the middle of it all.

******

After securing some funds from the local banks, Jimmie and I returned to the YWCA. I received a message from Ramana asking if I would like to have dinner with her. We met at a place called *The Monkey Bar* at her recommendation. It was arranged that the taxi driver would wait outside while I had dinner. I felt bad making him wait so long but I was told this was the typical way in India. When we had visited the Taj Mahal, we had engaged in a similar practice, the driver standing by while we toured the grounds. What made the current situation even more unusual for me was that I had intentions of trying to take a ride home, not with this man back to my hotel, but with Ramana. I thought it best to make the driver aware of this.

"I'm meeting a woman here," I said. "If things go well, I might not need a ride back. Do you understand?" He smiled and confirmed his understanding.

I went inside and found a seat on the second floor which overlooked the lower level and waited patiently for the girl I had come for. I watched as she came in from the front of the restaurant. She looked good in a flowing midnight black dress, her legs appearing rhythmically from underneath as she glided through the dim lighting. Her gait was controlled and easy as she moved across the floor. She found my eyes and I felt electricity run through my body. My smile was a beacon and when she ascended the steps, I met her with a warm embrace.

"Hey," I said. "You look great."

"Thank you." Her smile like dynamite to the heart. "You look pretty good yourself."

"You flatter." I gestured to the booth. "Care to have a drink with me?"

We ordered finger foods and gradually worked up to the entrees, a steady stream of mixed drinks accompanying each new dish. We ran with the night and talked about our lives back home and our aspirations for the future. She told me more about the school she had gone to as a young girl, a convent as it turned out. It was wild to think I could be so far from the south, or all of America for that matter, and still be running into Catholic girls so easily. As we talked and laughed, I let my hand slip from the table and rest on her thigh. My fingers eventually migrated and found other surfaces to explore: her back, her arm, a squeezed hand. After two hours we were lazily slumped in our booth, full of food and booze, my arm around her waist, our talk more subdued now as I urged her to cease her words of departure.

"Don't go," I told her. "Stay with me a little longer."

"I can't," she said with eyes glazed with dream and drink. "I have work in the morning."

"Then take me with you."

She gave a great sigh. She ran a hand through my hair while I sat there sunken into my seat, my body leaning up against hers, taking in the scent of wildflower from some lotion or hair product. "I have to work tomorrow," she said, and then, after a time, "the weekend would be better."

A gave a sightless grin. "That would be nice."

The waitress brought the check and I finished the last of my lime tonic. We got up together and made our way downstairs. I wasn't sure when our hands came together as we walked side by side, but it felt natural and my stride was all the lighter. We came out into the night with the parking lot just ahead of us.

"Hey. Come here," Ramana whispered in my ear and was suddenly pulling me through the grass away from the bar. Saying nothing she brought me to a low tree encased by a raised wooden box. Before I could ask, she pushed me down to sit on the wooden frame and then fell on top of me, grabbing my head and pushing her lips against mine. With an aggressiveness that both astounded and pleased me, we made out like we were living in times of war. One of my hands ran through her forest of hair and found its mark on the back of her head, the other grabbing at her hip. In my drunken state of surprise, I had to remind myself to take a breath every now and again to avoid suffocation.

The pack of wild dogs was on us before we knew what was happening.

Out of the darkness they had come at a full run, at least eight of them, homely looking in their disheveled furs. I couldn't say where they had come from or what sent them into such a frenzy to charge us as they did. All I know is one moment I was running my hands over Ramana and the next we were surrounded by a group of canines more heated than we were.

"What in the *fuuuck*," I said as I pushed Ramana away and stood up tensely. I kept one arm around her and held her close in case one of them tried to move on us. They formed around us in a half-circle and continued barking ceaselessly.

"Hey! *Heeeeey*! Get out of here!" I yelled at them realizing none were brave enough to attack. "No! Get!"

Ramana laughed as I tried to communicate with the lot of them. Most of them wagged their tails as they yelled back at me. "I don't think they like you," she said.

"What goes on in your country that there are just roves of cock blocking dogs that patrol the streets? Seriously." I thought back to the dog that had first boxed me out when I had tried to sit closer to her in Dharamshala. I secretly hoped she didn't have one of these disruptive breeds at her place.

"Don't worry about them," she said and, since we were already huddled together, began to resume where we had left off, much to the dogs' collective dismay. We were barely in on each other again before they doubled their efforts to cause as much noise as possible. People were coming out of the restaurant and looking at this strange sight with confused expressions on their faces. "Okay," I said, pulling us away again prematurely, "I don't think this was the scene either of us expected. Let's call it a night and just save it for the weekend, alright?"

"Sounds good to me," she smiled and we walked away from the dogs, glancing back as we went to make sure none of them had suddenly become bold. I said goodbye to Ramana and we kissed one last time before she climbed into the taxi. I turned around and looked about the darkness. I began walking through the parking lot, my legs feeling somewhat like jelly, my stomach fluttering with a newfound romantic interest. I came to the passenger side window of one of the cars parked along the street and pressed my face against the window. I knocked on the glass *tap-tap-tap* with my knuckles. The man inside stirred and raised from his seat. I climbed in opposite of him.

"Okay now?" The taxi driver said.

"Yes," I said. "We can go now."

******

I had a day to pass before meeting with Ramana again. I took her suggestion and made the most of my time by purchasing a ticket for the city Hop-On, Hop-Off bus circuit. I left Jimmie behind as her health was too poor that morning to adventure out into New Delhi's soot-black skies. It was blazing hot as I had come to expect. I took a map of all the destinations I would have available to me and waited patiently for the next arriving bus. It came and I climbed aboard, taking a seat near the back under a cool vent that was a much-welcomed change from the sun's malevolent outpour. As we cruised along, I took note of all the strange sights the city had to offer. The animals and people walked the streets as if it were some rural farm town. Sidewalk vendors and old cars that looked like they were held together by duct tape and chewing gum.

My first stop took me to the National Gallery of Modern Art, a massive complex with over seventeen thousand works from more than two thousand artists between the main complex and its regional centers, some of the oldest pieces dating back to the late 1850s. The original structure served as the former residential palace to the Maharajah of Jaipur House and was established in 1954 by the Government of India with additional branches in Mumbai and Bangalore.

I walked about the museum's large surrounding lawn, reading as I went, occasionally stopping to admire the many interesting pieces that scattered the grounds. Statues and sculptures of bronze, metal and clay depict all visual novelties familiar and foreign. A metallic tree fifteen feet in height with dozens of monochrome kitchen utensils and appliances instead of leaves. An old, rusted-over white bus from decades past. Stone faces protruding from dense green shrubs. Dozens of small potted trees perfectly distanced and exceptionally trimmed. Inside, floors upon floors of hanging pieces, too staggering in number to describe. I spent an hour walking staircases and taking elevators to different areas, admiring the many varied works spanning over a century. Groups of school children walked noisily through the otherwise quiet complex, too young to appreciate the extensive collection in full, many preferring to locate and point, giggling at paintings depicting nude men and women.

Knowing I still had many locations to visit I abandoned the museum grounds and returned to the bus stop where I was soon picked up and shuttled away to a new location. One noteworthy site was the impressive Red Fort, regarded as one of Delhi's most famous monuments, considered by many to represent the zenith of the Mughal empire. Built as the capital of Mughal Delhi by order of Emperor Shah Jahan in 1638, it now served as a complex of museums. It is also worth mentioning that it was the same emperor who commissioned the building of the Taj Mahal.

The Red Fort is Delhi's most expansive historical monument at over 250 acres, all enclosed by one and a half miles of defensive walls with bastions and turrets that range from sixty to over a hundred feet in height. It was here that Jawaharlal Nehrus gave his "Tryst of Destiny" speech to declare India's official independence on August 15 of 1947. Every year on its anniversary of freedom, the

Indian Prime Minister delivers a nationally broadcasted speech from the structures ramparts and raises the country flag, a symbol of unity for the people of India.

If the Red Fort is the biggest monument, the Qutab Minar is most certainly the tallest. A structure made of dense red sandstone which rose against the midday sun as if the flaming star served to be cradled in the high balcony overlook of the tower. I admired the intricate work of its build, observing the way the different shades of clay played with the high noon rays and reflected them down to the gardens below with families and vagabond types sprawled out across the landscape.

After a while, I found my way back to the bus stop and carried on my journey. There were many intriguing sites along the way. The famed gate of India resembling the Arc de Triomphe of Paris which was dedicated to the British Indian troops who died in the first world war. An impressive structure standing at forty-two meters completed in 1931, the year New Delhi became the official capital of India. To this day it is regularly used as a site for civil society protests and other matters of national affairs. There was Humayun's Tomb, the precursor to the Taj Mahal and the Lajpat Nagar, one of the oldest markets in India.

But the most amazing of all the locations I visited was the strikingly beautiful Lotus Temple located in the southeastern corner of New Delhi. The entrance to the grounds was about a quarter-mile or so from the structure, which peaked through tall trees and lush vegetation seeming to invite its visitors forward from afar. Its magnificent architecture was so captivating I found myself with butterflies in my stomach as I made my approach down the pathway. The open green space felt out of place in the otherwise cramped city and the degree of detail given to every aspect of the site made it seem of another world entirely. I felt like I was in a scene from Jurassic Park. The droves of people filed along quietly, save for a few children so gitty with excitement that they hopped about eagerly with anticipation. The great mass of people was hushed into awe, their gazes hungry to take in all before them, as if we were all collectively wondering: Where do they keep the T-rex?

The way adjusted and we came toward the temple head-on, the path between flawless bushes, neatly set apart from one another with thoughtful precision. The sun fell from the sky seeking dusk. It seemed to burn dull compared to its usual murderous rampage and instead took a soft orange hue and fixed itself neatly behind the sacred structure which sat on rising plateaus of green Earth, masterfully raised and leveled at the hands of diligent workers. Twenty-six acres of open, bright land. Clean and quiet. The great white temple consisted of twenty-seven free-standing marble walls, arranged in clusters of three to form nine "petals". This design was what gave the building its lotus shape. The central hall inside was accessible from nine different doors, reached from the interconnected pathway that ascended between nine identical clear blue ponds that surrounded the structure's base, giving the appearance that it was floating, elevated above one single body of water. I marveled at the site as a nearby uniformed Indian woman stood off to the side, addressing the row of people entering the building next.

"The Lotus Temple is a Bahai House of Worship, dedicated in December 1986," she said. "The temple is open to all peoples regardless of religion or creed and is one of the most visited sites in the world. Development took eighteen months and the equivalent of approximately ten million dollars, most of which was used to purchase the land for the site. This was achieved largely in part thanks to Ardishir Rustampur, a Pakistani man, who gave his entire life's savings to the cause in 1953. A portion of the construction went to building on-site greenhouses to study indigenous plants and flowers used on the grounds.

"Iranian architect, Fariborz Sahba, who now lives in La Jolla of California, is responsible for designing the Lotus Temple. This temple is the first of its kind in New Delhi to utilize solar power, which saves over one hundred kilowatts of its monthly five-hundred-kilowatt usage. The petal-like walls are made of white marble from the Penteli mountain of Greece and have received numerous architectural awards for its beauty. The site receives approximately 3.5 million visitors annually and, within the last few years, surpassed one hundred million visitors since its opening."

The line moved forward slowly as she spoke. We were now directly in front of one of the entrances. "You will be entering the temple in just a few moments," she continued. "The central hall's capacity is two thousand, five hundred people. Inside, any sacred writings may be read, sung or chatted, regardless of language or origin. Nonscriptural texts are forbidden as well as any sermons or lectures. No musical instruments are permitted. No set pattern of worship services or ritualistic ceremonies are conducted in the temple. No images or statues are allowed to be displayed. No pulpits or altars are to be utilized, though simple lecture stands are acceptable. No cameras or audio recording is permitted once inside the temple. After entering the temple, you are welcome to sit anywhere and may stay as long as you'd like."

Finally, we were waved forward through an open door held by a smiling man. As I entered, the door closed behind me again. There was a serene ambiance to the massive, circular room, its ceilings dome-shaped and stretching some forty meters high. White marble everywhere with lights along the walls casting a brilliant glow upwards to the dome's apex. There were many stiff, dark wood benches facing toward the center of the floor. Many of them were occupied with visitors who sat quietly in reflection.

I took a seat on one of the benches. It lacked any sense of comfort and the backrest was perfectly straight and hard, forcing visitors to sit erect at full attention. I gazed at the ceiling above me and noted how sound traveled throughout the central hall. The acoustics inside the building were fascinating and I wished I could be present for some musical performance of any kind, though such performances were not permitted. Even still, I thought it would be a treasure just to possess an audio recording of some event within the hall. A choir singing praise. An uplifting speech. If I could just play one song on my acoustic guitar at the center of the floor, I thought. That would be an experience in its own right.

I felt no pressing reason to leave the temple in any hurry. This felt counter to the point of everything the holy place stood for, so I instead found stillness over my body and reflected. Letting my thoughts wander with the experiences of my journey. People met. Places seen. My chance encounter with Ramana in the mountains. I wondered what she was doing now. Then I thought about the other Dharamshala travelers and hoped they would continue to see good health and fair fortune in their journeys. I thought of the exiles of Tibet and the oppression they endured. I marveled at the progressive attitudes of the people who had constructed the temple I sat in and contemplated how much better the world could be if such humane ways of thinking could be extended to those in other parts of the world being torn apart by political and social unrest. If man could be turned from their individual dogmas to find unity in the human condition as a whole.

I engaged in an exercise of gratitude. Thankful for my life. For good health. To be born in the United States, free to speak, practice, vote, travel and love as I choose. Luxuries often taken for granted by those born into such fortunate circumstances. A condition of existence promised to no one. I thought of my parents. My brother and sister. For the happy accident of meeting Jimmie, whose friendship allowed me to be here now. I wondered what she was up to and sincerely hoped that she would see better health in the days ahead. She had been coughing and wheezing much more since we returned from the clear mountain air to the polluted city. I thought of her son and hoped that our travels had provided her with something meaningful and that we could continue to honor his memory safely in the days ahead.

After a time, I closed my eyes and let my thoughts go, the soft surrounding noises amplified in the darkness. This brought another wave of appreciation for the acoustics of the room. The energy here was of another world. Slowly the sounds became but a whisper to my idle ears, my breath the sole testament to life.

Minutes passed.

Internal silence.

Peace in thought.

Feelings of infinite space.

I opened my eyes gradually. The crowds continued to flow about the room like the spectating spirits of an ancient pilgrimage. After a time, I slowly rose from my seat and departed the temple.

******

Traffic was so terrible that it took almost two hours to get across town to where Ramana lived. I was relieved when, after conferring with Jimmie, we had agreed to cancel our train ride that Friday night, opting instead to take a flight from New Delhi to the last leg of our trip in Mumbai. Had it not been for this change of plans, I would have been unable to see Ramana again, but Jimmie saw the interest I had taken in the Indian woman and was more than willing to accommodate. The driver was on his phone speaking Hindi when we slowed next to a white SUV on an isolated road.

"This is her," he said. I thanked him then climbed out of the cab and walked around to her passenger door.

"Hello," she smiled as I took my seat.

"Hello back," I returned.

"I was thinking of going to meet my guy to get some hash. Is that okay?"

We drove a few minutes to a completely unfamiliar part of New Delhi. "Be right back." She got out and spoke briefly with a young man who seemed to appear from nowhere. They conversed for less than a minute and then she climbed back in the driver's seat again. "Does this look like enough to you?" She held up a small, palm-sized baggy with a thick paste of brown goo inside. "You're asking me?" I questioned. "Hash isn't my specialty. Don't you know quantities?"

"I've been using this guy a couple of months. I think he's solid and I've never had problems with him."

"So, what now? Out to see your friends? Something to eat?"

She put the car into gear and pulled out onto the road. "Actually, I thought we could go back to my place and roll one first. We can figure out what we want to do after that."

The drive to her place took less than fifteen minutes. She lived on the third floor of a lovely condo. Jimmie had seemed impressed when I told her what area Ramana lived in and by looking around I could understand why. We went up a winding staircase and came to the large wooden door that served as her flat's entrance. The inside was beautiful and elegant. Marble and wood. There was a small four-person table in a spacious foyer, two big couches in the living room facing one another, and not a television in sight, which made me happy. Christmas lights hung across the walls and gave a soft glow to the room. A large wooden door went out to a forward-facing balcony. I put my things down and we went to the couch.

"I'll roll us a spliff. My roommate may join us if that's okay." Ramana said.

"Can you teach me?"

Ramana showed me how to go about twisting the cigarette between my fingers so the tobacco came loose and fell onto the table between the couches. Then she demonstrated the tedious task of breaking pieces of hash with her fingernails from the chunk we had acquired. This proved to be quite an arduous affair, but we happily passed the time conversing and talking about the different cannabis cultures we grew up in. After several minutes I had made a small pile of hash clippings that, individually, were no bigger than the head of a pen. She then took this pile and mixed it in with some of the loose tobacco before producing a pack of rolling papers from a small box.

"I texted my roommate," she said, eyes never leaving her task, "she will be coming out shortly."

Just as she was completing the project, a door opened at the far end of the condo.

"Come on. We're starting!" Ramana said. Her roommate came in and took the couch opposite of us. "This is my roommate and longtime friend, Aahna."

We exchanged formalities over the now-lit spliff. As smoke filled the room our conversation opened up to less serious matters and we began to relax, laughing together. I admit the taste and thickness of this foreign way of smoking was still harsh to me. As we passed the joint around, we became relaxed and found ourselves sprawled out on the couch. Across from us, Aahna was giggling and sinking into her own cloud. We finished our first roll at a leisurely pace.

"Let's do another," Ramana suggested, to which I agreed. We went through the routine again, this time Aahna breaking the hash at Ramana's request. "You can break it up better than I can!" she pleaded to her roommate.

"Lazy. You just don't want to do it yourself," Aahna retorted. I watched their sisterly exchange with amusement. I was willing to bet life with them was a comical act from day to day. Before I knew it, another joint was rolled and ready before us.

"I'll leave you two to this one," Aahna said, rising from the couch, "I have a few things I need to do. Enjoy," she said with a coy grin and

241

went back to her room, leaving Ramana and me to sink deeper into our lounging positions. She reached for the lighter. "What about your friends?" I asked curiously. "I thought they were expecting us."

She gave a sleepy pause. "*Mhmm*, I don't know. It's been such a long week…and I'm so comfortable here."

"It is very comfortable," I said stroking one of her long legs. It's so nice she has two of these, I thought in my semi-high state. How fortunate it is that so many of a woman's best features come in pairs.

"We can still go out though," she said. "Are you hungry? We could go meet my friends for a little while and get dinner."

"*Hmmm*," I contemplated.

"Or we could stay in and order a pizza," she suggested.

"That doesn't sound so bad."

"Baking Bad."

"I'm sorry?"

"Baking Bad," she repeated. "It's this great pizza place. You custom make it the way you like."

"Groundbreaking stuff."

"Shut up, it's really good." She gave the lighter a flick and ignited the end of the paper, inhaling a deep breath and letting it escape her slowly. "Besides," she said in the forming haze, "I already told my friends we would be staying in." She handed me the spliff.

"Clever girl."

We spent the next few minutes in the slightest of stupors, trying to navigate our phones to a readable menu for the pizza shop. "Just so you know," I said, "if they named their business after one of greatest dramas in the history of television, I am going to have very high standards for the food."

Eventually, we found a picture that displayed the options available to us. Continuing to smoke, we tried to decide what we wanted, but this was a restaurant of options and our brains bounced from one possibility to the next. Calzones? Subs? Salads? Then all the options extending from each possible choice. Meats, cheeses, breads, thickness, size, beverages, vegan, extra meat, etc. Such variety when choosing dinner is enough to hold up even the soberest of eaters.

In our indecisiveness, we decided to work on another spliff in hopes it might inspire a more concrete decision. As we worked with our hands, we debated the proper pizza, figuring out what toppings would make for the best experience. What dough consistency did they offer that defined us as people? The second stick burned down somewhere along the line, and the third took its place. The aroma of tobacco filled the room, a laced mist of tranquility. We were lying down together now. We talked and laughed at things that were nothing to the outside world, but they were everything to us in those moments.

I was looking down into her eyes, which appeared all the dreamier as the gentle effects of the plant pulsed through her body, relaxing her. We were kissing deeply now, sinking into each other, lazily letting the moment unfold. I savored her lips and my hands searched for the bare skin of her hip below her shirt. We pulled closer to one another and seemed to rock gently on a wave of serenity, losing ourselves in intimate connection that saw the minutes melt. A noise in the condo caused her to jump from our singular trance. Aahna was moving through the foyer to get something from the kitchen and disappeared into her room again as quickly as she had come.

"Oh my gosh," Ramana was saying. "Did she see us? So embarrassing." I shifted over her slightly, no less deterred.

"What's the big deal? She knows what we're up to, right?" I forgot she had been hesitant at the bus stop as well. I found her modesty a little unusual but was certain it was just cultural differences. "She likes to kiss guys too, right? No need to be embarrassed." But she still squirmed at the thought that her friend had seen us. I found her cautious demeanor rather adorable.

"Oh, the pizza!" She sat up on the couch and grabbed her phone.

"Come on. We need to decide before we…get distracted again." After the order was placed and we felt confident all was taken care of, we eased back into the couch to fall into each other once more, stopping only briefly to light the half-finished joint still sitting on the table.

******

I woke up in Ramana's bed not long after the sun began to rise. Her room had a balcony with large windows that allowed the morning light to pour in through the thin curtains she had put up. What sounded like a family reunion of pigeons could be heard just beyond the walls, mixed with the not-too-distant chatter of workers on a construction project and the faint but festive tones of Indian music over someone's radio. I squirmed off the night's sleep, bringing motion into my body. My leg brushed something under the covers. I reached down and found the gym shorts I had been wearing when I first got into bed. I flung them down on the floor, where they landed next to other articles of clothing that had been discarded throughout the night.

I rolled over onto my side. Ramana's bare back was facing me, her long black hair flowing all about in defiance of any fashionable order. I wanted to reach out and run my hands down her skin but just lay there thinking instead. Ramana and I had shared an incredible night. I searched my mind for when we had gone to sleep. It seemed like midnight, but I knew it was likely closer to one or two, sitting in her bed smoking the room into a cloud. Despite our decision to preserve her chastity, she had still floored me with all the alternatives. It was hard to believe this sweet, relatively inexperienced girl was capable of being so much fun.

We wanted it bad for each other and all our bottled-up desires manifested in all kinds of enjoyable rough play. Biting, nail digging, ass grabbing and physical exploration to name a few. I was shocked she could be so wonderfully aggressive and exciting and then become the innocent girl all over again. It went like that all night. Thinking back, it made sense. We were raised Catholic, so it seemed natural that we would both be freaks behind closed doors. I recognized her as a girl who was committed to the idea of celibacy till marriage and didn't wish to ruin that, knowing we were two souls from the farthest parts of Earth who may never see one another again after this blissful encounter. Still, our boiling passions that bordered on animalistic challenged both of us. I wanted the decision to come from her but knew she was unlikely to agree to such a thing, knowing our unique circumstances. I scooted next to her, cradling her backside. I kissed around her shoulder, her back. I caressed her arm and breathed her hair in, the lingering smell of our mixed chemistry hanging in the room. She gave a delighted moan and turned on her side to face me.

She put her arms around me and said good morning. A long, sustained kiss. Restless hands working overtime. We talked about breakfast. I told her I wanted to make something for her, but we had other appetites so fierce that we began reenacting our midnight activities within minutes of her waking. The presence of the sun gave new light to the scene, allowing me even more eye candy as I studied over her exquisite features. When we had exhausted ourselves of one another, I brought up the idea of breakfast once more.

There wasn't much in the kitchen to work with. Dressed-up oatmeal and scrambled eggs were about the only real foods I could muster up in my two days with Ramana, although her housemaids did come in that Saturday to clean and brought ingredients to prepare the most terrific lunch of potatoes and curried chicken with buttered naan. They couldn't speak a lick of English and were very surprised to find an American boy in gym shorts and a T-shirt cooking in the kitchen. You didn't need to speak the language to know both maids were gitty at this new friend Ramana had made who stood barefoot, stirring oatmeal in the first hours of light. They giggled and gave me glances. I smiled back mostly, the universal expression of good vibes.

We spent the entire day lounging. We seemed to be in a world of our own. We talked once or twice about going out that night or making a day trip somewhere—all empty ideas. We were content to just stay in, eating off the wonderful food her helpers had prepared and the last slices of pizza from the night before. "Why do you do that?" she asked several times in regards to my habit of standing while I ate.

"I stand up when I eat all the time," I said. "I started cooking more frequently several years ago and began to snack during the process, and then it just evolved into eating everything else like that. More physically engaging. Better for digestion too. You know a lot of the Germans eat standing up."

"Oh, you're so cultured," she said sarcastically. "I think it's odd."

"You're just not hip to my practical sensibilities."

I pinched her butt as she went by. She turned a grin on me. "Whatever you say hot stuff." She was wearing an oversized white T-shirt and not a whole lot else. I took in her bronzed legs and bare feet as they carried her seductively across the room.

"Where are you going?" I asked.

"Why don't you come find out when you're done?" she replied from down the hall, holding my eyes temporarily before slipping slowly through the bedroom door. I leaned against the counter and looked out the window while I ate, the sun rising and bathing the kitchen in light. A group of pigeons flew by and took perch on a powerline outside, more faint sounds of the city coming to life. When I finished, I washed my plate and set it in the sink, then went down the hall to Ramana's room where I found her waiting under the covers.

******

We lay side by side on our back in the dying light. She ran her hand over my chest. My left arm draped over her dark shoulders, the other tucked behind my head. A classic scene.

"Do you really have to leave tomorrow?" she asked.

"I'm afraid so."

We lay quietly for a while. Things had become noticeably more intense as my stay with her continued. A shift had come over her. It was in her eyes, the way she was kissing me now, the telling details in the pauses in between conversation. She held me differently. The energy of the encounter was shifting. There was an air of seriousness now. This was a sensitive matter, one not to be taken lightly. I needed to bring forth the reality of the situation. We were both aware of it of course, but I felt that reality slipping and giving way to the dreamlike experience we found ourselves engaged in. The fact of the matter was I was leaving for a plane to Mumbai the next day. There was no mystery to it. No alternate possibilities. Nothing waiting behind door number two. Ramana knew my business here, where I came from and where I would go. We were both completely honest with each other from the start and had discussed it more than once.

Despite our openness, I still felt something developing contrary to the way things were.

"Do you think you'll ever talk to me again once you go home?" she asked.

"Of course. Just because we live far apart doesn't mean we can't be friends. You're an incredible person. I don't want you to fade out of my life just like that."

She seemed to think on it. "Yes, you are right."

"Of course I'm right," I said, running a hand through her hair. "This has been an unforgettable weekend. Nights like these are the things of fantasy. Guys go their whole life without ever getting to experience something so incredible. Nothing on this trip could possibly top my time with you. This is something that I'll remember the rest of my life." I thought for a second. "Who knows, maybe we will make more memories together someday."

Shit, should I have said that?

She seemed closer to me at my words. "You're not like anyone I've ever met before," she said.

"I feel the same way about you. I guess that's what makes it all so great, if not a little difficult." I kissed her on her head. She looked up at me and returned one directly, but it was long and slow, then she was on top of me. We started to fool around but everything was getting mixed up with words and emotions. The scene was set with fire. It was harder and harder to keep myself from her. I thought it best to take control and rolled her for the dominant position. I tried more subtle play but the shift in her breathing said it all. She wanted me as much as I wanted her and restraint was losing out by the second.

She reached down below my waist and grabbed me. I knew what she wanted and I wanted it too. Still, the All-American caring boy inside me with his sensitive, good intentions suggested I try one last time to preserve her.

"Are you sure?" I asked.

She gave a deep exhale. "I think it would be good."

"It certainly would," I said without much arrogance in the least, "but it's in your hands. You've held on to a special part of you for all this time. I don't expect you to give that to me." After a moment I added, "You should wait for someone who deserves it...someone special." I felt her other hand slide up the small of my back, her gaze, serene as it was, burned deep.

"I think you're pretty special," she whispered. We kissed again and our bodies found motion. We were two people moving in time to the slow, passionate dance of love and, somewhere in the act, both heartfelt and innocently indulgent, became a part of one another at last.

******

At four in the morning, I felt her at my side. It would be a day full of travel and I wanted to be rested, so I tried to go back to sleep. She started clinging to me, pecking me with her lips. I turned my head away, trying to find distance in the subtle movement, but she didn't let up. She rubbed her bare legs against me and then wrapped them. Knowing good and well I would not fall back asleep I turned to satisfy her, knowing it would be our last time together. We experienced each other without boundaries, having removed all chaste limitations from the night before.

In the late darkness of early morning, we explored the possibilities in this newfound aspect of her womanhood. It fired me up to know I was the one to share in these moments with her, to be the guy to show her new avenues in her blooming sexuality. Now, she was even more beautiful than ever and it made the connection we shared all the more powerful. It was all I could do to keep myself from only loving her physically, but how could I? She possessed all the qualities that a man could want in a woman. Beauty, character, kindness, intelligence, work ethic and, on top of all this, she was dynamite in bed. She exhibited complete confidence in her abilities and it made for the most liberating experience. Show me any man who would not be pleased by all of this and I will show you a man of the homosexual persuasion.

A sound came to our ears. It was the slow, ascending music of the alarm I had set to not miss my plane. Now, instead of a call to rise, it served as a stop clock, bringing our morning delights to an end. I rolled over and silenced the obtrusive noise. "I have to get ready now," I told her.

"I know." She was away in thought. I sat up in bed, the comforter falling to my waist. I ran a hand through my hair and looked for the first light outside the bedroom window, but it lay somewhere dormant, as if clinging to the previous day gone by. "I'm going to go take a shower," I told her.

"Okay," she lay still on her stomach, her chest nestled in the fading heat of our bodies. I ran my left hand over her naked back, one of the most gorgeous parts of the female anatomy.

"Do you wanna join me?"

"No, you go ahead," she said. I went into her connecting bathroom. I washed slowly like I was savoring a warm summer's rain. A small window near the ceiling allowed the steam to escape and, when I turned the nozzle shut, the sound of perching birds filled the room.

I squeegeed the floor, pushing the water to the center drain. I brushed my teeth and tended to what hygiene duties remained. When I came out, Ramana was sitting in her bed. I flashed her a smile and went about the room looking for clothes to put on. After this, I began collecting what few belongings I had with me, putting them in my gym bag one at a time. I ate a granola bar and rechecked my things. Ramana sat by, hardly saying much as I prepared my departure. When I believed myself to be thoroughly packed, I came and sat with her.

"Hey, sweet girl."

"Hey."

"I think I'd better call for a ride now." She reached over and picked up her phone. "I will do it. Are you sure you're ready? Once I call, they will get here pretty fast." I gave it a thought before replying. "Yes, I'm ready." She made the call. It wouldn't be long now. "Come here," I said and wrapped my arms around her. We exchanged words of farewell that I will not share here, but instead keep as parting memories between us. The departure felt both open and final. It was hard to say where things would go after this. We held our embrace as long as we could.

I looked at her sincerely. "I want to thank you for making this the most incredible couple of days. Here I am, taking the trip of a lifetime, thinking nothing could top the journey itself and then I meet you, undoubtedly one of the sweetest, most beautiful girls in all the world. This is something I'll never forget."

Her eyes hung low. The morning sun found my back through her window and a distant smell of incense reached me. "It doesn't seem fair," she almost whispered.

"How much of life truly is? But if I had the choice between having this experience with all its parting sorrows versus never having known it, I'd take you over the latter anytime." We became a part of the hushed stillness that engulfed the condo in that early hour. Her phone broke the trance, its vibrations muted by her comforter which I was sad to leave behind. "The car is here," she said.

"Will you come down with me?"

She nodded and found some shoes to slip on. I slung my gym bag over my shoulder. We descended the staircase and walked outside. I opened the iron gate out front and we made our way to the street where a four-door sedan was waiting, a man behind the wheel. He waved at us and rolled down the window. He spoke Hindi to Ramana who replied affirmatively. I opened the back seat, tossed my bag to the far side and turned to her. "Okay, sweetheart."

She hugged me one last time but refused a kiss, as we were outside in the open. I squeezed her hand and climbed in behind the passenger seat. We pulled away and I watched Ramana go back through the iron gate, closing it behind her, disappearing from my sight and quite possibly from my life forever.

Mumbai

The morning was dark, a foggy over-cast that reached out over the skies as the sun exposed the rising pollution that never slept. My mood was somber, but despite what I was being driven away from, I tried to keep my thoughts on the journey head. I reflected on this last leg of my trip to Mumbai. How was anything I was yet to experience going to top the weekend I had just had? This was it, I thought. Yet I still had almost a week left in another major hub of India. I just hoped the conditions in this new city would be more bearable than the current chaos of Delhi.

We reached the airport in twenty minutes. I tipped the driver. His thanks were the most I heard out of him. Now it was time to find Jimmie. I went in with my bag over my shoulder and scanned the floor, finding Jimmie fairly quickly among the crowd.

"There you are. I was beginning to think I was gonna have to leave you," she said. "Good weekend?"

"Great weekend," I smiled. "Probably the best I'll have while I'm here."

She laughed again and stifled a rising cough. "Very good, alright then. Well, I guess we better get a move on. Do you see the foot traffic around here? It's unbelievable. I'm gonna need another wheelchair. Come on, let's go this way, try not to fall behind."

"Oh, sure Jimmie, I'll try not to slow you down."

She laughed.

"How are you feeling," I asked as we crossed the floor to the check-in counter. In her expected fashion, she bypassed most of the line without breaking conversation. "I'm still not well. I feel a little better, but I can't shake this cough. I think I'm doin' well one minute and then it kinda comes back on, ya know?"

"Okay, well let's try to take it easy until we get settled into our spot in Mumbai."

"Definitely, although I don't expect to hold you up. If I start feeling off you may just have to go off without me at times."

"I'm sure I won't go too far. I feel the best of India may be behind me now." Little did I know there was still a great deal of fun left to be had with a whole new group of interesting characters. We spent a few minutes acquiring a pair of tickets and a wheelchair. Within a few hours, we were airborne and in transit to the mega-city of Mumbai.

Several hours later we flew past India's central coast into the Arabian Sea before making a U-turn and descending onto the landing strip below. As the aircraft lowered, I got a spectacular view of Mumbai's diverse urban landscape. It was massive and, with significantly less pollution, I could see just how far this industrial monstrosity went. There were skyscrapers, large commercial buildings, apartments and condos. There were huge areas of slums but, because Mumbai is home to many of India's wealthiest citizens, there is no shortage of impressive structures hinting at the money that flows through the city.

When we finally landed, a worker helped to push Jimmie through the airport which was impressive in its scale. Outside, an arranged taxi picked us up on the curb. "Oh, a woman driver," Jimmie said as the lady approached. "You don't see much of that in India." The woman was stiff-lipped and muscular. She opened her trunk and threw our bags in without much how-do. It was around noon when we began the drive. It seemed even hotter here with the sun's rays unhindered by dense pollution. Not quite as beautiful as Dharamshala, but a significant improvement over New Delhi's drab curtains of filth that appeared to be forever suspended in those scarred skies.

The drive was a long one, but we did pass a great deal of interesting architecture. This, fortunately, became more frequent as we neared our destination at the YWCA on Madame Cama Road. The buildings that surrounded us reflected the many years of British occupation. I felt like I was driving through parts of New Orleans at times, but you could just as quickly turn down a road that led to a run-down area where shambled homes and loosely clothed people sat along the streets in tattered wears. The traffic and the sheer number of people made it clear that this was a true sibling of New Delhi, though I did feel a little more at home in our new location. We pulled up to our hotel and bid our driver farewell.

"You did a great job," Jimmie said to the woman who smiled sheepishly. "All those men think they run the show, but you keep at it and show them how it's done!"

We made our way inside. Two large glass doors on the first floor led to the small lobby with its check-in counter. Two sofas near the double doors faced each other from opposite ends. A woman sat reading a book and a girl who looked slightly younger than me was on a laptop. Jimmie approached the counter where a beaming middle-aged Indian man waited behind a computer. "Hello, we have reservations for a room. I'd like to check-in."

"Yes, ma'am," the man said and began to type away at his terminal. I took our bags and stood off to the side while Jimmie handled the room situation. I passed time on my phone for a few minutes, checking emails, glancing over my social media and sending a brief message to Ramana, letting her know we had made it to Mumbai and that everything was going smoothly.

"What the hell do you mean!" I heard Jimmie's voice rising.

I had spoken too soon.

The man behind the counter was mumbling some response as he looked down at his computer. I stood, stowed my phone away, approached the counter and leaned in. "No, this is unacceptable,"

Jimmie was saying. A second staff member joined the first man and they made a show of studying the screen together. "We've already paid! I made this reservation when I was staying here several weeks ago. I want the same room. The room I *paid* for!" Her arms rested on the black granite counter that came up to her chest.

"What's the problem," I asked.

"Unbelievable! They have given our room away! I made arrangements weeks in advance, but they have filled it anyway. They don't do business here like we do in America. The hell kind of operation are you people running here?"

"Oh, geez," I muttered, shaking my head. "Now what?"

"Well, they're going to give us that room, that's what" she asserted. "Y'all gotta fix this." But try as we might the situation couldn't be altered, even after Jimmie spit venom at the manager on duty as well. We lost out on the room with the phenomenal view overlooking the water and a supposedly stellar WiFi connection. Jimmie exercised her frustrations to me and the poor guy who had to help carry the bags up to the room we were offered. The worker was all too happy to bid us farewell after unlocking the door and handing us the keys. We entered and looked around the room as we settled our bags about the floor. It was without windows and a bleak darkness filled the room. There was an ashy smell to the fading walls painted a light shade of some distasteful color.

"Somebody has been smoking here," Jimmie said matter-of-fact as if she had defeated someone at their own game. "And you wouldn't need thirty years of experience to know it. I *specifically* told them not to put us in a room that had been smoked in." She breathed an exhausted sigh brought on by the hike up to our room. She snatched up a brochure laying on the nightstand and fanned herself in an attempt to cool down. "And why's it so goddamn stuffy," she said as she approached the small AC unit along the wall. Turning on the system, she cranked the velocity up while simultaneously dropping the temperature. She stood there a few seconds, her hands out, monitoring the machine's output, then turned away and shook her head in disapproval. "Don't bother unpacking," she said. "I'm calling down to get our rooms changed right now." She went over and picked up the phone and was soon connected to the front desk. "Hello, yes, it's me again. Listen, this room is terrible. A *major* downgrade from the room I was in. I can't stay here. I'm old and this room is bad for my health. You must have something else!" A few minutes later, we walked the halls of a different floor to another room. This one was a little better. Jimmie still found it inferior to her previous accommodations, but I sensed she was becoming too tired from all the drama and began to accept our situation.

"I could fight these people till I'm blue in the face," she said hotly as she began arranging her belongings, "but what the fuck good is it going to do? They don't have our room and I don't have the energy." She gave a harsh cough, which I had noticed was becoming more frequent.

"And if you keep getting worked up, that cough of yours is liable to get worse," I said.

"Well, you probably right about that."

She shuffled more items around in her bag. "It just really fries my nerves thinking about how they could do us like that. Can't rely on anything being a constant around here. It's like everything is a roll of the dice. But if you can get past that part and accept that these things are common in India, then it's not so bad." I hoped sincerely that this phase of acceptance she spoke of was soon to find her.

******

We hung out in the room for a few hours waiting for dinner. I began reading the first few chapters of *House of Leaves*, a favorite of mine, before drifting off into an unexpected nap. Jimmie woke me about an hour later and we went down to the dining hall for supper. I scoped out the other visitors while we ate. There was a mix of people, including a small group of girls that I gathered must surely be Australian or New Zealanders. A pair of older Asian women picked at their dishes of chicken and rice. An Indian woman in long white garments read a newspaper and sipped tea the color of mud.

I noticed a girl sitting alone in the corner at the far side of the room, eating her modest meal of potatoes and masala. Her blonde hair and deep vanilla skin distinguished her from all others. What was her story, I wondered. Jimmie and I had chi tea and were served ice cream after our meal. I was worried all the sugar and caffeine would affect my sleep this late in the day but, after dinner concluded and we returned to our room, I wrote briefly at the small desk beside my bed before my eyes began to sag and I succumbed to a deep and undisturbed sleep.

The next morning Jimmie decided to venture out with me down the street to a local grocery store a block away. We enjoyed a simple breakfast in the dining hall consisting of eggs, toast and tea before setting off. We went out and found the day bright and clear. We walked up two blocks to the corner of the Colaba Causeway.

"That's the Regal Cinema there," Jimmie said, pointing to the old theatre we passed. "It's a landmark of India. They built it in 1933. First theatre in the whole country to have air conditioning. People would pay money just to come and fall asleep in a cool room." We turned east to the next street over, passing a series of nice cafés and restaurants. Glancing back over to the same street with the Regal, I saw dozens of pop-up merchant stalls with a small mass of people filing through.

We went inside the grocery store and collected some supplies. We returned to the hotel where Jimmie announced she was done for the day. She had developed a series of coughing fits as we moved through the streets. "Why don't you go on and have a look around?" She suggested. I recalled being disinterested at first, blaming the temperature for my laziness. Really, I think I was beginning to feel the first desire to return home. I was also worried about going out and discovering the city's true colors, a reflection of the maddening chaos that I associated with New Delhi. Jimmie ultimately persuaded me otherwise.

"No, you should go on," she said. "We will only be here a couple of days and who knows if you will ever come through again."

I loaded up my backpack with a bottled water, some almonds and two packs of raisins. I took a business card from the front counter with the hotel's address. I had a paper with important phone numbers in case of an emergency. I walked down to the first floor and out the side entrance. I pulled out my music player, a near ancient black second-generation iPod Classic, which was navigated with a scrolling wheel. This was the first time since leaving home that I had listened to my music and there seemed only one song on my mind for my walk. I hit the repeat option and found Kashmir from Led Zeppelin's *Physical Graffiti*.

I walked the city for several hours, weaving through streets and back alleys. I'd stop into a restaurant and order a dish, continue walking, then stop for ice cream, walk some more, then order something from a populated street vendor. I did this until the sun was past its apex and the worst of the day's heat was beginning to fade. I had crossed paths with a wide range of people. Nearly every street had a vendor of some kind, even if it was just a blanket on the sidewalk with a man or a woman sitting alongside an assortment of watches, shirts, jewelry and other artifacts, none of which I trusted to be authentic. Food stalls filled the air with tantalizing aromas that blended with the sweet smoke of incense used to keep bugs away. British architecture ruled the skyline, whether it was giant cathedrals, a massive clock tower, high-rise apartments or classy restaurants.

Art museums and schools provided well-kept grounds to cross

over. Traffic was a constant blur of motion at my peripheral. People were less pressing of tourists here. Rarely was I pursued down the streets, followed by an eager salesman or persistent child asking me where I was from, where I wanted to go, did I want hash, did I want to see a girl and so on. I had found it smart to use my sunglasses and the music to see more while being seen less. What few times I was approached by beaming merchants or locals that wanted a picture because of my extraordinary paleness, I merely had to give them a blank look and keep walking, waving them away if they pushed to sell me something. At a time when all I wanted to do was walk aimlessly, see the city and be with my thoughts, I found this method incredibly effective.

But, even under the cover of my glasses and music player (I was now listening to the B-side of Tool's *10,000 Days*), I could not keep away the harsh realities of a country trying to rise above its third-world status. Beggars sat on dirty rugs in the sidewalks, filthy and unshaven, tin cups down by their feet. A little boy followed me down the street tapping my leg and holding a hand out, then returned to a woman who sat off in the distance to collect what money he could retrieve. Standing on a crowded corner, waiting for a crosswalk green light, I heard something metallic at my feet. I turned and stepped aside as a man with no legs rolled past on a small square of plywood that he propelled with his arms and a cylindrical metal tube that balanced the underside of the board. There were fewer stray dogs here than in New Delhi. Some of the kinder vendors would throw scraps of meat to them in attempts to further sustain the poor creatures. As I walked, people gave stares of wonder and uncertainty.

Somewhere in the distance, a church bell was ringing. Catholicism still played a role here from when the land was ruled by the British. I found myself alone on the waterfront of Mumbai's southernmost tip admiring the Gateway of India, perhaps Mumbai's most famous and distinct landmark. Erected just over a hundred years ago for the arrival

259

of King George V, it was now the city's biggest tourist attraction. Several young men approached me as I walked. They smiled enthusiastically at my presence. I could hear them asking me questions but I moved on all the same.

After leaving them behind, I approached the cement barrier where the water began. A stunning view of a hundred or more tiny vessels, the oars resting idly in their hauls, lay stationary in the calm waters. It was a magnificent sight to behold and begged to be painted by a hand much more skilled than my own. Even more incredible was how almost all of the boats were absent of any captain. They just floated there in the great body of water without a soul to govern them. Bobbing up and down with the water's gentle sway as flocks of birds and hundreds of people swarmed the surrounding area. I wondered how on Earth people were so trusting to leave their boats unattended like this, especially since many of their livelihoods depended on the fishing trade. I continued to walk along the water's edge and into the streets, dodging traffic, as it was particularly heavy at this hour.

After a time, I came full circle on exploring the area, removed my baseball cap and hung my sunglasses around my neck. I could feel the sweat seeping through the back of my shirt as I adjusted the straps of my bookbag. It was incredibly hot for November. The weather here was what you'd expect of a warm spring day in the deep south. I had gone through my water supply in the peak of the afternoon heat. I resolved to return to my air-conditioned room at the YWCA to rest and check on Jimmie.

Climbing the stairs, I stopped on the first-floor lobby, where I had the best chance of connecting to the internet. I sat down on the couch nearby and began checking emails and social media outlets. As I was doing this a woman came in and sat down at the far end of the couch with me. It was the girl I had seen by herself in the dining hall the night before. I struck up a conversation with her.

Her name was Erin and this was her second time in India. She was a school teacher back in Australia, teaching a mix of English and theater. I was surprised to find that she was alone in her stay. Erin first came to India in 2010 with the company she worked for. She had been in her late twenties then. Her employers had selected a group of seventeen teachers from all around Australia to participate in a type of "cultural immersion experience". Through this school-funded program, this group of seventeen was able to tour several Indian schools in the area as well as various Non-Government Organizations.

"We got to see the social work and educational trends that were developing in the country," she explained. "It was fascinating. Initially, I didn't think New Delhi was as bad as I expected, but then again, the Common Wealth Games had just come to pass, so they had done a significant cleanup of the city and moved a great number of beggars and homeless to the outskirts. They didn't want visitors to see that. Obviously, you can't get rid of all the poverty and I was still exposed to it on a daily basis. As I began to see more of it, I remember being...just very quiet. Like being emotionally affected by it.

"It wasn't until they took us to Agra that I was truly confronted by how severe the peoples' conditions were. We took a train from Delhi to Agra to see the Taj Mahal. After finishing the tour, we started making our way back to Delhi. It was late at night, about ten, and we were at the train station. I'm sure you've heard stories about the train stations. There were many people there that night, but my eye caught these two kids who had just entered. One was a teenage boy with really bad elephantiasis. So severe was his condition that he had to drag himself along using a skateboard. It was pitiful. With him was this tiny little girl, about five or six, and in her arms she held a baby that was covered in rags, all three of them looking as homely as you could imagine. The guide we were with told us, 'Don't give them money. Their pimp could be watching and if you give them something you will be supporting these kinds of industries.'

"This other woman who wasn't in our group felt so bad she gave the girl an apple. Our guide said, 'Oh, she shouldn't have done that. They will be beaten now for taking that. The pimps want money, not food.' There was a strong smell in the station and I felt like I needed to sit, but there was nowhere to sit, so I just went down onto the floor. The crowd was swarming around me. I felt light-headed. Through the mass of people, I could see almost clearly across to the other side of the station. Seemingly out of nowhere, a naked child walked out of the sea of bodies, totally unnoticed by everyone around it. It's hard for me to say it was even a child. It was practically a baby, maybe three or four. It came out a little way and stopped in a small opening among the people, squatted down low to the ground and urinated on the floor. The child stood up and before I knew it, disappeared into the swarm of passing strangers. I was still trying to process everything I had seen since I had arrived in India. New Delhi, the city of Agra and now, what I was witnessing in this run-down, crummy train station. It all just hit me in one wave and I began crying uncontrollably. I couldn't help it. I had never seen people living like that. It crushed me.

"The little girl who had received the apple saw me crying. She gave the baby to the boy and came over. She couldn't understand it. She couldn't understand why I was crying like that. She started tapping me, trying to communicate with me. When that didn't work, she started trying to tickle me. Then she wanted to play clapping games. All of this just set me off even more. I was so overwhelmed by what was going, especially to these children, and this little girl...she was trying to cheer *me* up."

She was distant for a time, staring ahead to the wall across from us. After a moment she went on. "We were debriefing after dinner the next day and my group asked me what it was about that moment that made me so emotional. I thought about that for a while and told them it was the fact that they were just kids. They were children. It was past ten at night and they should have been tucked in at home with their parents. Someone should have known where they were and what they were doing. Someone should have loved them.

"That was my moment. I can note that experience as a pivotal point in my life where it felt like I grew up almost overnight. I was twenty-five at the time and a bit selfish, perhaps even a little hostile in my own world. I was in a really bad relationship, overweight and in a rut with my job. It was then that I realized I had so much control over things in my life. I didn't have to be in a bad relationship. I didn't have to be overweight. I had every opportunity in the world to change my situation and those children didn't. So, I had this transformative experience and, after that, I saw things in a different light. Everyone in my group began to know me as the 'girl who cried first'. They started keeping an eye on me because they thought I was fragile, but, after that moment, I was determined to learn everything I could and make the most of the opportunities given to me. I fell in love with the country. Everything I saw I was so inspired by. I knew I had to go back someday and that's why I am here now. I took service leave and came back on my own terms to experience this place by myself, without a group, so I could reflect on my life and better understand my purpose."

The mostly vacant lobby seemed to swell with her words as we sat side by side on the couch. "What other parts of the country have you seen?" I asked. "How does Mumbai compare?"

"Mumbai is a very vibrant city to me. It has a certain romantic appeal that I can't quite put my finger on. In the past, when I've read novels about Mumbai, there was always this talk of the south Mumbai "underworld" and all these mysterious components it possessed. I took a lot from the book *Shantaram*. It shaped my views and fueled my imagination.

"When I first came to this country in 2010, I went to Kolkata and that was my favorite city by far. I had a real love for it. I spent time at a great school there. I remember walking through the city and thinking people were really friendly and warm and extremely easy going. I always related that to back home, because Australia has a lot of really laid-back people. It reminded me of the city I came from so it was easy to connect to. It was on a river and I remember Kolkata having more poverty than any other city I had been to, but I had enjoyed doing simple things like sitting with people in the streets, an activity that we were encouraged to do by our group leader.

"He was the head of my company and he visits Kolkata once a year. He told us if we ever had leftover food to just take it down to the street and give it to the people, maybe even sit with them for a time. People would hand you their baby while they sat and ate. They were very kind people. I've been to other parts of the country and have liked them for different reasons. Rajasthan is beautiful in regards to the architecture and the scenery. Kerala is lovely because it's very laid back and just has a different feel to it. I think I am drawn to these big cities because they are full of people. For me, the draw has always been people and culture, so I love the cities because those are places I get to interact, which makes me very happy. Also, as a teacher, it fills a natural curiosity."

I inquired further on the slums and the poverty she had witnessed. I wanted to know more about what her experiences had been like with those people and places. She shifted a little in her seat. "Are you aware of the poverty tours?"

I shook my head.

"Have you heard of Dharavi?"

Regarded as Asia's largest slum, Dharavi is located in the heart of Mumbai with an estimated population of one million people, all crammed into the tiny space which measures less than a single square mile. Though rent in Mumbai is regarded as some of the highest in the world, spaces in Dharavi can be had for the equivalent of a few U.S. dollars per month. Searching the city online produces images of mothers bathing their children in brown water, single-room houses built atop piles of garbage, clothes strung along public bridges or train tracks to dry, aerial shots that make the city look more cancerous than urban with a sea of filth and waste as its backdrop.

"Those tours are a bit controversial," Erin was saying. "Not everyone agrees that there should be businesses based around the city's poverty, but I was interested in the industry and the people. They do a great deal of recycling there with almost twenty-five thousand of the city's population doing some form of recycling work. The city also exports a lot of goods around the world. Leather, jewelry, textiles to name a few. With this in mind, the average income per year usually doesn't exceed much more than the equivalent of a hundred U.S. dollars.

"You go into these slum areas and it can be pretty bad and it can be upsetting and a bit confronting at times. I would take some friends and go out to do food distributions and one of them was quite upset seeing the kids scramble for food and water. But a lot of times you meet them and they are always smiling and saying, Hello, Teacher! Hello!' If you go into some of these places the sense of community and the level of happiness that the people possess cannot be bought. Many are happy despite the fact they live in extremely difficult circumstances, so it's a double-edged sword you might say. You have to look at it from different angles. In my experience, when I was in slum homes, even though the occupants dealt with incredible hardships, they were still very happy and warm places. You'll never meet hospitality anywhere else like you will in India. The people will give you the shirt off their back if they can. It's hard when I spend time in places where you are forced to see a lot of that poverty and have a Western filter about it. All these thoughts running through your head. 'Why isn't this provided for? Why isn't this, why isn't that,' but you also see the flip side of it where there are elements in those communities that I think are largely absent in the West. You know, we don't have..." She seemed to trail off in her thoughts. She looked down at her hands in her lap and became silent for a time. She looked up at me again.

"It's a wave of emotions, thoughts and reflections that I can't quantify. I don't have specific answers. Perhaps that's more to the point of why I'm here again. I want to understand more about this place. Perhaps that's why you're here as well. If so, I hope my stories have been helpful." I assured her they were and thanked her for sharing them with me. We spoke a few minutes more and then I excused myself and returned to my room.

******

I rested upstairs for a while and then went back down to the lobby. There was still time to pass until dinner and I didn't have much of a desire to venture out into the streets again. I was starving from all of the walking I had done that day. Jimmie had let me borrow her tablet and I was messaging with my family back home when an American girl with dark hair came in and sat down on the couch.

Her name was Janie and she was here for an internship program through the University of California. She said several others students were staying in the hotel with her, all from different parts of California. They had been there several months and were only a few weeks away from going home. This program she spoke of was the first of its kind for their school. "I guess you could say me and my classmates are guinea pigs," she said.

"What has it been like living and interacting with all these other American students in such a foreign place?" I inquired.

"It's kind of cool when you meet a group of other people and they are all working on a common goal, in our case, those goals have been primarily socially driven—doing work to help others. It was a wonderful experience getting to meet so many people like that because I didn't feel like I got that in my undergraduate years in the States. I knew people in similar programs for social entrepreneurship but ultimately felt like I hadn't connected with them as much as I wanted to. But to be placed into an environment where me and all these other people began to form a bond and work side by side was a unique experience. We had to get used to each other very quickly because we had four months together ahead of us. Even through the struggles of living in a foreign country and constantly dealing with new challenges, our unity made it easier to manage. We relied on each other."

"What were your initial impressions of India?" I asked.

She gave a reflective sigh. "Difficult to describe. Just the chemical concoction of pollution and city life. It was weird and uncomfortable but I knew going into it what to expect. It varies depending on where you are, particularly the way the people are and how they treat you, in my case, a woman from America. Here I am, accustomed to mostly laid-back people from California and then I come here and there's a whole new culture to adapt to. So yes, uncomfortable, but in a way that's what I was looking for. I wanted to feel that vulnerability, that sense of challenge.

"There's so much variety in the people themselves too. You meet so many different personalities. There's the woman who sells little bundles of flowers and you just want to talk to her and hear what she has to say." She laughed. "Then you get the obnoxious guy who is walking the streets trying to sell these giant balloons and he's yelling at you because he wants you to buy them. Who needs a giant balloon? What kind of profit margins are in a business like that? The merchants would have different tactics for dealing with customers in the shops. Some were more aggressive; some were more helpful.

"To be honest, one of the best places to see people in action is around the train station. It's the intersection for a great deal of diversity. I've seen men covered in...boils or scars or something terrible. Then there are kids playing barefoot and filthy in the dirt because that's where they live. That is *how* they live. Next thing you know, you see these beautiful cars with personal drivers at the wheel. It's a very co-existing community, more so than in the States. There isn't as much overlapping of classes as there is here. There are exotic nightclubs next to slums. Nice houses next to abandoned shacks."

I asked her what moments had most impacted her while she had been in India. What images did she believe would be the most enduring to her?

"I can say that I encountered a lot of moments that inspired me to reflect on my own life. I had a new scope to further consider how the world worked. I think many of those thoughts came from working at the non-profit attached to the program. It was a small, two-story building. The bottom floor was for classes and, upstairs, there was a bathroom and two additional classrooms. It was all run by the Catholic diocese, which was very interesting because although they were Catholic, they also taught Hinduism and Islamic traditions.

"It was very difficult communicating with the people I worked with there. Most knew two languages but usually only a little English. I would be in charge of writing down their programs and operations and putting them into an online format. I got most of it done, so that was cool, but that kind of work takes so much dedication. I'm sure they weren't paid a great deal and they had to deal with nearly a hundred kids! All of them running around and climbing on top of each other. It was an education NGO that dealt with rehabilitating young kids, so they would usually either be in school or have dropped out. Many of these kids were called "rag pickers" which means they come from a background of rummaging through trash to find things to resale. They could be ten or eleven years old and have no prior education, just this lifestyle that was their means of getting by. To be able to work with the team there, despite the conditions, was an enriching experience. It taught me a lot of patience."

"What other places did you see since you've been here?" I asked.

"I took some time off to go to Thailand. It was nice to be

somewhere else and not have to work. I was dealing with a lot of physical stress, not to mention the weather made my hair a total wreck most days. But besides the little hygiene stuff, I also needed a break from going to work and seeing...some of the saddest things I've ever seen in my life. So when I went to Thailand, I thought, wow, this is really nice. I can wear shorts. I can eat cold vegetables. I can go swimming. Being able to have that time off and to have a few familiar western indulgences was great, but it also made me reflect on the hardships of India. It made me appreciate the freedoms and luxuries that are so common in my life."

"Having spent so much time here," I pressed, "do you think you would ever come back to India?"

"Apart of me didn't care for India at first and I got fed up with it, but after the two-month mark, I started to enjoy it. I liked the work. I liked the people. Apart of me wishes I had met more locals in my time here. I also wished I could have traveled more, but it's hard to travel somewhere and enjoy it when you're only there for two days.

"I do believe I would like to come back. I've become such a different person in so many ways, at least I think so. Stronger, more resilient. It does that to you. It teaches you. You're living with Hindus and Muslims who come from their homelands and they have their own perceptions and intentions. Meanwhile, you, the outsider, have to adapt to a new environment where all these unfamiliar variables occur. I don't think many Americans are taken out of their comfort zone to that degree very often, if ever. All the little things add up and make you more grateful for your usual liberties.

"I am so thankful to have been able to get an education. I am so thankful to have been able to go on this trip and support myself. You start to internalize those things. Not to say that I took my freedoms for granted, but there is a big difference between understanding what you have and living without it. Working here, I was surrounded by people who had nothing at all. That was humbling."

We sat for an hour talking. When we stopped to check the time we realized that the dining hall would be opening soon. I asked her if I could join her and her friends for dinner. We parted ways and I returned to my room to shower and make myself more presentable. After stepping out from under the running water, I examined myself in the mirror. My facial hair was beginning to crowd my skin, but I resolved to forgo shaving for the time being. I soaked my clothes in a bucket containing a small amount of castor soap and gave them a quick wash before wringing out the excess water and hanging them to dry where the steady breeze of the ceiling fans could reach them.

Jimmie, who was already prepared, told me she would meet me downstairs. I was only a few minutes behind her getting out the door. I walked down the stairs, the faint sound of evening traffic ever-present just outside the old walls. I went down the lobby hallway and entered the dining hall. I looked around and spotted Jimmie in the back corner. At another table at the far side of the room, I saw Janie with two other girls. I checked in with Jimmie first. "Hey, I'm going to go eat with the American girl I told you about. That's her over there. I'd like to meet her friends and talk to them about their travels."

She nodded her head as she finished taking a sip of her chi. I had already told her of my encounters with Erin and Janie thus far, and Jimmie was thrilled to hear there were more outsiders my age for me to pal around with. "That's good," she said. "Make yourself some new friends. There is so much to see and do in India, but our time is limited. It will be through the experiences of your peers that you will gain a better understanding of what this country means to others and how it resonates with them." I took note of her words and then went and collected a plate before going over to the girls' table.

"Hey ladies, is it okay if I join you?" I asked.

"Yeah, of course," Janie said. "These are my friends Kate and Ying." We exchanged greetings and I sat down with them. Halfway through the meal, Ying and I were talking and I became very intrigued by her personal story. She was a recent fourth-year college student majoring in biochemistry and molecular biology at Santa Cruz, a self-proclaimed "non-competitive" but ambitious student who wanted to come to India to gain clinical experience by working with under-serviced communities.

"I grew up with many Indian friends and I was always immersed in their culture when visiting their homes," she explained. "I was also raised Buddhist and, since Buddhism has a lot of ties with Hinduism, it made sense to connect with that on a deeper level. I wanted to learn a little bit more about my religious background. I love to travel and to experience new cultures but didn't want to go to stereotypical countries that people our age usually go to, Europe specifically. So, when considering all of these factors, I felt that India was the ideal place for me to learn and work.

"I did have the usual foreigner difficulties with getting used to the language barriers and certain cultural etiquette, like being expected to freely jaywalk and knowing that a taxi driver would likely rip me off. I'd say the most demanding aspects have come from my work directly with the Desire Society. I've been working as the principal investigator for an NGO that takes and cares for children who have been abandoned or orphaned due to HIV and AIDs. One day I noticed that a child suddenly became sick after having already recovered from a previous condition only a short time prior. I told the administration about my observations and was very adamant about taking the child to the hospital for further evaluation. For reasons I can't disclose, they were unable to get the child to the hospital until three or four days later. They discovered she had contracted Dengue Fever, as well as Tuberculosis. She passed away two days later."

"That must have been very difficult," I said, touched by her ability to share such a story.

"It was, but I am preparing myself for a career where those incidents will occur. I want to be a doctor one day and I know I will need to be mentally capable of handling that level of stress if I hope to make a difference."

The next night, I met the girls again for dinner after they had gotten off of work. I was quiet as Kate and Ying chatted about their day and what they accomplished at their jobs. Janie was just getting back from her gig and was expected to join us at any moment.

"You'll have to meet Griffin later," Kate was saying as she put her fork down and set her plate to the side. One of the ever-vigilant workers came and removed it at once. "Griffin is a film major. He is working on an interesting piece about the lady-men down by the river."

The surprise on my face was not missed. "The who?" I asked.

"The transgender men who go down to the river just up the way from here, near the Gateway of India." I thought of where all the unmanned rowboats were docked from my previous walk. All the "men" who had surrounded me and tried to get me to stop. Their beaming faces and touches. Their insistent questions and more aggressive attempts to follow me. The situation was given new light. Janie arrived in the middle of our conversation and sat down with a tray of food. Before long, we talked about what everyone was doing later that evening.

"We could go out to some of the bars," Janie offered. "Griffin should be getting off soon and I'm sure he'd like to meet us down there for a drink. What do you think?" We all agreed to the idea. We would return to our rooms to get ready and then go down a few blocks to some of the popular bar destinations. I would finally get a taste of the notorious Mumbai nightlife.

******

Jimmie was not doing well. When I found her back in the room she was lying in bed and coughing severely. The television was tuned

272

to BBC, one of the few news outlets she found worth paying attention to. "Boy, I tell you I got it bad," she was saying. "It has slowly crept up on me. I don't know that I will be able to stay as I had planned, although I'd hate to miss the chance to spend time with the friends I have yet to see here in Mumbai." She projected another series of strangled coughs. "Shit," she muttered. "I was going to stay a few weeks more and really enjoy my last time here. I know if I leave, I most likely won't ever see my friends again." She gave a deep sigh and regarded to TV ideally. "It makes me sad to think it."

I told her to think it over but not be distraught if she couldn't keep her stay. "You've got to do what's in the best interest of your health," I told her as I gathered some belongings for my outing. "You're always saying how you never get sick and I can tell you are not well at all. Between this smog, your asthma and everything else, this place has got to be wearing you thin."

"It is," she said clutching a tissue. "God, it is." I moved around to my bed across from hers and sat down. "Where are you going," she asked when she noticed I had gotten changed.

"I was going to go out and have a drink with the California students. Would you rather me stay?"

"Oh, well that sounds nice. No, there isn't much you can do for me here. I just need time and rest. I'll sit here and watch the idiot box and then fall asleep in the next hour or two."

My phone vibrated in my hand just then. It was a message from Marijke, my newest and only Dutch friend.

"Hey, how are things going?" it read.

"Doing fine. We're in Mumbai. I've met a bunch of college students from the States. We're going down to a place called the Bar Stock Exchange." I responded.

"The Bar Stock? I think I've heard of that place..."

"Really?" It must be a famous place I thought. *"What are you up to?"* I added.

I finished getting my belongings and was about to leave. "Are you sure there isn't anything I can get you?" I asked Jimmie.

"No, I'll be alright. I've got everything I need here. I just ate, I have a little water and the room is nice and cool." Cool was an understatement. It was downright freezing. One night I actually had to pull my rain jacket over me to keep warm. The beds and blankets here were far too short for my tall frame and I had to wear socks on my feet which protruded out from the end.

"Well, if you're sure then," I said.

"Yes, I'm sure. Be safe, and remember, we don't have much time left here. This may be your last good outing in Mumbai, so enjoy every minute of it. You'll be departing India very soon."

"Sure thing, Jimmie."

I met Janie, Kate and Ying downstairs in the lobby before trekking off towards the Regal Cinema. Instead of crossing the street to the movies at the corner, we went right and then another block or two. People and cars zipped by as the flow shifted with the changing of traffic lights. I noticed a group of local men watching us as we passed and openly jaywalked across the street to the row of bars.

Inside the Exchange, I was delighted by the intricate details of the building's interior ascetics. I felt like I had walked into a scene from *The Great Gatsby*. All the wooden tables and marble bar tops were polished to a shine. Beautiful light fixtures hung from the ceilings. Servers were dressed in up-class attire. Music played at a volume that kept the party lively but wasn't so loud you couldn't hear your conversation. A few televisions were broadcasting cricket and UFC fights.

"This is quite a place," I said impressed.

"It's one of our favorite bars," Janie was saying as we walked to a table at the far end of the room. "And if you look up at those screens, you'll see why it's called the *Stock Exchange*," she pointed to a television that had that cycled through all the different drinks they were serving, a long list of assorted beers, mixed drinks and liquors. Across from each name were numbers with green and red arrows that corresponded to whether the beverage price was going up or down in cost.

A server came over and I deferred to the rest of the girls while I studied the menu. One of them ordered an apple martini. Another a beer. Another a mixed liquor. I became overwhelmed by the choices and the more foreign options. I wondered what the Great Gatsby would drink at a time like this. I didn't much feel like my usual whiskey on the rocks tonight. I thought of Leonardo DiCaprio ordering a vodka cranberry in a den of gangsters during one of the scenes in *The Departed* and settled on that.

After a few minutes of conversation, a young man with curly hair and glasses approached our table. Janie waved from her seat. He pulled out a chair next to her, putting him directly across the table from me.

"Glad you could make it," Janie said. "Griffin, this is Stefan. He is traveling through India with his grandmother and Mumbai is their last stop." We shook hands and struck up a conversation immediately. Back home, Griffin was going to UCSB and majored in literature. "It's a hippy-dippy school. They didn't even give us grades," he said. He had held a production coordinator job at a college radio station making PSA's for community events in Santa Barbra.

"My desire to come here spawned a lot from Wes Anderson films," he said, "and the food, of course. I always thought of India as being some kind of pilgrimage to be undertaken."

"What were the hardest adjustments when you arrived?" I asked.

"Believe it or not, I wouldn't say the language was the biggest issue or getting sick for that matter. Physically, I didn't get sick for the first two weeks. I thought people were making a bigger deal of it than it was. I had gotten a medical exam, a mental exam, was prescribed malaria medicine and was given some vaccinations, one of which was a rabies shot. So here I am thinking it's all being blown out of proportion and I get a little cocky. I ate some street food and, not too much later, I was vomiting from both ends. But the biggest cultural realization is that personal space is so much different here. I thought the way people treated each other in the streets was bizarre. The way they push past one another. As a westerner, it looked like a lack of manners but, over time, it started to feel like that's just the way things were done. In America, we're more aware of personal space, but that concept seems almost absent here.

"You also realize after a few weeks how much everything is group and family orientated. People in their twenties and thirties are still living with their families, sometimes until their parents die. That is so radically different from what I've been taught in the States. Independence is huge in America. In India, it's different. There is a greater emphasis on being in touch with your family and making your parents happy. I saw this cricket movie while I was here and they spend *so long* with the protagonist's relationship with his parents. You would never see an American sports movie do that.

"During my time working for a Bollywood audio post-production house, I've come to realize there is way more organization in America. Films in America have a set linear plan during production. Here, they just do things until the end result is achieved. That level of chaos extends to so many social aspects here. A good image of that is the freeway. Even back home, as I'm driving through Los Angeles, everyone is in a line and going one at a time. That is a beautiful thing to me now. Sure, everyone hates Los Angeles driving, but in India, it's fucking crazy. The entertainment industry here is very similar. At first, it was frustrating, but I got used to how they did things over time. I don't know that I agree with it, but at least I can work in the space without losing my mind now."

"What have been your most memorable moments," I asked.

"I did a lot of traveling while I was here. I went to this little place called Panash outside of Mumbai. It's a renowned spiritual town and I took the train and a rickshaw to get there. It was in the middle of nowhere. People had smartphones and stuff but the pace of living was so incredibly slow. A lot of them were living in these little huts. It felt like a different time, a different world. All they did was go to temple at four in the morning, again at noon and once more at dusk. There were hot springs they'd go to but, besides that, they pretty much just raised their kids and not much else. It was an incredible little town.

"I went to check into this hotel and the first hour I was there this guy says, 'Hey come to my gift shop,' so I go in and he speaks pretty good English. He tells me he has a room and he seemed trustworthy, but I was cautious. So I shake him down and get a reasonable price. I get the key, get the room and it's a done deal. I start walking out of my room and I see this guy across the street selling chips, cigarettes and other stuff. I go buy a pack of cigarettes and he says, 'come, come, come.' He barely speaks English. I go back and he takes me behind the store to this house where he is running his operation and shows me he has six chickens in his living room which he keeps under baskets. Well, this is weird, I'm thinking. He starts showing me all these dirty playing cards with women. He starts saying, 'you like, you like' and I'm like, *Ummm* ya, they're great. Next thing I know he is reaching for my dick. I quickly start backpedaling and make for the door. No, no, I'm saying, that's okay, thanks. As I'm retreating, he says, 'tomorrow, same program.' I went back over and talked to the guy who rented me the room. He laughed and said, 'Sorry, I meant to warn you about that guy. You should stay clear of him. He's crazy.'"

I was trying to contain my laughter when Marijke appeared alongside us with a booming, "Hello!"

"What on Earth!" I said in astonishment. "What are you doing here?"

"I told you I expected to come down to Mumbai. When you text me earlier, I recalled the name of this bar as I passed it going to my hostel."

"That's great! Well sit down and get acquainted with the group."

Marijke sat down and began introducing herself to the other students. Before long we were all laughing and telling stories about our travels.

After several drinks, we decided to try another spot. "Let's go to Leopold's," somebody suggested, so off we went back up the street and across a few blocks to a restaurant mixed in among the many street vendors that were still in full swing despite the hour. In the short walk to our destination, I was offered hash, prostitutes and other back-alley goods. We sit down at a table and begin looking over the menu. The bar is packed and, despite several fans oscillating about us, there was an oppressive warmth to the room. We scanned the prices on the menus before us.

"*Hmmm*, that's the thing about this place," Griffin was saying. "They can be a bit overpriced." He was right. I couldn't understand why the costs here were so much higher here. Maybe their clientele valued the stuffy atmosphere more than the ritzy glam of the Exchange. In the end, I don't think any of us actually ordered a drink. Griffin had a far better plan. "I have a bottle of gin in my room," he announced. "Why don't we go get a Sprite off one of the vendors and have a few drinks in the commons room back at the hotel?" Even though alcohol was forbidden at the YMCA we were all just buzzed enough to agree.

We found a vendor who gave us the only thing he had that resembled a Sprite. Worse yet, it was a diet version, but we were undeterred and quickly returned to the hotel to hold our secret committee of prohibited drinking. We again jaywalked across the road we had first crossed at the beginning of the night. The alcohol, in combination with the pleasantly cool night air, had put me in a blissful state that set me weightless across the city streets. We passed the night guard posted outside the YWCA without being stopped, then climbed the steps and went in through the front.

"We'll need some glasses," Griffin said as we walked past the lobby and into the hallway which led to the small commons room. "I'm on it," I said and proceeded to the cafeteria. One of the girls said she would check her room for an extra cup. I walked down the hall to the diner by myself. *CLOSED* read one of those signs that hang from a wire outside of businesses. I reached for the handle. Locked. I stood there listening, trying to ignore the lite chatter from the students down the hall.

Somebody was moving around inside. I knocked on the door without much thought to the action. I could hear someone coming around. A latch thrown. The door cracked. "*Hellooo*," I said, immediately becoming self-aware of my winded greeting toward the confused-looking man wearing a white apron. "I was wondering if I could possibly borrow some glasses from you. I don't think any were ever placed in my room."

"Glasses? Drink?" He pantomimed a drinking motion with his hand.

"Yes," I said with a hiccup, "the very same."

He came back with a single small drinking glass. I was a little underwhelmed but thought surely we could make it work. I walked back down the hall and found myself in the commons room. Janie and Ying were already seated comfortably on the small couch in the middle of the room. There were two other chairs across from them. It was a tiny room, so I sat down on the floor with my back against the wall to complete our circle.

The gin and soda were passed around in earnest. Ying appeared to be most enthused and proceeded to pour herself an overly generous drink. "Geez, Ying, are you thirsty?" the other girls joked. "I can't drink so much," she said, stirring her glass. "The Asian stereotype holds true for me. Even just a little bit and I will feel it."

"I think you have enough to feel it for both of us," Janie added.

She responded by taking a long drink of the clear, fizzy liquid that emptied a quarter of her glass. "We're going to see Ying drunk!" Kate said, excitedly clapping her hands.

"*Sssh*!" Janie hushed her as a staff member walked by and peered in. Marijke had just tucked the gin away in a book bag and placed it behind a chair. The girls waved. The man smiled and continued on. We all took turns passing the bottle around and making drinks or taking shots to expedite the process.

We sat around and laughed for a half-hour before the unpleasantness of the stuffy room became greater than the euphoria of our surfacing buzz. "Okay, are we ready," someone finally said. "Let's go to the bar around the corner." We cut through the night with renewed energy, passing a handful of people along the way, the traffic still pulsing between street lights. We turned the corner across from the Regal Cinema going east and came to a stop at our destination.

However instead of going in through the main door, we went through a side entrance that led to a narrow staircase of wooden steps. *HQ* read a sign above the door. This bar was located above the infamous Café Royal, which I later discovered used to be a shed for horse-drawn buggies in the early twentieth century for the Maharaja of Mourvi. The café was now an iconic fine dining destination approaching its one-hundredth birthday and yet another visited location of Bill Clinton. As we climbed up, we could peer through the glass on our left to get a glimpse of the restaurant that had a small crowd of diners seated at tables. At the top of the stairs, the floor opened up to a large room with a bar at the center. We stood at a high-top table nearby and waited as a server came and took our orders. We were the only ones there. It was close to ten now.

A DJ manned a corner booth, actively scrolling through a music playlist. With an audience now present, he eagerly sifted through his library to provide us with background entertainment. Our drinks were brought out. I took Janie's advice to order a mixed beverage called the Celtic Six, which consisted of Bacardi, Triple Sec, gin, vodka, tequila, and other types of liqueur, lime juice and Sprite. It was strong. I examined just how big the glass was and I knew the night would become significantly more interesting by the time it was finished.

******

We were drunk.

This was made most apparent as Ying became full of gesture and was noticeably more talkative than I had ever seen her. The quiet, studious girl I had met earlier that week was nowhere to be seen. We all laughed as she became red in the face and loudly announced her thoughts on music, society's problems and the underrated merits of strong gin. Janie had asked the DJ to switch to more nostalgic 90's music and we found ourselves singing along to *Steal My Sunshine, Say It Ain't So* and *Tubthumping*, a song I thought was surely lost and forgotten in time after the first decade of the 2000s. It was close to eleven. Several people had entered the upstairs bar at this point. Somebody ordered birthday shots for our entire table, though we would never be able to recollect *whose* birthday it had been that night.

The tray reached the table and Ying, through half-moon eyes, reached out at once with an unsteady hand, spilling a small amount over the edges as she brought it up to her face. Everyone gave a birthday toast and downed their liquor. A minute later, I saw Ying looking like she would be better off sitting down as she shifted her weight uneasily onto her arms, the tabletop she stood at rocking under the sudden shift. She closed her eyes and swayed to an invisible sea.

"Are you doing okay there, Ying," I said across from her. She nodded her head yes, a little too long after the question. "Let's get her some water." Kate went away and asked the bartender for a glass. At about this time, Ying turned to her side and aggressively deposited everything that she was carrying in her stomach onto the floor. We jumped away from the table as she let loose a second round.

"*Shiiit,* Ying," Janie said, wanting to help her but still not sure if she had finished. "Can we get some towels?" Kate was already coming back with the water. The girls got to her side and held her steady. "Ying? Can we get you to the bathroom?" She mumbled some incoherent reply and we waited a few more seconds, gauging her condition.

"Let's get her moving," I said. "You guys get on her sides and I'll be right behind you." We secured her the best we could and began to move her across the room to where the bathrooms were. "Okay Ying, we're moving to the bathroom now, alright?"

"*Muhhhemmmmmmm,*" she tried to explain.

We were almost to the bathroom when she spoke up. "*Ssstop.*" We did as she asked and held her steady. "I'm na...nah gon ma-ket," she struggled to admit.

"Don't throw up again," Janie encouraged. "We're almost there Ying. Can you hang in there a little longer." We waited for a reply but nothing came. "Ying? We're going to keep going okay? We are almost there." We began moving again. I left them at the women's door and turned to go back to the table. Griffin, Marijke and the bartender were moving the tables away from where she had been standing. Kate came back just then. "Is she okay," I asked.

"Janie is with her. I don't want the bartender to feel like he has to deal with this." We cleaned up the area as best as we could. I was surprised that everyone seemed to have a much better stomach for the task than I did. I still had very displeasing memories of cleaning up the vomit from patients at The Winded Willow whose detoxes were a hospital-wide dreaded affair. Memories Jimmie and I were both happy to think less of these days.

After a time, Janie and Kate brought Ying out from the bathroom around their shoulders. Ying dragged her feet, her head sagging and her eyes closed. "We need to get her back to her room," Janie said.

"I can look after her," Kate said. I took up next to Ying and, with Janie's help, we got her down the staircase. Griffon and Marijke stayed behind at the bar. Once we got out onto the street Ying said she wanted to sit down.

"No Ying, we need to keep moving." But she became planted there. "Are you going to throw up again?" There was a moment's pause and then she began to nod her head.

"Let's bring her over to the sidewalk," Janie said, "next to those bushes." Still holding on to keep her propped up, we took positions slightly behind Ying as she bent herself over the small grassy area. We waited there but nothing happened. "You might just want to make yourself throw up," Janie offered. "You will feel better if you do." She took her advice and stuck her finger down her throat, letting loose another stream of vomit.

We patted her on the back and told her how great she was doing.

Finally, we had her under control enough to get her walking down the street again, her arms hung over our shoulders once more. The whole way back she mumble-talked to us. We managed to get her down the street and up to the hotel's front door. We took the elevator up and half-dragged her to the bathroom in her room where Kate placed her in the shower to soak and contemplate further puking.

We stayed around a little longer, ensuring she was alright and had enough Ibuprofen to get her through the night. Once everything appeared to be taken care of, we bid farewell to Kate, made our way back down the elevator and promptly returned to HQ where Marijke and Griffin were. They continued to drink, undeterred by what had taken place where they stood less than a half-hour ago.

In our absence, they had befriended two South African gentlemen. One who wore a well-tailored suit and firmly believed it was better living through chemistry, which was made more apparent by his lively character ignited far beyond what typical alcoholic beverages could inspire. He held an iced-down whiskey tumbler that moved about the air as he gestured elaborately and told loud stories while his face gathered beads of thick sweat, signs suggesting a biological tango of MDMA and cocaine. A little less dark in complexion, his friend was sober and sturdy, like an off-duty cop. He wore a plain T-shirt with cargo pants and had dreads that went to his shoulders, prompting me to call him Zach Da La Rocha for the rest of the night.

"We party everywhere we go!" Suit Man was saying. "Everyone we meet, we just want to have a good time. We can go all night, whatever it is you want to do. You guys like to dance? What are you, Americans? Great dance clubs around here. We can take a cab if we have to, it's on me, no worries. No worries! We just want to have a good time. What time is it now? Oh, man! We got to keep moving, it's getting late and the clubs around here will close. It's no problem though, there are clubs on the other side of town. It might take an hour but if we go now-" and on it went. The Da La Rocha look-alike (who had never actually heard of the performer) stood by with total composure and laughed as his friend soared higher into his state of ecstasy. I imagined this must be an entertaining partnership to witness on a usual basis.

In the end, we decided to return to the Stock Exchange across the street, as it was the closest bar that stayed open the latest. We left HQ in a convoy of laughter and merry antics. As we exited onto the street and rounded a corner in good spirit, we became hushed at the sight of a shirtless man and his son sleeping there on the pavement. There was only a cardboard box between them and the cold ground. We moved past them quietly and, though I can't speak to the others' feelings, the moment resonated with me deeply. Here we were, rich in comparison, drunk and parading through the streets to fill our bodies with more of what it didn't need. The sudden encounter was a wrecking ball of awareness, sobering to the heart and mind.

This was the reality of India. Its darker side was so prominent it couldn't be hidden or swept away. You had to learn how to accept it and live with it as they did. I believe this was one of the many powerful aspects that people speak about when describing their travels to India. Just turn the corner and you'll find another reason to appreciate what you have in your own existence. The inspiration to give at the realization that you are in possession of abundance. As soon as we were down the street from the pair, the group's volume began to pick up again. Conversation formed and took to other matters. Energy was being restored. We moved on and entered the Stock Exchange for the second time that night. There was almost no one else in the bar. Suit Man bought everyone a round.

We danced to whatever loud, thumping music was playing at that hour, exorcising the last of the night's buzz until the bartenders threw us out at two that morning. The music stopped and our new friend from South Africa began to protest. "What happened? Why did the music stop? Come on. We are paying customers, don't stop the party!" But the two bartenders and the large bouncer on duty were insistent on closing. "Okay, okay," Suit Man said, "we'll take the checks now." The bartender behind the register was grim-faced as he began printing our receipts. He handed the first to the South African man who began looking it over, swaying with intoxication and exhausted from dancing. I paid for the one or two drinks I had purchased myself and began tucking away my money.

"Hey, hey, hey," Suit Man was saying. "What is this? What are all these charges? I didn't buy all these drinks. You've made a mistake here. You need to fix this." He was waving the check at the bartender. The bouncer by the door slowly walked towards us, his hands casually locked in front of him, though his expression seemed less passive. The man behind the register pointed at the receipt paper and tried to explain the charges, but the South African was talking over him and getting increasingly loud, his companion stepping to his side as the bouncer approached the growing argument. The debate escalated; the men were shouting now. A powerful flash of white light engulfed us. Suddenly the overheads had come on, aggressively bright in the previously dim bar. My head swam with the abrupt, nauseating brilliance, my vision waxy like I was waking up inside of a fishbowl. "This is bullshit. I did not buy these drinks," the man continued. "You cheat us? You try to rob me?"

The bouncer was now stepping in between them. The South African took a step back but continued to protest. "What? What are you going to do? You want to start something, huh?" More shouts. The girls glanced around uncertainly. The De La Rocha look-alike placed his hands on his furious companion, trying to calm him down. I stood leaning against the counter still feeling very tipsy. It was terribly bad timing to be as drunk as I was. I took another sip from my glass and watched with passive interest to the affair. Finally, after a series of insults and accusations, the men eventually resolved their conflict without violence. We went out into the street and bid farewell to the South Africans who we would never see again after that night.

******

The phone on the nightstand rang out and abruptly woke me from a deep sleep. My legs kicked up and my heels came down hard on the wooden bed frame that was too short for my height. I silently swore and rolled on my side. The phone rang again. What time was it? I looked at my Casio on the nightstand. It was three-thirty in the morning. Through the dark, I noticed Jimmie's covers thrown back on her bed and her mattress vacant. Oh shit, I thought. I picked up the receiver on the sixth ring.

"Hello?"

"I need you to do something for me," Jimmie said on the other end.

"What's going on?"

"I need you to bring my bag down to the lobby. It has my money in it."

I didn't bother asking questions. "I'm on my way," and hung up.

I jumped out of bed and turned on the bathroom light as my body adjusted to the sudden demand for forward momentum. I found Jimmie's book bag and put on my pair of ten-dollar bath sandals. I moved quickly down the hall with all its bright lights and descended the stairs. I rounded the last steps and stopped at the glass lobby doors. Jimmie was sitting on a roller chair at the clerk's desk. She held a phone to her ear with one hand and leaned against the counter with her free arm. The night clerk sat on the other side reviewing his computer.

I let out a deep sigh, pushed the door open and walked with an easier pace towards her. As I came upon her side, she turned to look at me. "Oh good, thank you," she said and reached out to take the bag from me.

"Is everything okay?" I asked.

"I am too damn sick. I'm going home. I don't think I can stand to stay any length of time longer here than what I have to so when you go, I'll go too. I'm on the phone with the airlines, have been for almost an hour now. They need my credit card number. It was a big ordeal at first but I've been talking to this nice lady. American, I think. She said this isn't normally something they do but just talking to her she can tell how sick I am so they are going to go ahead and change my flight for me."

And so, Jimmie's journey would end with my own. She hated to conclude her travels prematurely, as this would mean she would be unable to visit with her other friends. This would be a decision that would weigh heavy on her, but her condition had worsened. She needed treatment and her doctor in New Orleans was the only real option for her. I asked her if there was anything else she needed. She told me she didn't and I should go back to sleep.

******

My time in Mumbai passed quickly. I didn't venture out so much, preferring to stick around in the local area or read a book in the hotel to beat the midday heat. One day Jimmie asked me to accompany her to her friend's place, a forty-five-minute drive from our hotel. We spent a lovely afternoon with her friend Mary and her family who served us a simple, but delicious Indian lunch with tea. Mary was originally from India but now lived in Los Angeles. She had returned to her home country to visit her family. Her daughter's husband took a special interest in me and we conversed at length about the cultural differences between America and India. Politics, technological developments and world affairs among other subjects.

Before we left, he showed us a room used solely for spiritual reflection and homage. He opened a sliding door and revealed a room full of pictures depicting important religious figures. A shrine with trinkets and offerings was spread across the length of the wall. A place to kneel and pray. A candle inside a glass lantern produced a dull flame that the family claimed had been burning for over forty years with ghee being its only fuel source in all that time. We were only allowed to observe the room from the door, as we were not Hindi and because our host insisted entry could only be made after the cleaning of one's entire body.

Besides this trip, not much more was to be done in Mumbai. The afternoon we were scheduled to leave, I went down to the streets where several dozen vendors were lined up along the busy merchant corners. I bought a pair of pink-flowered earrings for my niece and an elephant bracelet for my nephew. Besides the prayer flags and beads I had gotten myself, these would be the only keepsakes I would take home from India. Our money situation had never permitted much else and people were still struggling with the situation as we prepared to take our leave.

I said my goodbyes to Marijke and the students around the hotel at the time of our departure. We made plans to stay in touch. I hugged everyone goodbye and then hoisted our bags out to the waiting taxi.

"Only one stop left," Jimmie said from the front seat.

"Where is that?" I asked.

"My son loved Mumbai," she said. "It would not be right for me to leave without making some effort to take his ashes somewhere in the city."

"Where did you have in mind?"

We arrived at the Gateway of India in no time at all, as the historic landmark was only a mile or two from the hostel. "Okay, you'll wait here for us then," Jimmie said to the driver who nodded soundlessly. We stepped out into the sun and made our way slowly through the dense square toward the large arch-monument, the Arabian Sea flowing out as far as the eye could see from behind it. We came right up on the structure and took a moment to observe its magnificence.

"They built this at the turn of the century for the arrival of the first British monarchs coming to India. When the King and Queen arrived, this structure hadn't even been built yet. Instead, they put up a big cardboard cutout. Kinda humorous when you think about it.

"When India saw its Independence in the forties, it was this same Gateway that the last British troops departed from, their many years of conquests and expeditions complete. So off they sailed away from this ancient civilization, back to the homeland from which they came." I looked down to find her misty-eyed and silent. I brought my gaze back to the Gateway of India. After a moment she spoke again. "Over these waters you and I came to Mumbai and, once again, we shall leave by the same means." She rummaged through her pockets and produced the vile in her hand. "Seems only right that this should be the last place I take him. His love for the city was strong and this gate is the heart and eyes of Mumbai. Come. Let's go to the water's edge."

We went slowly to the wall that overlooked the sea. The many small boats I saw days before continued to drift, unmanned in the waters before us. Birds shuffled and took to the air on our approach and we were granted a clear view all the way out to where the sea found union with the blue sky. The smell of salt and fish filled my nose and my hands rested on the rough face of the stone wall. Jimmie uncapped the vile and stood looking out. With no measured regard, she released the final contents of the container out over the water and then let her hands rest upon the wall.

"And that's that," she said.

We stood quietly for a time, the noises of the city surrounding us from every direction, the sea stretching on into the unknown.

"I must say," Jimmie finally said. "I have been surprised by just how much has changed since I was last in India. Seems like every time I turn around these days the whole world shifts on me. It's all movin' so fast now. I think back to my childhood years in the south, livin' in the countryside. Going out into the night by candlelight. Cars you had to crank just to get them started. Everyone used to write letters to each other. What has our country become now? It's not the place it once was. When I came to India all those years ago, this country was still livin' in simpler times. It was a breath of fresh air from what America was turning into."

She raised her head to the sky and surveyed it with cautious eyes. "Now you can't even breathe the air in some of the places here. America got to it. The Indian people wanted our cars, so now they got 'em. They wanted to work and make the money we made, so they stepped up to the world stage and adopted capitalism. It's not everywhere and it'll take a long time before it is, but it's coming. I just hope the world doesn't move so fast that people lose touch with what's important. We gotta remember where we came from. You lose sight of your roots, and your future's foundation is easily lost.

"You've seen the conditions here. You've heard the stories from your new friends. The human spirit here is unlike anywhere else. It'll be your generation that has to contend with the issues of the future. You'll be the ones to manage the population, the pollution and all the politics. If anything, I hope you've taken away some good lessons from this trip, because our country is the big brother to the world now. What we see and do affects everything on this planet and if we become shortsighted to what's important, then we're gonna lose the ancient wisdom of the people and places that came *way* before us."

We stood by the water's edge a few moments longer, the sky becoming a watermelon red that the rippling ocean began to adopt into its own reflection. After a time, Jimmie directed us back to the taxi and held my arm as we made our way across the square through the shadow of the great Gateway now behind us.

******

The drive to the airport took about an hour. I played a nearly ten-year-old conversation with Graham Hancock on an early episode of the *Joe Rogan Experience*. We were several hours ahead of schedule, but we didn't want to leave anything to chance. Just as when we had come in, we found ourselves sitting in the Mumbai airport at the same little tabletop, drinking strong chai tea from the same vendor near the large floor-to-ceiling windows that looked out over the incoming motorists.

We talked about the world we were returning to and everything we were leaving behind. I could see Jimmie was bothered by her premature departure, but not as much as by the growing sickness draining her. It had to be a miserable position to be in. She spoke of her son. So much of these travels had been in his honor. He would be here now if he were alive, most likely in my very seat. I would be in the states, merely dreaming of such an expedition, wondering how I could ever make it come to pass. And here it was almost two years and months of setbacks in the process, now complete.

It was done.

We waited over an hour in the main lobby before Jimmie began to pull our tickets from her backpack. "Well, I guess we should start making our way," she said. I took our trays, cleared the table and checked the trolley bags to make sure everything was accounted for and secured. We found a wheelchair nearby and then checked in with the clerk who provided us with our boarding passes. We were on different flights, separated by an hour and a half between departures. We went through the usual process of making our way through the airport until we reached the security checkpoints. Oddly enough, this was the first time I was not permitted to go through an express lane of some sort to keep alongside Jimmie. This time, we decided there was no need to stick together.

"It's separate ways from this point on," I said to her. "Unless you want me to stand by and wait for you on the other side."

"No," she said, her hand resting on her bag. A boy from the airline was holding the handles of her chair waiting for direction. "I'll be fine with this young man. You'll need to make sure you make your plane. Don't worry about me."

"I don't worry about you too much. You generally seem to know what you're doing," I smiled.

"As old as I am, I better know how to do somethin'," she said.

The airport was a hustle of bodies and baggage moving about chaotically, but Jimmie and I seemed to be enclosed in our little bubble as our journey came to an end. "Give me a hug before you go," Jimmie said. We embraced momentarily. As I pulled away, Jimmie held my arms and I kept on to hers.

"Listen," she said. "I want to thank you for coming with me to this place."

"I'm the one who should be thanking you," I returned. "Without you, I'd have been lost here."

"I understand, but you have helped me a lot too. I don't have the health I once had and it's not easy for me to get around like I used to. Having someone along with an open mind and a hunger for the unknown makes a world of difference."

"Don't think anything of it."

"But I do," she said tearfully, "You helped give me closure with my son. You helped me honor his memory. I'll never get my boy back, but I'm going to have these experiences with me for the rest of my life, however long that might be. Working with you at the Winded Willow, getting to know you, gives me some hope for the younger generations. Many nights you and I stayed up over coffee at the hospital. I've shared with you a great deal of my life story, but now you have your own stories to tell and maybe, just maybe, these old tales of mine will find themselves weaved between the experiences you share with others. My memories will live on through your memories and for that, I am more grateful to you than you could ever imagine." She grinned and gave a playful tug on my arm. "You've got a good head on your shoulder and one day, when you're old and gray like me, you'll look back on this time and it'll make you smile."

"I don't think I'll have to wait till I'm old to appreciate my time with you, Jimmie," I said. "I'm thankful now."

"Just don't lose touch with the people you've met along the way. Keep up with the good ones you find in this world, because they will keep the spark in your life new and exciting."

"I understand."

"And if you ever find yourself thinking you might be in love, don't hesitate on it."

I laughed, somewhat caught off guard by this statement. "Jimmie, do you think I'm in love with someone?"

"I'm not saying that. I'm just saying if you do feel that way, that certain something in your gut, don't ignore it. Remember the story I told you about Alma and the sharecropper." I thought back to her tale of the young girl with the black stallion, of Frank, the boy who pulled her along bare-footed in those sunny Louisianan fields decades ago. "It might not have been a happy ending for them," Jimmie reminded me, "but the choice is in your hands. You choose your own path. You create your destiny. When you take control of your life, the universe will give you what you need at every turn."

I was somewhat surprised by her sudden outpour but nodded my head with respect to her words. The crowds continued to move around us, reminding us both of our destinations ahead. "It's time to go, Jimmie. I'll call you when we get Stateside," I said.

"Okay. Love you, Darlin'. Take care of yourself," she said as the young boy began pushing her forward in her wheelchair.

"Love you too...Grandma!"

Her head went back in a great laugh as she was pushed forward and disappeared into the shifting crowd.

Of Heart & Home

As expected, I never found Jimmie in the main terminal after passing
through security. It was getting late. Almost nine o'clock. I still had
almost two hours to kill before my boarding time. I found a long seat
to lay down on, facing the tarmac. Hundreds of little lights from
passing planes and walkways and tall towers replaced what should
have been observable in the night sky. Still, I found the sight tranquil
in a way. I was watching the workings of my departure as it formulated
on the runway just on the other side of the glass.

I lay there but kept my eyes open, thinking about what my future
held. I had spent so much time waiting for this adventure to transpire
in the last two years. I had stayed in my home state, kept my job and
had remained compliant with the status quo. When finally it was upon
me, I had totally thrown myself into the experience. Every moment I
had done my best to absorb the littlest details, embrace the cultural
differences and abnormalities I was unaccustomed to. I was liberated
completely in these past weeks. I did not dwell on my return or think
about whatever work awaited me back home. Though I did miss my
family, the journey had occupied me completely in the day-to-day.

But what now, I wondered as I lay in the massive airport. What is
the next journey? What is my next move in *life?* I had thought about it
for many months leading up to the trip. I had talked about it with
friends and family and co-workers. I was going to turn twenty-seven
soon. I had been working and establishing my young adult life and, by
all accounts, it was going well as far as I was concerned. I had a little

house, a nice car and a few streams of revenue in motion. Being financially stable and without a wife or kids to keep me stationary, there was not much holding me back. I just needed to figure out what it was I wanted to do next.

This all said, I assumed once I got back from India, I would begin looking to relocate to another state. I was certain for years I would find myself in Colorado, having visited it several times in the last few years. At the time, I already had some friends who had relocated there. My thinking was: I'll just worry about India until India happens. Then, the headache of moving, finding a new job, a new place to live and selling my house would be dealt with when I returned.

Now that moment was here. I was still physically in India, but the rest of the country was behind me now and yet, the idea of setting those wheels in motion for the next big thing didn't strike me as I thought it would. Free to open myself up to the idea, I expected to be flooded with new excitement for the next great adventure.

But I didn't feel that. Strange, I thought. What was I missing?

All the burdens of moving came to mind again as I lay there. It would be a lot of work. Then I began to worry about other factors. What if I went through all the trouble of moving, selling and acquiring new property and material goods, only to discover I didn't like my new home or the line of work I found myself in? What about *all* the other places in America I had never seen? Now that India was done, I wondered where I would go if I could go anywhere. I had a newfound appreciation for my country. I imagined all the places I had never been to and if I could actually take the time to explore each one as I saw fit.

Whatever weariness was over me disappeared as my mind became awake, calculating a dozen different possibilities as I stared out into the blackness ahead. In my last year of college, I often half-joked about wanting to buy an SUV or van and put what belongings I could in it; My guitar, podcast equipment, blank notebooks, a small bed and then travel around the country. It was the typical aspiring musician road warrior routine. Living life out of a suitcase. I gave it serious thought for many months. It never happened because real life set in. I didn't feel like I had the money to do that kind of thing. I wasn't established enough. How would I ever make money on the road and prevent myself from starving to death? Where would I sleep at night? These were the pressing concerns that loomed over me at the time, the thoughts that pushed such ideas out of my head.

But, as I contemplated all those gloomy questions, I noticed something different. I wasn't near as afraid of the answers now as I was then. I had some money now. It wasn't much, but it could be made to last with the right management. I had more experience as a guitarist and my podcast was doing fairly well. My house was a major asset. My car could be sold if needed.

I sat up in the chair and my gaze fell to the ground at my feet. A commercial airplane hummed and rolled towards a position of flight. The rest of the airport was quietly subdued with only a few people nearby resting their eyes, reading a book or swiping their phones. I unzipped my backpack, pulled out a notebook and considered the financial aspect of it.

Funding such a trip would mean I would need as little money going out of my bank accounts with options on the road to generate income. Ideally, I would want to have some sort of revenue stream coming in regardless of whether I was working a job or not. I began examining the first of the list. How much of my monthly income was currently going towards debt? Which of them could I eliminate if I gave myself a year? I jotted down numbers of things I owed. I knew rough estimates and made conservative figures for each. I started adding up the numbers of what I brought in from my current job at the hospital, then, I found what my biggest money sinkholes were. What methods or modifications could I employ to reduce those costs? I bunched together monthly bills and, in general, what left my pocket regularly and subtracted it from what I brought in at the end of the month. What did I have leftover? How much of that could I throw at debt comfortably while still working on savings?

This can be done.

What's more, this didn't have to be the same idea I had when I was in college. I was an established young man at this point. I was making enough to purchase a house and a car, so why couldn't I exchange those assets and that *lifestyle* for a nomadic living situation? A high-top van or a truck and trailer pull behind. There were truck campers and bigger RVs too. The technology of the day was getting better and better every year. Solar power, cellphones, WiFi, cooking appliances, electric bikes, computers; all compact, convenient and highly efficient. How much did one need to be comfortable?

I started my research on my phone right there in the airport. An hour later I had ordered several how-to books from authors actively engaged in nomadic lifestyles, Bob Wells being one of the most reliable and knowledgeable in the community. I researched vehicles and noted the devices that would most benefit me while living within those circumstances. Every question I seemed to ask myself was met with an answer, a way around the impossible. Instead of being filled with fear at such a drastic life-altering decision, I was energized with a newfound excitement that was more powerful than anything I'd felt before. I wasn't just daydreaming about it now, I was envisioning it with purpose, with intent. I saw it not as a fantasy but as a manageable reality.

After another half hour, I put my pen down. I had several newly inked pages before me, a combination of notes and financial calculations. My brain was still producing a low buzz of information, a series of neural roadways to various considerations. I let them be. I looked up into the darkness outside and watched the slow dance of giant metallic birds as they coordinated out onto the runway. I was ready to be home now more than ever.

******

The day after I returned to the U.S., I called Jimmie. She was at her house, readjusting to home life after the long, cross-global transit. Her journey had transpired without a hiccup. She was back at her house in Chalmette with her many cats and dogs. Her daughter next door was glad to see her wild and roaming mother back from another worldly expedition. She had gone to her doctor and was working hard to get better.

I told her about the ideas I had. Going mobile and traveling around the U.S. and seeing many of the places she had seen herself from decades past. Exploring the greatest country in the world at my leisure, however I saw fit from the comfort of my tiny little home on wheels.

"You could do it," she said over the phone. I was at home in my bedroom and outside my window, the evening was beginning to take shape. "Me and my husband used to travel around the country like that. He would do contracting work for all those different restaurants. Those were good years. We had our dogs, and we had each other."

She had lived the lifestyle and, in some sense, perhaps she was seeing it all come together again for another person at the age she had been when she first began taking those leaps of faith. "Oh, the things you will see," she said with a soft chuckle. "It's a marvelous world out there."

A silence developed between us for a brief moment and, as I sat in my easy chair, a dim light cast across the room onto a scratch-off map of the U.S. which my sister had so tastefully given to me as a Christmas present. I had already filed away a few countries and American states. My eyes studied over the wide stretch of North America and I imagined how much more colorful the map could become in the years to follow.

During this time, I kept up with Ramana as well. I first contacted her again a few days after I got back home and had settled into my work routine once more. I had not shaved since leaving India and told her as much. She was a fan of facial hair and had affectionately admired what little I had during my stay. "Show me!" she had insisted.

"You don't want to see this wild face," I said. "I'm starting to look like Dave Grohl over here."

"Stop teasing and just send me a picture."

I told her about my travel plans and she was excited for me. It was always difficult to find a time when the other wasn't asleep or working, so we usually just messaged each other. As I was doing this one day, I was going through some of the pictures from India. My eyes studied a shot from the Seed Café. "Look at this," I wrote and sent her the picture. It was from when I first walked through the door of the café. The layout of the place had compelled me to take a quick, thoughtless shot with my phone, slipping it back into my pocket as fast as I had taken it out. Studying the picture now, I made out Ramana sitting by herself in the back corner where we'd first spoken. Her head of dark hair hanging over the book she held before her, a lamp directly overhead like a spotlight announcing her presence, compelling me forward. In taking a picture of the little café I found so unique, I had simultaneously captured the first moments of our meeting.

We communicated like that, back and forth for months. Sometimes this basic form of communication felt crude, our feelings mixed up with words not so easily conveyed. It was still unclear why we spoke to each other as we did. As far as I could tell, neither one of us believed there were grounds for a real relationship. I knew for certain that neither party would ever live in the other's country. It didn't seem meant to be, but I thought at the very least we could remain friends. Sometimes I wanted more and sometimes I think she did too, but we were in impossible positions. We would go weeks without talking and then, I would ping her, asking her how she was doing and sharing a few sweet words.

At times I thought I should cut contact with her. Other times I missed her a great deal and told her as much. She eventually quit her job and began traveling as she said she would. I watched on social media as she posted pictures of breathtaking landscapes, corners of the world I would have enjoyed to stand with her at. On more than one occasion I suggested she come to the U.S., but she wouldn't hear it. She was still too unsure of the political unrest that gripped America. The uncertainty of our country and how people like her would be treated there.

One day Ramana told me she was going to spend some time at "the center". I didn't understand this and asked her what she meant. "The meditation center," she said, "in Dharamshala." My mind went back to the sleepy little community in the mountain where Ramana and I met for the second time. She told me she had signed up for a ten-day retreat. I asked her what had inspired her to do that and was surprised when she said she felt depressed and somewhat lost in life. "I'm not able to understand life and myself anymore," she wrote. "I'm hoping some meditation and spiritual realignment can help clear my head," I asked her what was wrong. What was *really* going on?

"A guy," she finally admitted.

"Who is this guy?" I asked.

"The only guy I ever dated. My first love."

I thought about this for a time. "Do you want to talk about it?"

But I never received a reply from her and it would be several weeks before I would hear from her again.

The messages stopped and her social media was vacant. I wondered where she was, what she was doing, but did not message her even after the ten-day mark of her retreat. Weeks went by until I saw her post a picture online one day. She was hang gliding through the air under a clear blue sky, snow-tipped mountains off in the distance, a smile on her face. I looked further into one of her pages and found a video of her taking off on a solo flight from the edge of a mountain. She gripped the handles of her glider and ran at a full clip, her feet giving way to a great distance of nothingness below before she began to fade into the stretch of sky. The video went on long after she had become a dot on the horizon and I felt a strange sense of longing to see her again.

Almost two months after Ramana told me she was going to the meditation center I received a message asking how I was doing. I told her I was good and returned the question to her. She told me she was doing well and that she had learned to fly. She told me more about the travels she had undergone and her aspirations for graduate school. She had spent a lot of time looking into different programs. "I got into Rochester," she said to my surprise. "I was also accepted into Milan, Italy, so I must decide between them." After a moment she added, "Where ever I go, maybe you can come to visit me there." I congratulated her on her accomplishments. She asked how close Rochester was to where I lived and I told her it was nowhere near me but, if circumstances permitted, I would visit her. She asked me if I still planned on traveling the country. I affirmed that I was.

She asked me if I knew anything about Rochester. I said I didn't but immediately read through community forums, sending her links to resources I found particularly useful. "When do you have to decide by?" I finally asked.

"By tomorrow," she replied.

"Tomorrow! That is *really* soon. You should have told me!"

I checked in with her half a day later. I was curious to know what she had decided. "Did you make a decision? Which did you pick?"

"I am going to choose Italy," she responded simply. It was all I needed to hear.

"Ok," I said. "Follow your heart."

A few days went by before I heard from Ramana again.

"Hey," she said. "I wanted to tell you I enrolled in Milan today."

"Nice!" I exclaimed. "I'm proud of you. You will do great there and will have a wonderful time I'm sure."

"If you plan to visit Italy sometime, do let me know."

"Sounds like a great excuse to travel."

"I'll be here a year," she said.

******

It was late October of 2017. I was still working my job and dreaming of future travels across the U.S. and abroad. I still talked with Ramana occasionally and called Jimmie every couple of weeks. I was spending several hours a week looking at the latest and greatest large capacity transit vans on the market, reading about modifications to create a mini-RV, blog posts of young couples taking the leap of faith to roam the country as spontaneous and lighthearted lovers.

I felt as though I was on track. All I had to do was stay focused and, above all, keep making the money I needed to finance and execute my plans. However, an unexpected twist came that month on the last day of October, one that would prove to be both a misfortune and a blessing.

I received a call while working at my job from Erica, the program director for my contract company. "I'm afraid I have some unfortunate news," she reported. Erica went on to tell me my contract had been suddenly cut, that the higher-ups in the military had suddenly terminated my position in an attempt to save money. This termination was not based on conduct, but for financial reasons. I sat processing the unexpected news.

"How long do I have left?" I asked.

"This is it I'm afraid. This is your last day. I'm so sorry."

With two hours' notice, I went from having a steady job to being unemployed before I knew what happened. I thought to myself, what could be scarier than losing your job with no backup plan on Halloween?

"You're one of our best employees," Erica went on. "This is not how we like to do business and, quite frankly, I'm a little upset that we weren't given more notice. I can only imagine how this must make you feel, but I promise, if any position becomes available here, you will be the first person I contact."

"Thank you, Erica. I appreciate that." We spoke a while longer before beginning to wrap up our conversation. Erica asked if I had a plan, genuine concern still in her voice. An idea of what I would do next. I smiled with the phone to my ear. "Yes," I said, "I think I'm going to sleep in tomorrow."

******

November marked my first day without a job. I ran the numbers on my finances and analyzed what I could scale down on. It looked like I would get by okay, but I was worried about what this would mean for my future aspirations of mobile living. In the back of my mind, I wondered if my current circumstances were justification to do some of that traveling now.

I thought about that for a time.

I decided I would make sure my situation was stable first and use some of my off time to catch up on work projects around the house. I called Paul, a previous renter with whom I developed a strong friendship with before he relocated to Seattle. I had visited him there in Washington that August and, now, he was living in Austin, Texas.

"You should visit us!" he said. "Come have Thanksgiving with my family. We will have food for days!" I had visited Austin a few years, renting a hotel several nights and then camping in a college student's backyard. The thought of going back again was a pleasing one. From there, I could shoot up to Colorado. I called a few friends in Denver and Boulder. In the course of a day, I had several possible destinations planned out.

In the three weeks that followed I mostly focused on my house projects. I pressure washed rain gutters, trimmed shrubs, chopped wood, cut grass and put an old couch for sale which I eventually just gave away to John, my old co-worker from the Winded Willow. I found the time to enjoy myself as well, playing my guitar more than I had in three years and writing new music. I thought of new podcast guests to reach out to and what the show's future would look like. Within a few months, I would host some of the show's more high-profile guests, comedians and musicians touring through my hometown's local casino circuit.

I was using the time thoughtfully and enjoying myself while keeping an open ear for new work opportunities and applying for various positions online. During this time, I also communicated with the people I had met in India, finding out what they had done in the year since our paths crossed during those travels.

Nearly all of my travel companions had stayed busy after we parted ways. I spoke with Janie and Griffin over the phone on separate occasions. They were both working in California and making future plans for their careers and world travels. Marijke had returned to the Netherlands, moved into a new apartment with her boyfriend, and was still teaching theater.

After I left, Alex and Jay enjoyed themselves in McLeod Ganj, befriending locals in the Shangri-La Café, who they now refer to as their Tibetan family. They also volunteered at Tibet World, helping the many Tibetan refugees displaced from their homes. "It was heart-wrenching, but an incredibly memorable time," Jay told me. "We met the most wonderful people and I can't help but get emotional thinking about them. People who have fled their homes in Tibet and have had everything taken away from them, yet, are so humble and would offer to help others at a moment's notice."

They spoke of meeting Tenzin Palmo, a highlight of their trip and a woman I had to look up to understand the full value of the encounter. Palmo, one of the few Western yoginis who studied intensively in the East, moved to India after reading a book on Buddhism at the age of twenty. She lived at the Khamtrul Rinpoche monastery, the sole nun among 100 other monks and experienced discrimination that resulted in information being withheld from her studies due to her sex. "They told me they prayed that in my next life I would have the good fortune to be reborn as a male so that I could join in all the monastery's activities," Palmo would later state. "In the meantime, they said, they didn't hold it too much against me that I had this inferior rebirth in the female form. It wasn't my fault."

The balls on these monks, I thought.

Tired of the unfair treatment, Palmo left the monastery and spent twelve years living in a remote cave in the higher reaches of the Himalayas, with three of those years dedicated to strict meditation. Starting in 1976, she began living in a ten feet wide, six feet deep cave where she would remain for more than a decade, surviving temperatures below -30 degrees Fahrenheit in snow present at least half of the year. She grew her own food and, under her traditional teachings, never lay down, but instead slept in a traditional wooden meditation box for only a few hours a night. Palmo became a voice for women's rights and opened a nunnery in 2000, giving education and training to women from Tibet and the Himalayan border.

I asked what their most memorable moments were after Dharamshala. "Something I really remember," Jay said, "was catching this rickshaw and we were piled in with an Indian family who did not speak any English. They started handing us fruit and were so welcoming. The elderly woman of the family put my hands into hers and looked into my eyes. At that moment, I discovered that language isn't the most important form of communication.

Feelings are. There any many languages that don't include speaking. Sometimes things just need to be felt." She then read me a journal entry that she had written after the encounter. "Being here makes you realize that compassion is a language of its own. You don't need to speak a specific language to give or receive it. You just need to learn how to feel.

"Our big goal right now is to save. Initially, it was for a house deposit but, someone said something to me while we were in India that has stuck with me. They said, 'you don't die with your possessions. You die with your memories'. Our travels haven't finished yet, so now we will save as much as we can for the next two years, and we will use that to travel again, hopefully, for at least a year, more if possible.

"India feels like home to me," she went on, "a place where you can be your true self, and if you don't know who or what that is, India has a way of helping you find it. We had an open heart and open mind the entire time, which I truly believe helped us on our journey. We put faith and trust in the Indian people, and they didn't let us down. India has my heart, and I know it'll be a place that I keep returning to for the rest of my life."

A few days later, I got word from my other Australian companion, Erin. Still in love with Mumbai, she decided to move there after a brief return to her home and began teaching English and theatre for an international school.

"Shortly after my travels, I returned to Australia and began missing India right away," she said. "I applied for a job there, not thinking anything would come of it, and was surprised when they offered the position to me. I thought, it's now or never, and decided to go for it. My boss in Australia gave me a year without pay so that I could come back if I changed my mind. The situation presented itself as pretty risk-free, so I jumped on the opportunity." She would remain there until June of 2018.

Some of the most exciting life developments came from Ying, who was much more conservative with her choices in liquor these days. Having travelled for a few months before she arrived in India, she looked forward to returning home to catch up with family and friends. However, she went to Spain almost immediately after her Mumbai departure, as she was accepted to a pre-med fellowship in the country.

"I had applied to this program, the Atlantis Project, when I was backpacking in Japan," Ying told me. "It was one of those programs that I always wanted to do but didn't have the time or money for before. I didn't think anything would come of it, so when I received the offer, I of course jumped on the opportunity. After over half a year of traveling, I wanted to touch base back home, but the program was scheduled to start three weeks after my time in Mumbai. I decided it wasn't financially worth it to return to the U.S. and instead began a mini-tour backpacking through Italy because, in my mind, I thought, why not spend Christmas in one of the most Christian places in the world? I started up north in Venice and worked my way down to Naples before returning up to Rome. From there, I flew out to Spain."

She went on to tell me about her time returning home after the fellowship.

"Coming back home after almost a year of nonstop traveling brought mixed feelings," she admitted. "On one hand I was happy to be able to return home to family and friends who truly know me, but as soon as I got back, I quickly got bored, as there was rarely anything new to anticipate besides studying and working. It was almost too laid back and mundane compared to having to constantly plan your days to be productive while traveling."

Now back in America, Ying worked as a medical assistant for a physical medicine, rehabilitation and pain management clinic. She said it was stressful work but a unique learning experience nonetheless, as the opioid crisis continued to escalate in the U.S. since our time overseas. She expressed satisfaction because she was able to give back to her country, as many of the center's patients were veterans.

"I expect I'll be working here for some time," she continued, "and don't expect to do any major traveling before my graduate program begins. For now, I just sustain off the memories I've made in those long months past."

******

Three weeks after losing my job, I was in my back yard, hot, sweaty and out of breath. I came out from under the sun and set the ax in my hands against the house. I had just finished chopping the last remnants of my recently downed pecan tree. I removed my work gloves and set them aside, then took a seat and surveyed the backyard, which looked good with all the maintenance I had been giving it. The birds chirped in the trees and the neighborhood was otherwise quiet as many of its residents were still at work. I took a long drink of water and picked up my notebook. I turned to the page that displayed the running to-do list that had guided my activities in the last few weeks. I scrolled down, item after item, to one that read *CHOP WOOD* and drew a single line through it. Looking over the rest of the page, I concluded that I had completed all the major tasks I had created for myself since leaving work. I closed the notebook, clipped the pen to the spiral binding, set it back down on the table next to me and stared out over the yard once more. I sat there for ten minutes before picking up my phone and dialing Paul's number. After a few rings, he picked up.

"Hey man," I said. "Does the offer for Thanksgiving dinner still stand?"

The very next day, I got into my car and began my tour across the U.S., almost exactly one year since I left the country for India.

******

Over the next three weeks, I wandered through different parts of the U.S. I spent a week in Austin, catching up with Paul and meeting the rest of his family. They showed me the up-and-coming town of Buda, which was beginning to see exciting developments as the influx of new Austin residents continued to surge into the already popular city. My next stop was Paulo Duro Canyon, just south of Amarillo, an eight-hour drive that would serve as the halfway point to Colorado Springs. I had been looking for somewhere to camp when one of Paul's friends told me about the site over dinner. Often referred to as "The Grand Canyon of Texas," Paulo Duro is the second-largest canyon in the U.S. stretching some 120 miles. The park rangers couldn't tell me if a fire-ban would be in effect when I arrived but, I was assured a primitive campsite at any hour, as seasonal traffic was very low that time of year.

Not wanting to be unprepared, I stopped at a Cabela's outside of town and spent a hundred dollars on pre-cut wood, fire-starting fuel, a hatchet and a few other items. I drove eight hours straight. The chilly winds began to bite across the open plains as I passed through the Roscoe Wind Farm, one of the world's largest capacity wind turbine sites, with over six hundred colossal units in operation. I pulled over on the solitary road to see the industrial machines working like silent giants. They spun hypnotically as far as the eye could see while the sunset played an amber hue across the eastern overcast and the wind ran unimpeded from one corner of the earth to another.

I pulled into Paulo Duro at 9 pm. The temperature dipped to just above freezing as I approached the now unmanned front gate with a posted sign that clearly stated, *BURN-BAN IN EFFECT – NO FIRES PERMITTED!*

It was going to be a long night.

I made my way down into the canyon, going lower and lower, as I crept along in the dark. It was pitch black and I had only my headlights to guide me as I leaned over my steering wheel. I kept my focus on the road just ahead of me but, outside, I felt an immense presence just beyond my car, as if the darkness was consuming the land around me and leaving a vast emptiness in its wake. The road curved and twisted as I descended further.

I quickly set up a small tent and a cot inside. Besides some thermal layers and a hoodie, I had little else to stay warm. At two in the morning, I woke from unfulfilled sleep. It had taken me several hours to doze, but now, the temperature had dropped into the twenties and I knew my plans needed modification. Defeated by Mother Nature, I crawled into my driver's seat with my sleeping bag and waited for morning.

At first light, with only two hours of broken napping, I got out of my car and began breaking down my tent, which I discovered had been ransacked by a mouse who had located my food stash and made a troublesome mess. It was another eight hours to Colorado Springs. I only made it a few hours in before taking a room at a hotel in northern New Mexico which, with its large rolling hills, provided the perfect visual precursor for the coming Colorado mountains. After checking into my room, I discovered I was the only person on my floor. Going down to the parking lot, I discovered I was the only guest in the entire hotel. I went and swam in the indoor pool, lounged in the hot tub and worked out in the tiny exercise room, with not a single other person to be seen.

Back in my room I settled into bed and began reading Louis Zamperini's biography *Unbroken*, which I had borrowed from my roommate for this expedition. It proved to be one of the most gripping biographical accounts I had ever read, made more intriguing by its setting of World War II. I made a mental note to recommend it to Jimmie.

I proceeded on to Colorado Springs the next morning. I gassed up in Colorado City and asked the cashiers what there was to do there. "Not much," they both responded. I drove on until I finally reached Garden of the Gods and spent the rest of the day walking through the natural structure and chatting with people on the trails.

I pushed on into the night, making my way to Boulder where I met up with my old friend, Will, who introduced me to his girlfriend before we hit the town for dinner and a beer. I was pleasantly surprised when a single pint gave me a comparable buzz to two or three at sea level. I spent part of the next day walking to a nearby library where I accessed the internet to check emails, communicate with friends and consider future destinations. I had received a text from another friend, Kale, who offered me a place to crash in Denver for a few nights, which gave us opportunities to go grab food in downtown Lo-Hi, make a day trip to Fort Collins, hike Horse Tooth Peak and order a beer at the New Belgium Headquarters.

Reflecting on my previous trips to Colorado, I realized it seemed an injustice to have never actually driven through the Rockies themselves. I had never driven through *any* mountains for that matter and my car was in no way equipped for snowy conditions, should they occur. I wasn't familiar with the area, nor did I know anyone living in the mountains, but the idea of seeing the major ski towns of Vail, Keystone, Breckinridge and Aspen, were all reasons enough for me to go for it. I decided to book a hostel called the St. Mortiz Hotel in Aspen. I would stay at St. Mortiz one night then proceed south to another town where I would rent a different room, repeat the process the next day, until I hit Colorado Springs for a second time, coming full circle to Denver once more.

******

I drove west into the mountains. When I had covered several miles and made significant gains in elevation, I pulled into a gas station to refuel. I stepped out of my warm car, still in shorts and a T-shirt from the pleasant, sunny weather in Denver. A rush of cold air assaulted me. I covered my arms instinctively and reached for a jacket. Oh God, I thought. It's coming.

I gassed up quickly and changed into full thermal wear from my front seat. Continuing on, I realized the grave mistake I had made in not doing more to wash my car, as the grime from two weeks of travel began to freeze over on the windshield, severely obscuring my view. Before long the snow was on top of me. My driving came to a crawl as I peered through small slits of visibility above my dashboard. I engaged my wipers in hopes some level of clarity would be gained, but the blades just smeared the dirt and road salt into an abstract painting of disaster before me. Other vehicles, better equipped than my own, seemed to shoot past me as I gingerly tapped the gas and tensed as sudden descents and sharp turns appeared out of the thick curtain of falling snow. An eighteen-wheeler pulled out in front of me, flinging a pinhead-sized rock at my windshield. It cracked and almost instantly developed into a hairline fracture that stretched from the passenger seat to the driver's seat in a frowny face expression. I gripped the wheel and hunched over, sincerely hoping the storm would pass. In time, it did, and I immediately pulled over and used a shirt from my laundry bag to wet down and wipe off my windshield.

The clouds broke and the sun began to warm the ground. I had to bypass Breckenridge and Keystone because of the unexpected delay, but proceeded to Aspen without further difficulties. With the weather now fair and clear, I witnessed the grand scale and beauty of the mountains. In a very short time, the drive went from horrifying to one of the most incredible joy rides of my life. The windmill farm and Garden of the Gods had been one thing, but the beauty of the Rockies surpassed them entirely.

At St. Mortiz, I met several other young people from around the world who came to Aspen for work at the ski resorts during the winter months, including a guy from South Africa, two girls from Argentina and another from France. Speaking with the wonderful staff at the front desk that night, a man sitting by the lobby fire overheard me say I was from the Gulf Coast.

"What part?" he asked from across the room.

"Mississippi," I responded.

"Oh, I'm from New Orleans," he beamed with an accent that made the city sound like *Nawlens*. I took up a seat across from him and he offered me a glass of his wine. The man's name was Tim and I liked him almost at once. He radiated with that familiar southern friendliness and a spirited zest for life that one might expect from a true New Orleans native. He was a car salesman, the owner of his own business for almost twenty-six years. Just recently he had begun bringing his son in to learn the business side of the dealership. Shortly after, he bought property in Cripple Creek, some three hours away, and began making regular trips to Colorado every month. St. Mortiz in Aspen, he told me, happened to be his favorite lodge in town. So much did I end up enjoying Aspen myself that I rented my room a second night. Then, when my friendships continued to develop with my fellow world travelers and the staff at St. Mortiz, I decided to stay an additional three nights, thanks largely in part to Tim's kindness. He had booked a room with an extra bed, expecting family or friends to come with him. His generosity continued to inspire as he often offered to drive our party to outings in his truck and would often try to take the bill when we dined out. One night our group celebrated his birthday over margaritas and dinner and even then he tried to pay!

Having sustained a knee injury earlier that week, Tim gave me his ski pass for the nearby Aspen and Snowmass slopes. With the girls in tow, he drove us to the mountain and we spent several hours gliding down the open runs before meeting for lunch at a Mexican restaurant accessible from the ski lift. The following night, we ventured into Aspen's small downtown to a cellar bar with a six-piece acoustic folk band. Tim and I got drinks from the bar and went down to the floor with the girls. One of them, being only twenty, began to take sips from what drinks we had among us as the music began. In her country, such behavior was perfectly acceptable but, by the second song, a man came and tapped the underage girl on the shoulder and we watched as she followed him to the front. We went behind them and found a group of bouncers, police officers and management interrogating the girl. We were all quickly kicked out and banned for six months, but it could have been much worse.

Earlier that day, we asked our new Argentinean friends Lucia and Maria, what the nightlife was like in their home country. They told us weekends were for dancing and nobody does this better than the people of Argentina. After we were removed from the venue, we agreed the best course of action would be to return to St. Mortiz, open a bottle of Tim's wine and throw a proper Argentinean dance party. A Bluetooth speaker in hand, we barged into the St. Mortiz lobby at 11 pm, already dancing and somewhat tipsy, as two stunned guests watched us from chairs near the fireplace.

Lucia and Maria quickly shuffled from one song to the next, providing a wide range of dance music from their home. For two hours the atmosphere was loud and energetic as we danced and drank. It was a miracle no one complained, but there was hardly anyone around to object since it was the off-season. James, the front desk worker, even encouraged our good time before heading off to his quarters. The two guests whose peace we had dismantled, a young guy and a strikingly beautiful blonde-haired girl, both from Las Vegas, went on to join us in our midnight festivities.

Several days later, it was time to continue the journey. Tim suggested that I come by his cabin in Cripple Creek. "You can crash for the night. There's a loft upstairs with an extra bed and a comfortable couch in the living room," he said. "Tomorrow, I'll catch my flight out of Colorado Springs and you can carry on with your trip."

We rode four hours straight to Cripple Creek, driving through its small downtown buzzing with a handful of packed casinos. Tim's cabin was nestled alongside a large plot of BLM land that stretched on for miles. The pipes had frozen in his absence and he quickly worked to warm them into operation as we settled in. After a midnight dinner of broccoli, sweet potatoes and red wine (we were short on supplies), I went upstairs to the spare bedroom in Tim's loft. Before going to sleep, I stared out window and marveled at the undisturbed night sky which, in such a rural place, seemed to present every star of the universe to me, the distant mountains adding to the extravagant scene.

The next morning Tim and I said our goodbyes and I followed him down the long dirt road and onto the highway. Before long, his vehicle was far ahead and disappeared from sight. I drove on past Pike's Peak and made my way through Colorado Springs for the second time. I began the hour-long drive to Denver. I rented a room at another Airbnb after securing a Chicago-style deep-dish pizza and proceeded to eat it while watching a Jim Carey documentary on his portrayal of Andy Kaufman.

The next day I began my return to the Gulf Coast with the intent to be home for the approaching holidays and to find a new job. I stopped briefly in Denver to retrieve a forgotten guitar at

Kale's apartment, where I stumbled into the middle of a coke-filled birthday party and ended up playing a few songs from Johnny Cash, John Fogerty and Jack White. Leaving Denver, I made my way across Kansas and Oklahoma where I stopped for the night in a cheap hotel just after midnight. Although it was small and a roach crawled out of my bed the next morning, it was still one of the best nights of sleep I'd gotten in over a week. I continued and drove through the Ouachita National Forest, taking in the beautiful views that I was previously unaware existed in Arkansas.

I stopped for a steak and potato dinner at a local restaurant and considered my options. I had been logging in ten-hour drives the last two days. It would make sense to bed down soon and finish the return drive tomorrow, but I ultimately decided to get back onto the road again. I expected to stop in Jackson, Mississippi, but as I crossed over the open lands of the Delta and approached the state capital, I considered how nice it would be to sleep in my own bed that night. On I went, through Magee, Collins and finally Hattiesburg, hitting Highway 49 due south. At 3 am I finally pulled into my driveway. I left all my belongings in the car, save for the two black-out curtains I had brought with me, which I promptly put over the windows in my room before crawling into my long-vacant bed and falling into a deep sleep that lasted till noon the next day.

******

The next morning, after taking a hot tea and going out into my favorite sun chair on the lawn, I rang up Jimmie and together we shared our recent trips around the country. She had been visiting friends in different states and had attended a World War II convention in Illinois.

"Do you remember," she asked, "the man I told you about who

went through my brother's belongings after Iwo Jima?"

"Sure, Louie, right?"

"Louie," she repeated. "He was going to come to New Orleans and catch the train to Illinois with me. He bought his ticket and everything. He was on the golf course and he got a little dehydrated and had a small stroke. Remember, he was already in his mid-nineties and he was going blind. The doctors told him he could never play golf again because he couldn't go out into the sun. Then I started talking to him every day because I was a nurse and I would give him advice and tell him about his medications.

"Well, a few months ago I was talking to him on the phone and I knew something had happened because his whole demeanor had changed. He said, 'I wanna thank you so much for the cards you have sent me. I want to thank you so much for thinking about me and helping me. I appreciate so much all that you have done. You have been such a good friend.' He had never talked like that to me before.

"He hung up right before dark and went to bed. After night fell, Louie's neighbor saw that he still had his flag up outside his home. Louie never left his flag out overnight. The neighbor went over, went inside and found him dead in his room. Louie knew he was dying and I was one of the last people he called."

"Oh, Jimmie, I'm so sorry to hear that."

"You and me both," she said softly. "Next year I will attend the 75th reunion for the Iwo Jima veterans in San Diego. I don't know how many more they will have after that." I could hear the sadness in her voice. "They are all dyin', those men. They are like me, in their late eighties and nineties. Good men. The finest this country's ever seen. But we are no more. That generation is on its last chapter." She was silent for a time. I waited patiently, sensing she still had more to say. "I will go there and I will pay my respects to my brother, Harry, the veterans that are still alive and to my dear friend, Louie. I practically had to beg him over the phone before we had ever met to come to that reunion. He didn't know anyone. All his buddies from the war had already passed. But he came anyway. He came and he met so many good people. And he brought me that flower..."

"The red rose," I said softly. Her silence on the other end confirmed the truth.

"When I go back this final time, I will go to where Louie was laid to rest in San Diego," she said. "But this time, it will be me bringing him the flowers."

We sat in silence for a few moments. I knew she didn't need me to talk as much as she needed to be heard. "It can be hard, you know? On the one hand, I have lived such a long life and made so many friends along the way, from all parts of this world, but then when you get to be my age, some of them start to fade away. That can be hard to deal with at times, but you have to remind yourself that it's the love those people gave you that makes your life worth living. We all go someday and when you do, it's your memories you are left with. It's that love that sustains you and takes you to the other side, whatever that might be. I don't pretend to know. I follow no book. I go on gut instinct and experience.

"You will meet a lot of amazing people in your young life. You met several in just a few weeks with me in India. You must not let those connections fade. The people you call friends and family are everything in life. The money, fame and parties are all secondary to what matters. One day you'll get to be my age, you'll look back and you'll think of me and you'll say, 'That old bat was crazier than all Hell...but she was right about what she said.'"

"I understand, Jimmie," I said.

"I know," she said. "And that's what gives me hope for future generations. It's the ones that understand who make the difference." I thought about those words and would continue to think about them for a long, long time to come.

"So go out there and make the difference," she said.

******

As luck would have it, my old job was offered back to me shortly after I returned home. I celebrated Christmas and New Years with family and friends and returned to my job a few days later. In all, it had equated to a two-and-a-half-month vacation and I felt I had squeezed it for all it was worth. I went back to work and enjoyed my once again regular paychecks. I even landed a second job as a yoga instructor at a new gym in my town, but it wasn't long before my dreams of travel began to disrupt my forty-hour-a-week desk job. I felt like I had a fire burning inside me that, if left ignored, would smolder and expire. I would be twenty-eight soon and, though I had achieved a great deal and had traveled to many places, I was still where I had always been. I wanted change. Drastic change.

I went to my parents for guidance. There were two possible paths as I saw it: I could move to a new state, establish a new home and find a new line of work there. Or, I could begin a life of travel, perhaps in the van life scenario I had envisioned and worked towards in the previous months. The other option was to remain here in Mississippi, a route I did not particularly favor at that stage in my life, but saw it as a sensible option in financial gain. I was well established as a homeowner and employed with an organization that might lead to a significant step up in my current field, even though I was growing tired of that line of work and wanted a new direction. My mother was the first to speak up.

"Let me tell you what I think you should do," she said, resting her hands on the kitchen table. "I think you should work your job a few more months, save up some money and just *go*. Move to Colorado or Austin or California. You've been wanting to do it for years. Sell your house and quit your job. If you keep waiting, you may never go and then you will feel like you missed out on something. This has been calling you for a long time. You know if *I'm* telling you to do it, you should," she finished with tears in her eyes. She wanted so badly for me to stay but, at that moment, I think what she wanted more than anything was for me to do whatever would bring me the most happiness in my life.

A certain weight lifted when my mom gave me her approval to move on from my hometown. I felt like she had given me the green light in some way. My mind went from calculating *if* to *when* and I began working toward the latter. I spoke with Ramana on the phone for the first time in a long while. We stayed on the line for an hour and it felt wonderful to talk to her again. Her MBA in Milan was going well and she had traveled to many European destinations when her schedule permitted.

"And I have some great news," she said. "I have been accepted to a three-month study abroad program for my school…in North Carolina!"

"Oh, wow," I said, "that *is* exciting. You'll love North Carolina. It's a very diverse state. You'll be just a few hours from coastal beaches, mountains and the iconic, artsy city of Ashville.

"That sounds wonderful!" she beamed.

"Who knows," I said, having just told her about my future travel aspirations. "Maybe I'll be able to show you around to some of the other great places in my country."

She gave a gentle laugh at that. "Maybe," she said. "We will see."

******

For weeks I analyzed my options for renting in another state. The cost of one year's rent in places like California, Colorado and Austin could be upwards of eighteen thousand dollars. There had to be a better way to utilize my money, I thought.

"If you're serious about living mobile, look into the fifth wheels and the class C's," my parents continued to suggest. They were not big fans of my converting a transit into a camper van. I had pushed this notion away, as a van conversion seemed most ideal. Better gas and I could park it anywhere a single space was available. It would be almost unnoticeable if I opted for the occasional urban camping. But further investigation sparked my interest. I was surprised to find gently used fifth wheelers and class C vehicles fairly priced, significantly more spacious and more practical than a van. Gas and stealth would be out of the equation, but perhaps I could take measures to offset these factors.

Additional research revealed an even more exciting option. New models of truck bed campers were astonishingly upscale. I marveled at the Lance's and the Canadian-based Bigfoot units with their open view window designs and modern furnishings. They were even outfitted for all weather conditions and able to withstand temperatures below freezing. Better still, many had powerful electronic leg mounts to make load up and removal from your truck bed a breeze. This would allow me to have a truck by itself, which would be great to drive off-road or in the snowy mountains with a four-wheel drive.

I continued my online hunting. I read forums, watched videos and called local RV salesmen for advice. Eventually, I came to a truck camper that seemed like it would more than fit my needs. It was exceptionally designed, totally winterized, wired for solar power, it had slide outs with a dinette drop, kitchen, queen-sized bed, a wet bath, surround sound, dimmable LED lights, an abundance of storage space and arched ceilings for extra headspace.

I surfed the web for a dealership. I planned to secure the camper first and then find a gently used, but well cared for truck. I dialed the dealership's number with a great sense of excitement. The phone rang several times before a pleasant salesman picked up.

"Hello," I said. "My name is Stefan Lawson. I'm looking for a camper."

"What is it you hope to do with your camper," the man asked.

I told him of my desire to travel great distances across the country. To live off the grid if I so desired and reintegrate with city life just as easily. I wanted a unit that could handle all the conditions I threw at it. Something robust and ultra-functional. Something upscale enough to live in if I chose to and rugged enough to handle the unforgiving backcountry terrain. I had a hunger to explore the world and I needed something that could handle the job.

"That sounds wonderful, Mr. Lawson!" The salesmen exclaimed. "I think I have just what you're looking for."

Winds of Change

I stared out toward the Pacific from one of the many benches lining the harbor walkway adjacent to the U.S.S. Midway in sunny San Diego, California. As another sea breeze met my face head-on, I closed my eyes and took in the ocean's breath as my own, an exchange of life made possible by the travel of untold miles. A fleeting, temporary experience made all the more valuable for its finite presence. On the wind, the call of sea birds was carried. A pair of musicians played to a small crowd nearby, the soulful notes of *As Long as I Can See the Light* radiating through the heart as much as the ear. The long rumble of a steamboat horn signaling a departure from the shoreline, my exhale finding unity in the comforting sound. I opened my eyes and the breeze seemed to ease its course in a quiet moment of solitude.

I brought my eyes down to the single red rose that I held in my lap.

I looked back up to the U.S.S. Midway, a massive aircraft carrier that served as the longest operating ship of its kind in the 20th century. Though it was built for World War II, it missed the global conflict by a week and would later be used for efforts in the Cold War. Now almost three-quarters of a century old, it served as the most visited naval warship museum in the United States since its opening to the public in June of 2004.

It was hard to believe it had been a year ago that I had met Jimmie Wakefield here in San Diego to accompany her to the 75th

Marine reunion. It was held annually at Camp Pendleton, some fifty-five miles north along the California coastline. During that evening, Jimmie and I, along with dozens of others, toured the Marine base and participated in a banquet where we shared dinner tables with actual Iwo Jima veterans who had fought on the island seventy-five years ago. It was yet another amazing journey I had shared with my grandmother from another mother.

But Jimmie and I wouldn't be going to the Iwo Jima reunion together at Camp Pendleton this year.

I brought my gaze down again to the rose on my lap. So much had changed since we had returned from India. I started living out of the camper in my backyard almost as soon as I purchased it. It was a truck camper on hydraulic legs that fit snuggly in the back of a six-foot short bed. For weeks I practiced living in the little unit. I cooked, showered, slept and familiarized myself with all the technical components, from the electrical functions to the water systems, to the gas-powered generator. I liked my camper, but it didn't take long for me to realize my new home away from home was on the small size. Even with the slide-out that gave me considerable elbow room, it was still a tight squeeze. When it became clear that I wouldn't even be able to carry a regular-sized guitar with me, I started considering other options.

Most of the nomads and RVers online had one thing in common. They all said you rarely get your mobile home right the first time. Even with weeks of research, the mantra ultimately held true for me as well. There was a good chance I would end up selling the truck camper and look for something a little more spacious. If I didn't want to sit on it, I would likely have to sell it at a loss.

But that was okay. There was more to life than just money.

My brain had been spinning with new ideas and I had plenty of intriguing reflections to consider as I mulled over the lifestyle. I had recently begun sketching out some designs for a custom pull behind. My dad, a skilled builder, helped me bring the design to life when we sat down one afternoon to make in-depth measurements, analyzed weight distribution and calculated costs associated with the buildout. I had already contacted a cargo trailer company in Florida that specialized in lightweight, ultra-durable, all-aluminum structures, custom-built and direct from their production facility. I was amazed at how far my research had taken me since I had begun thinking about nomadic living at the end of my trip. Whether or not my life would go on the road as I envisioned…only time would tell.

As I thought back to India, naturally, my thoughts went to Jimmie as well. Besides my euphoric nomadic daydreaming, I often associated the end of that trip with the times ahead that would mark changes in Jimmie's health. The Indian air had wreaked havoc on her vulnerable lungs. As time went on, she fared worse or better depending on the treatments she took, the condition of the weather, her stress levels and several other factors that I suppose all of us will have to contend with one day.

Whenever we spoke over the phone, I could see her animated, age-pruned hands moving as she talked, confidently asserting that no damn cold was gonna keep her down. She didn't get sick. She wasn't one to just stay at home. She said the coughing would subside any day now.

But then the days kept adding up and passed into weeks. I remember when she started telling me that her asthma had gotten so bad that she was starting to consider canceling some of her future travel travels. That's when I started to get worried. That wasn't the Jimmie I knew. She always said she had trouble accepting her age and that one day life would have to put its foot down hard if it wanted to stop her. It pained me to hear those words.

Sitting by the water now in San Diego, I was just glad that time hadn't come to pass yet.

"*Heeeeeeey!*"

I recognized her low, raspy voice immediately. I turned around to find Jimmie Wakefield's head sticking out the back of an SUV's half-opened window. The next thing I knew, the face of a large golden retriever appeared next to hers, its tongue sticking out in a big smile. Then there was a second dog's head. Another retriever. All three of them looked out toward me as I approached the street where the driver had parked.

"Who are these characters?" I asked of the dogs. Jimmie was now pulling at the door handle, opening it wide.

"That's Roxie and Chipper," she said as she slid down from the back seat. She was so short, it looked like she practically took a leap of faith to remove herself from the large vehicle. "And they are *indeed* characters." The dogs wagged and waited obediently in the back as Jimmie and I embraced for the first time in many months.

"Oh, so good to see you, Darlin'. How are you?"

"I'm great, but look at you! All the way from New Orleans to California, by car at that. That's quite a journey. And you look as healthy as I've ever seen you!"

She wore a headband with two American flags protruding from the top. They blew erratically in the wind as she spoke. "I've had my ups and downs since our little trip, but these new steroids the doctor has got me on are strong as shit. Took me a few months to adjust to them, but boy, do I feel like a million bucks now. Most people don't even realize I'm pushin' ninety. And my asthma has even cleared up a little. In any case, I told ya I got too much to see and do, can't just stay at home."

Last year had been the 75th and final reunion for the Marines of Iwo Jima. There was only a handful of men left still alive to take part in the ceremonies and the number of attendees continued to dwindle. When it was announced that there would be no reunion this year, Jimmie asked if I would meet her in San Diego to carry on the tradition of remembering the men who fought for our freedom all those years ago. She had made many friends at the gatherings in the years prior. Her closest companions were a group of women her age whose fathers, brothers and cousins had fought on that treacherous Pacific battleground. They called themselves the *Iwo Sisters* and agreed to meet every year to continue their friendship and to remember the loved ones they had lost. In a few moments, they would be joining us for the afternoon to tour the U.S.S. Midway.

"Oh, what you got there?" Jimmie asked noticing the rose in my hand for the first time. She wore a custom-made T-shirt that her Iwo Sisters had designed for the occasion. An image of the *Embracing Peace* statue, a sailor hearing of the end of World War II kissing a woman in Time Square, the statue itself only a few yards away from where we stood. The iconic image was one of Jimmie's favorite art pieces. Over her T-shirt, Jimmie had a rainbow-colored shawl that hung loosely at her shoulders. To keep warm against the chilly Pacific wind, she had wrapped a scarf about her head, her face centered in the fuzzy, red fabric.

"This is for you," I responded. "I passed a flower vendor on the way here and when I saw the roses I just had to get you one."

"Well, that's sweet of you, but you didn't have to do that. I'm just happy you could be here." She took the rose, the delight apparent on her face as she tugged my arm toward the SUV she had arrived in.

"Come on. I want you to meet my friends from New Orleans. They are the nicest people you ever met and they came all this way with me. I been tellin' them all about you."

The couple was just now getting out of the vehicle. The man, pepper-haired and handsome, was making his way around to leash Roxie and Chipper, who appeared grateful as they hopped to the ground and began sniffing the nearby grass. A woman with sparkling eyes and a disarming smile stepped out of the passenger seat. Only a couple of months ago, Jimmie had started telling me about Jackie and Lyle. She had met the middle-aged couple through an acquaintance at a party in New Orleans and had become friends almost at once. They were tickled by Jimmie's quick wit and fascinated by her life story. Within weeks, they had become like a family trio, spending countless hours at dinner, watching old films at night and even going on trips together around the country.

As I shook their hands and made small talk, it was easy to see why Jimmie had formed such a close connection to the couple. Their smiles and laughter were as genuine as could be and I could tell instantly that they loved Jimmie as if she were blood. We talked for a half-hour before the nearby parking lot began to fill with incoming vehicles. A dozen or so men and women began to step out of their parked cars. Even from a distance, I could see all of their identical *Embracing Peace* shirts, confirming their affiliation to one another. They were mostly Jimmie's age by the looks of it and I had the feeling I was in for a day of interesting stories and humorous banter.

Jimmie threw her arm up in a wave. Several enthusiastically returned her greeting and then resumed the salutations they had been engaged in with the many friends they had not seen in over a year. Several of the women were already captivated by the musicians who played on to the passing crowds and a few were already approaching the players to chat them up. Jackie, Lyle, Jimmie and I walked slowly in their direction, all of us matching the old nurse's leisurely pace.

"This is so wonderful," Jimmie was beaming. "All of us here together like this. It's really something." She stopped in her tracks and held my arm, addressing the three of us as she spoke. "Sometimes I get to thinkin'. How it is that I'm just now meeting so many good people like y'all in the final act of my life is beyond me. I wish I could have known you all years earlier."

Jackie stood by her and gave her a great hug, the gesture as sweet as honeydew. "We're all just happy to have you in our lives now, Jimmie," she said. Turning to me, I thought I detected a thin mist over her eyes, but the grin on her face was a certainty. "You know, it wasn't long after my own mother passed away that we met Mrs. Jimmie. There was something about her that reminded me of my dear mom. Not a day has gone by that I haven't missed her, but being with Mrs. Jimmie has helped bring back some happiness in my life."

"Yeah," Jimmie replied, "it's nice just to have someone to spend time with, to make memories. That's what good friends are for. That's what life is all about." She turned to me then. "It's like with you. I met you not long after my son passed and look at all we've done together. I guess it just goes to show, life gives you what you need exactly when you need it."

I smiled. "I think you're right about that, Jimmie."

Then, she grabbed my arm and pulled me closer, her voice dropping to just above a whisper. "Oh, and I wanted to tell you. I've been reading your journal, the one you gave me about the Winded Willow and our travels to India." She raised her eyes in a show of surprise. "It's really something, to read it all like that. So many memories. I had no idea you were keeping track of it all. You might have something special on your hands there, Honey."

"Well thank you, Jimmie," I said. "I'm glad it has your seal of approval."

"The thing is," she said softly. "I'm reading it all and it's got me thinkin' about other things. Other stories I never told you. Things about my life you might find *very* interesting."

Her words caused my ears to perk up and I wondered what more she could possibly tell me. "Like what, Jimmie?" I asked, but the moment was destined for another time. Across the parking lot, a few of the women who had just arrived were eagerly talking to the bass player as the two musicians braked between songs. The man lit up with the exchange as the women began to point excitedly towards us. The bass player nodded with a grin and began speaking into his headset, his voice broadcasting out to all the people on the harbor walkway.

"Hey now, folks, I just heard we got some special guests in the house. We got the Iwo Sisters out here and they sayin' they come to party. They got a song request for us. This one's goin' out as a special dedication to their sister who came all the way from New Orleans! Mrs. Jimmie! Where you at girl? This one's for you, Honey." The men commenced plucking the first notes of *Stand by Me* as the Iwo Sisters began to dance to the music.

"Oh, I love this song. It's one of my favorites," Jimmie said as her body came alive to the sounds of the instruments. "Come on, you can dance with me. You gotta dance through life. It's the pulse of the world around you that moves your feet. If you don't dance, you miss out on half the fun in life."

"What's the other half?" I asked through a grin.

"That's for you to decide," she said as she grooved her body backward towards the music. "But don't try to figure it out now. Now we dance."

I laughed and waved her on. "Oh no, this is your tune, Jimmie. I wouldn't dare crowd your stage. Besides, I haven't learned to dance as well as you can. You go on, teach us all a thing or two."

She pointed her finger, an affirmation of her understanding as she bounced on her feet and slowly spun in the direction of the waiting crowd who clapped in time to the upbeat number. "Yeah," she said. "You wait here. I'm gonna show you young folk how it's done."

Her Iwo Sisters cheered and jived happily along with the band. The bass player crooned in his heavy voice, dancing with Jimmie as his fingers plucked the playful melody. Jimmie smiled through her thick red scarf, clutching her rose as the wind blew back her two American flag headbands, her rainbow shawl as alive as any colors ever have been. I took my place among the men as they stood by watching the spirited scene. A young girl and her mother took from a nearby bench and came to join the dancing troop, holding each other hand in hand and bouncing lively from side to side. The bass player sang on:

"*Ohhh, staaand by me,* come on Mrs. Jimmie, *staaand by me.* Yeah, she movin' now people." And she laughed and gently kicked her leg out, resting her hand on his forearm briefly to grin up at him through his dark sunglasses, his own smile wide and pearly white.

Then she is dancing again.

Dancing without a care, as if all of the world before her a stage where the music never stopped, the audience was absent of any stranger and the youth of her soul lived on forever.

Parting Words

Thank you for reading my story. After almost eight years of working on this project, it is satisfying beyond measure to finally have it out in the world. If you enjoyed this book, I would be eternally grateful if you would take the time to **leave a review on Amazon**. This will help the story find its way to other readers and will give me a better sense of how I did as a writer and storyteller. Of course, while online reviews are hugely appreciated, I am also a firm believer in the power of word of mouth, so thank you very much if you choose to share a kind word or post about Travels with a Gypsy Lotus to your friends. As the text has previously mentioned, **a portion of the physical sales of this book will go towards animal and humane causes around the world,** so every positive review or recommendation to others goes a long way in helping those causes. It's now more than ever that our good deeds are needed in this world and I thank you for being a part of this one.

Living and writing this story has been one of the greatest thrills of my life. Since I was a young boy, I have always wanted to author a book and this release marks the completion of that goal. That said, my mind frequently dreams of other stories I have yet to put to pen, and I sincerely hope that readers will want to see more from me in the years ahead. No matter what happens or where the journey leads, I am just thankful that you believed in this writer enough to take this part of the ride with me.

-Stefan

About the Author

Music has been my first love since I was a kid. I took piano for seven years and then found the electric guitar when I was fifteen. Since then, I've loved writing, recording and performing my music where ever I can. It is my hope that I will be able to record an EP or album in the next couple of years. More immediate music goals include sharing performances on YouTube or doing some kind of musical breakdown channel on my favorite tracks. Outside of music, I am a huge podcast fan and it is not uncommon for me to listen to 3-4 hours worth of content a day, usually while I'm outdoors running, swimming, doing yoga or lifting heavy stuff. I ran a podcast (Coastal Noise) for six years and have been very tempted to start a new one. My dream is to travel the world playing music, writing and producing content. At time of publication, I was living in San Diego, but new and exciting places are forever on my mind.

Here are a few places you can find my thoughts and other content I put out.
Please follow and drop me a line!

Stefanlawson.com

Instagram: @Stefanlawsonmedia

YouTube: @Stefanlawson

Stefanlawson.bandcamp.com

Twitter: @Stefanlawson

To get notifications of future releases I'm working on, join my NEWSLETTER at Stefanlawson.com

48140639R00204